Eradicating Smallpox in Ethiopia

Peace Corps Volunteers'
Accounts of Their
Adventures, Challenges and Achievements

Eradicating Smallpox in Ethiopia

Peace Corps Volunteers' Accounts of Their Adventures,
Challenges and Achievements

Gene L. Bartley
John Scott Porterfield
Alan Schnur
James W. Skelton, Jr.
Editors

PEACE CORPS WRITERS

ERADICATING SMALLPOX IN ETHIOPIA:
PEACE CORPS VOLUNTEERS' ACCOUNTS OF THEIR ADVENTURES,
CHALLENGES AND ACHIEVEMENTS

A Peace Corps Writers Book — an imprint of Peace Corps Worldwide

Book design, cover design, layout and editing: Marian Haley Beil

The translation of the Amharic description of the picture on the front cover is as follows: "Health workers giving vaccinations to children and adults everywhere." It is a photo of a panel from a larger oil-on-canvas painting by Ethiopian artist *Ato* Tesfaye Tave, which is on the back cover of the book. See "About the SEP Ethiopia Painting" in the Appendix to learn more about the painting.

For more information, contact peacecorpsworldwide@gmail.com.

Peace Corps Writers and the Peace Corps Writers colophon are trademarks of PeaceCorpsWorldwide.org.

ISBN-13: 978-1-950444-04-5

Library of Congress Control Number: 2019947759

First Peace Corps Writers Edition, November 2019

This book is dedicated to the honor and memory of our mentors and friends, Dr. Ciro de Quadros, the World Health Organization Epidemiologist who was in charge of field operations in Ethiopia, and Dr. Donald A. (D.A.) Henderson, the Director of the World Health Organization's Global Smallpox Eradication Program, both of whom were respected as inspired and brilliant leaders in the field of public health.

Contents

Appendix

Preface

This book is dedicated to the honor and memory of Dr. Ciro de Quadros and Dr. Donald A. (D.A.) Henderson, both of whom were giants in the public health field. All of the contributors to this book worked extensively with both of these men as Peace Corps Volunteers (PCVs) in Ethiopia in the early to mid-1970s. The stories contained herein reflect the profound respect and admiration we had for them.

We also honor the memory of our fellow Peace Corps Volunteer and smallpox warrior, Stuart Gold, who passed away on June 3, 2018. Chapter 7 is Stuart's account of "Finding the Last Outbreak of Smallpox in Southwestern Ethiopia," which describes his discovery and containment of a smallpox outbreak in Kaffa province, where there was not supposed to be any more cases. It is an excellent account of the successful search and containment operation that he led. Stuart was a very good, kind and honest man who always saw the bright side of things. As mentioned below, he attended the book project kickoff meeting that was held in Washington, DC, on November 19, 2014, where his cheerful presence and sense of humor helped to launch the project. He is missed dearly by everyone who knew him.

The objective of this book is to make a meaningful contribution to the literature and knowledge about the successful Smallpox Eradication Program (SEP) in Ethiopia. We have focused on the initial years of the program, 1970 to 1975, providing a wide variety of perceptive stories about the experiences of the PCVs after they were suddenly immersed in a global public health program in Ethiopia. The authors have written about their first-hand experiences with the implementation of the program under the challenging working and living conditions that existed in the country at the time. Many chapters include stories about working under the inspired leadership of trailblazers like Dr. de Quadros, the World

Health Organization (WHO) Epidemiologist in charge of field operations in Ethiopia, and Dr. Henderson, the Director of the WHO's global SEP. Our goal has been to provide readers with an understanding of what the authors were experiencing, accomplishing and thinking during the days when Ethiopia was reporting more smallpox cases than any other country in the world.

What became known as the "SEP Ethiopia book project" began on May 11, 2014, when Jim Skelton sent an email message to a group of former PCVs suggesting that we write a book about our memories of the SEP in Ethiopia in the 1970s. Jim received many positive responses to that initial message, the first of which was sent by Alan Schnur, who had been thinking about pursuing a similar type of book project.

Gene Bartley and Scott Porterfield joined Alan and Jim to form an Editorial Committee that would be responsible for managing the project and editing this anthology. The Editorial Committee has remained fully committed to the project, although it proved to be more challenging and time-consuming than we had imagined. Once we got organized, however, it became obvious that many former PCVs were eager to participate, and the book project took on a life of its own.

Our original plan was to dedicate this book to our hero, Ciro de Quadros, who was then very ill. We even hoped he would be able to write the introduction to the book. Unfortunately, Ciro passed away on May 28, 2014, which made us more determined to push forward with our project to honor the memory of this great man.

A group of us met in Washington, DC, on November 18, 2014, while attending a memorial event celebrating Ciro's life and career. This remarkable event was followed by a dinner at an Ethiopian restaurant with D.A. Henderson, his wife Nana, and their daughter, Leigh. For nearly two years thereafter, D.A. strongly encouraged us to pursue our book project about the SEP in Ethiopia, which served to invigorate us. He was so supportive of our project that he took the time to write the introductory chapter about his active support and mentoring of the smallpox workers, and allowed us to publish one of his old, informative and unpublished reports as the twentieth chapter of this book. He was also kind enough to write email messages to assist some of the authors in finding invaluable background information.

A formal SEP Ethiopia book project kickoff meeting was held in Washington, DC, on November 19, 2014, for the purpose of providing more definition to the project. The attendees were Vince Radke, Jim Siemon, Peter Carrasco, Stuart Gold, Robert Steinglass, Gene Bartley, Alan Schnur and Jim Skelton. The Editorial Committee prepared a record of the meeting, which was sent to all prospective project participants on December 23, 2014. That message also set forth the basic elements of the project, an outline of the potential topics to be covered, some specifications and guidelines for preparation of the chapters, as well as a preliminary time frame.

Although much has been written over the years about the worldwide SEP effort, it seemed like the unique stories that all of us had lived and breathed, and would always remember, had not yet been told. We believed those stories, which would demonstrate the personal challenges and accomplishments of the field workers, needed to be told and that those who lived and worked in the field under extremely difficult conditions were the ones to write them. We challenged the contributors to write a story or a chapter about their most memorable experiences, including details about the technical aspects of their work.

Much to our dismay, D.A. passed away on August 19, 2016. His loss had a profound effect on the entire public health community, and many of us attended a memorial event for him in Baltimore on November 4, 2016, two years after Ciro's memorial event. As a consequence of this painful loss, we also decided to dedicate this book to D.A. We take great pride in dedicating this book to the achievements, honor and memory of both of our mentors, Ciro and D.A.

Several other books on this subject have included assertions that the eradication of smallpox was made possible by the inspired leadership of men like Ciro and D.A., plus the enthusiastic, tireless and resourceful efforts of the field staff. In addition to being entertaining, informative and interesting to read, we hope this book will convey a sense of such attributes to the reader, as well as the technical efforts, and the feelings of adventure, learning, and achievement that comprised the authors' experiences with the SEP and the people of Ethiopia.

We are very grateful for the invaluable contributions of Marian Haley Beil, whose tireless editing, design and formatting work was so crucial to the publication of this book. Marian was a member of the first group of Peace Corps Volunteers to serve in Ethiopia from 1962 to 1964.

The Editors:
Gene L. Bartley
John Scott Porterfield
Alan Schnur
James W. Skelton, Jr.

November 2019

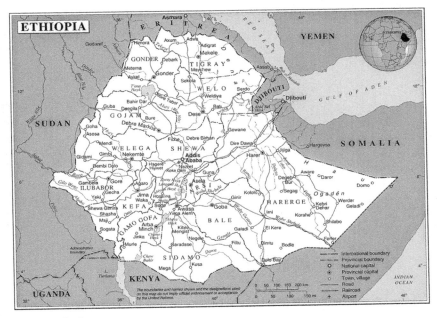

Map of Ethiopia

Note: this is a partially updated map of Ethiopia, utilizing the new spellings of provinces, cities, towns and places. The authors have used these new spellings in this book as well as the old spellings that they were accustomed to using from the maps that were available to them in the 1970s. The internal provincial borders show the provinces as they existed in the 1970s, although it should be noted that Eritrea was one of the provinces at that time. These borders were changed and redrawn when they were replaced by regions in 1995.

The map is based on a United Nations map of Ethiopia found at:

https://commons.wikimedia.org/wiki/File:Un-ethiopia.png#file

Eradicating Smallpox in Ethiopia

Peace Corps Volunteers'
Accounts of Their
Adventures, Challenges and Achievements

1

Global Eradication of Smallpox
An Historic Adventure

by Dr. D. A. Henderson, MD, MPH,
Director of WHO Global Smallpox Eradication Program, 1966-1977

THE BEGINNING OF THE ERADICATION PROGRAM

In May 1966, the World Health Assembly voted to begin a program to eradicate smallpox throughout the world. This decisive action, taken with many delays and doubts, finally launched the program. The Assembly consisted of national representatives from each country. It met each year at the Geneva headquarters of the World Health Organization (WHO) to decide policies, programs, and plans to prevent disease and promote health. The Assembly had only once before made a commitment to eradicate a disease. That was in 1955; malaria eradication had been the objective. A decade later and after the expenditure of more than $2 billion, the program was proving to be far too difficult and the program began to be phased out.

Smallpox was a far greater threat to human health than was malaria. The virus could spread in any climate and in any season: it was the most serious of all the infectious diseases. It had been spreading throughout the world for at least 3,500 years. Unless protected by vaccine, virtually everyone would eventually experience the disease; one in four would die and some would be blind. Those who recovered, however, were immune to a second attack.

In 1796, a vaccine was discovered by an English physician, Edward Jenner. It protected individuals from being infected by the virus. However, the vaccine was difficult to produce and had to be used within a few days after production. Thus, most industrialized countries gradually became free of smallpox, but most developing nations experienced outbreaks year after year.

In 1966, at the time of the Assembly's decision, nearly 40 countries were reporting cases. It was endemic (continually present) in 31. Studies revealed that between 10 and 15 million cases and two million deaths were occurring yearly.

At the Assembly nearly half of the countries voted against the proposal for a smallpox eradication program. Some believed that no disease could be eradicated. The failing 12-year-old WHO malaria eradication campaign provided evidence for this belief. Most delegates were especially skeptical for the potential of success in large countries with limited infrastructures for transportation and communication as well as primitive to nil health services. Nevertheless, the eradication of the world's most feared disease was achieved in just 10 years and 9 months. Smallpox is the only human disease that has ever been eradicated. Many individuals and organizations contributed to what has been called one of the most successful achievements of medicine in the 20th century. Peace Corps Volunteers served with distinction in Afghanistan, Zaire, and Ethiopia. Their role in the program in Ethiopia was more than significant; it proved to be one of the most critical contributions in eliminating smallpox in that war-torn country.

ORGANIZATION AND EARLY DEVELOPMENTS — 1967–1972

To oversee international planning and development for smallpox eradication, WHO established a smallpox eradication unit at WHO headquarters in Geneva. It was to consist of four medical officers; two administrative officers; and three secretaries plus one advisor in each of the four WHO Regional Offices where smallpox was endemic.

The WHO budget was set at $2.4 million annually. Programs would be needed both in endemic and nearby countries — perhaps 50 in all. The WHO budget itself was too small even to buy the needed vaccine. A major effort would have to be made to persuade potential donors to contribute resources and to convince the smallpox infected and adjacent countries to provide special funds and personnel. A special program would be needed to develop and expand vaccine production. How to communicate with the many different national programs, vaccine production facilities, and other agencies that might provide help was a daunting problem; virtually all had to be done by postal letter or personal visit.

EVOLUTION OF THE GLOBAL PROGRAM — 1967–1971

A new eradication strategy called surveillance-containment was introduced. In brief, it consisted of developing a national reporting network of health units to report cases of smallpox each week. In response, small emergency teams would go to the outbreaks to vaccinate family members and visitors as well as nearby neighbors.

The first five years of the program were astonishingly successful. In West and Central Africa, a block of 18 countries with more than 100 million people became smallpox-free thanks to a specially supported U.S. program. These countries had been experiencing the highest rates of smallpox infection in the world. By late 1971, smallpox had also been eliminated from the remaining countries of Africa except for Ethiopia, from all of Latin America, from Indonesia, and from Afghanistan. The strategy of surveillance and search for cases coupled with use of a heat-stable smallpox vaccine was working wonders. Detailed accounts of the challenges and progress in the programs are described in the 1500-page book *Smallpox and Its Eradication*, by Fenner, Henderson, Arita, Ježek and Ladnyi. It was published in 1988 by the World Health Organization.

In 1971, the remaining endemic areas were two. They differed greatly in character, but the problems in each appeared to be overwhelming. Success in the near term was unlikely.

The first was a populous block of South Asian countries (India, Pakistan, Bangladesh) with a population approaching one billion people and health services discouraged by failed heroic mass vaccination campaigns. An enormous input of available resources and international expertise would be needed.

The second area was Ethiopia. Its population was only 25 million, but the health system was rudimentary, roads were few, the population was widely scattered and many had never been vaccinated. It posed the most significant problem in all of Africa.

ETHIOPIA – A BRIEF OVERVIEW OF ITS PROBLEMS

From the beginning of the global program in 1967, we were concerned about Ethiopia. Information about the country was scant and little did we appreciate how diverse, and all but insoluble the problems would be.

Among the endemic countries, all had some sort of health system upon which a program could be built. Ethiopia, however, had only a limited number of health units and medical personnel. It was estimated that 40% of the population required a journey of three days or more to reach any kind of health unit. A locally produced thermolabile smallpox vaccine was given to a few hundred thousand each year, but, on testing, the vaccine was found to be inert.

The country is equivalent in size to France, Germany and the Netherlands combined. Most of its twenty-five million people lived in scattered villages or towns populated by a few thousand persons. Most resided in the mountainous highland area; 85% lived more than 20 miles from an all-weather road.

Planning was difficult as there were no national or local maps showing roads and towns in sufficient detail for practical use. In addition, several million nomads roamed freely over a large sandy desert. There were numerous tribal languages, but none was nationally recognized.

Each year, Ethiopia reported some 200 cases of smallpox but little was known as to where the cases were.

Soon after the global program was announced, I contacted the Ethiopian Minister of Health and asked that I be permitted to visit the country to learn more about the health system, the smallpox problem, and the possibility of WHO funding at least a small program to assess needs. For fully three years, the Minister steadfastly refused my requests simply to visit. It was virtually unknown for a government to reject such a WHO request.

Finally, in July 1970, I was surprised by a communication from Ethiopia welcoming a visit of myself and one of my staff. We immediately flew to Addis Ababa, the capital. Soon we learned that a mistake had been made. The Minister had been out of the city when our request was received and the Deputy Minister had acted in his stead to extend the invitation. On returning, a decidedly unhappy Minister reluctantly agreed for us to stay for two weeks to develop a possible plan and to present it to him for consideration. He assured us that he wouldn't need to read it in order to reject it.

The cause for his behavior soon became known. It was the American project director of a malaria elimination program funded by the U.S. Agency for International Development (USAID). The director was determined not to have competition from a smallpox eradication program. For malaria programs, it was a difficult transitional period as the global malaria eradication effort was in its final stages of collapse, as was the program in Ethiopia. Yet, as we learned, it still employed some 8,000 staff — more than twice the number in Ethiopia's entire national health care system — and it had a motor pool of some 250 vehicles.

We drafted a plan for beginning a modest exploratory program for smallpox control. It called for two WHO staff, five vehicles and 19 Ethiopian health staff. This was only a fraction of the absolute minimum number we believed to be needed. However, WHO couldn't afford more than this what with current efforts to cope with the massive smallpox epidemics in Asia. Hopefully, however, this modest effort would better define the problem and needs. In the meantime, I requested that we be permitted to borrow five vehicles from the massive USAID malaria motor pool. The malaria director rejected the request.

I was devastated as I attended a small reception on the night prior to flying back to Geneva. There, I met a stocky, knowledgeable, and enthu-

could be achieved began to provide special funds. This permitted the use of some fixed wing and helicopter aircraft.

The program continlued to make remarkable progress and by 1975, the cases had fallen to only 50 to 60 per week in no more than 10 to 15 villages. Smallpox was occurring in only three provinces; some two million vaccinations were being performed annually. It seemed possible that the program might reach "0" cases within a matter of perhaps twelve to eighteen months.

In 1975 disaster struck. The Emperor was assassinated, active fighting broke out, and most countries evacuated all but their most essential staff. Peace Corps Volunteers were obliged to depart. Foreign assistance projects were terminated. Only the smallpox eradication campaign was permitted to continue. It operated with a still substantial staff of Ethiopians plus Weithaler, de Quadros, and a handful of expatriate nationals. The only vehicles and staff allowed outside Addis were those from the smallpox program. It was extremely hazardous, several teams were kidnapped, although eventually released in Somalia. A helicopter was destroyed with a grenade and one was held for ransom. A courageous group team effort defiantly continued until, on August 3, 1976, the last case was discovered in a desert village in Dimo, Ethiopia.

Meanwhile, smallpox was imported into Somalia where it persisted unknown to the outside world, hidden by government officials who endeavored secretly and unsuccessfully to stop its spread. Finally, its existence came to light and the extensive epidemic was eventually stopped by WHO staff and smallpox veterans from many countries. The world's last case occurred on October 26, 1977.

POSTLUDE – WHAT IF?

By October 1975 India and Bangladesh were smallpox-free, thus leaving Ethiopia as the only endemic country. The pace of the program in Ethiopia had been remarkable considering the problems of geography, lack of infrastructure and health services. The vigor and dedication of the Peace Corps Volunteers contributed significantly to the rapidity of its achievements. However, the revolution and civil wars of 1975 plunged much of Ethiopia into chaos. Fortunately, the endemic areas were confined to parts of three provinces, each of which required special surveillance operations in order to stop the spread. The experienced staff was known to residents in the affected areas and skillful enough to rapidly stop further spread despite the risks and the chaos of a revolutionary war.

Had the Ethiopian program not made the dramatic progress it did, August 1976 would almost certainly have found endemic smallpox over an impossibly large area, which would have been impossible for search and containment missions given the violence of the revolution that began in 1975. As it was, the endemic areas were restricted to three provinces and containment was possible.

Had the Peace Corps Volunteer group not contributed so much as they did at a critical point and time in the history of smallpox eradication, "Target Zero" might be an unfulfilled dream.

The stories presented in this book have been written by Peace Corps Volunteers who were directly involved in the Ethiopian program. These stories provide a treasure trove of insights into their work, living conditions and the substantial challenges they faced almost on a daily basis. It is an inspiration to read of their dedication, as well as their creative efforts to resolve problems that others may have viewed as insolvable. This book is an important addition to the historical record about the first human disease to be eradicated.

•

2

A Brief History of Smallpox in Ethiopia

by James W. Skelton, Jr.

Ethiopia is unique among the nations of Africa for a host of reasons, only one of which is the fact that it was never colonized. The Italian army did occupy Ethiopia during part of World War II, and some of its citizens are of Italian descent, but the Ethiopian culture is distinctly different from other East African countries. Indeed, it is as different from most other countries as a society could possibly be. There are many causes of the exclusive nature of the country's social order, the most important of which may be the inherent sense of pride that its inhabitants share regarding their motherland's legendary history.

The country's renowned history is comprised of factual and legendary elements that have been considered by many scholars. For example, Donald Levine describes the myths "which hitherto guided the world of Ethiopianist scholarship," stating that, "Scholars have viewed Ethiopia primarily either as an outpost of Semitic civilization, as an ethnographic museum, or as an underdeveloped country."[1] As a sociologist, Levine relies

---

1 D. Levine, Greater Ethiopia: The Evolution of a Multiethnic Society, The University of Chicago Press, 1974, 17.

on "recent advances in general sociological theory" to overcome such limited views and "develop an image of Ethiopia as a complex sociocultural system that has evolved through determinate stages."[2] He theorizes that an evolutionary process occurred in Ethiopia that was enabled by five types of what he calls "modalities of adaptation," which he describes as

- Holistic specialization (evolutionary patterns that are shared),
- Internal specialization (both the formation of elites and the creation of free–floating resources),
- Mutualistic specialization (the inclusion of occupational specialists), and
- Despecialization and new evolutionary potential,

all of which allowed the country to move toward a modern system by the early 1970s, even though "the peoples of Greater Ethiopia remain anchored in the five types of evolutionary modality."[3] While this characterization of Levine's vision is necessarily simplistic, it provides an insight into the complicated cultural and sociological environment in which the World Health Organization (WHO) and the Ethiopian government initiated the Smallpox Eradication Program (SEP) in 1971 in Ethiopia.

Due to its status as a developing nation, Ethiopia presented many complicating factors for medical personnel attempting to implement health programs, especially in terms of the serious shortage of health facilities, infrastructure and all–weather roads. In addition, the extreme geographical features found in both the mountainous and desert regions, and the widely dispersed and ethnically diverse population, with many distinct cultures and languages, further contributed to the complexity of implementing a national health program like the SEP.

These issues, as analyzed in the second half of the twentieth century, have been succinctly described by the distinguished authors of the comprehensive book on the eradication of smallpox, *Smallpox and Its Eradication,* the so–called "Big Red Book," as set forth below.

---

2 Ibid. 25.
3 Ibid. 166–181.

Most of Ethiopia's population was widely distributed in small groups of huts scattered across the central highlands at 1500–3000 meters above sea level. Rugged mountains and deep ravines made travel extremely difficult throughout this area and impossible during the rainy season, from June to September. At the periphery of the country were lowland areas in the west and southwest, with fertile and more populated savanna grassland.

The villages, however, were unlike those in most other countries in that they usually extended over large areas, the distance between houses often ranging from a few hundred to a thousand meters. In the extensive eastern and southern scrub desert areas, which comprised half the country, nomadic groups with ethnic ties to the neighboring French Territory of the Afars and the Issas and Somalia wandered freely, not infrequently crossing open borders between the countries. In the southwest were tribal groups whose way of life was little more advanced than that of a Stone Age culture.

Roads of any type were few; more than 85% of the population lived further than 30 kilometers away from the nearest all–weather road (Ayalew, 1982). Travel from place to place during the dry season was largely on horse or mule back or by foot. When torrential rains occurred in the highlands, between June and September, large areas became completely inaccessible. Communications were poor: an unreliable, frequently unusable, telephone service linked the capitals of provinces, and the postal service was deficient.

Language presented a further problem. The people of Ethiopia consisted of 10 major ethnic groups speaking 70 languages and dialects. Frequently, programme staff had to communicate successively through two or three different interpreters to question villagers about the existence of smallpox and to explain the unfamiliar practice of vaccination. Some people were reasonably receptive, but refusal and sometimes active resistance were encountered among many who lived in the highland areas in the north and central parts of the country. Not surprisingly, smallpox proved to be particularly tenacious in those areas.

Health personnel and facilities in 1967 were concentrated in Addis Ababa, the capital, and in Eritrea. The largest proportion of the government's health budget was allocated to curative services, to which not more than 5% of the population had access. Government records for 1967 show a census of 84 hospitals and 64 health centers and a total of 362 physicians and 2800 other health staff. For 40% of the population, a journey of 3 days or more, and for another 30%, a journey of 1–2 days, was required to reach the nearest health unit.[4]

In addition to the substantial challenges noted above, there were numerous other problems with which to contend, and many of those are addressed in detail by the authors of the various chapters of this book. It is clear, however, that the geographical and social challenges that were faced by health workers at various times in Ethiopia's history prevented the implementation of a national disease control program until the second half of the twentieth century.

EARLY REPORTS OF SMALLPOX IN ETHIOPIA

According to Richard Pankhurst, one of the most authoritative Ethiopian historians, the first written account of smallpox was recorded by James Bruce, a Scottish traveler and historian, who reported that smallpox "reached epidemic proportions during the reign of Iyasu I (1682–1706), when it raged among the Gallas, or Oromos."[5] The later stages of a subsequent epidemic in 1768 were actually "described by Bruce, who himself treated some of the victims. He claimed the outbreak had started at the

---

4 F. Fenner, D. A. Henderson, I. Arita, Z. Jezek, I. D. Ladnyi, *Smallpox and Its Eradication* (Geneva: World Health Organization, 1988), 1004–1006 [hereinafter Fenner et al., *Smallpox and Its Eradication*].

5 Pankhurst, Richard, "*An Introduction to the Medical History of Ethiopia,*" Red Sea Press, 1990, p. 23 [hereinafter, Pankhurst, *Medical History of Ethiopia*].

coast, killing over one thousand people at the ports of Massawa and Arkiko. From there it advanced to Adwa in the autumn of 1769, and spread rapidly inland, reaching Gondar in the spring of the following year."[6]

At least half a dozen outbreaks were reported in the nineteenth century, or almost once every generation. One of those outbreaks was described by Nathaniel Pearce, a British resident of Tigray province, who wrote in 1811, "As the malady increased it became more like a plague than the smallpox, and in a great many towns and villages the people lost all their children, and numbers of grown–up persons, who had not had the disease before, died also."[7] The most devastating epidemic in the late nineteenth century took place from 1886 to 1898, which also began in Massawa and spread to Adwa, killing 500 people out of a population of 7,000, 60% of whom were children under the age of 14, despite the fact that a major vaccination campaign was undertaken at the time.[8]

The descriptions of these epidemics indicate that the type of smallpox that occurred in Ethiopia during the eighteenth and nineteenth centuries constituted the more serious form of the illness called variola major, which was associated with a high fatality rate. Variola minor, the less deadly form of smallpox, was documented in 1958, but in 1964 an outbreak with variola major was reported by an Ethiopian health officer in the highlands.[9] Variola major disappeared in Ethiopia sometime thereafter, but it is not known when that happened.[10] It was variola minor, the less devastating type of smallpox, which would become the exclusive type of smallpox in Ethiopia in the 1960s and 1970s when vaccination and eradication efforts were increased.

What is thought to be the last significant smallpox epidemic occurred in 1904–05, when the virus spread over many areas of the nation.[11] It is possible that no further epidemics were reported in pre–World War II Ethiopia due to the initiation of vaccination campaigns, but the disease

6 Ibid.
7 Ibid. 24.
8 bid. 25.
9 Fenner et al., *Smallpox and Its Eradication*, 1007.
10 Ibid.
11 Ibid.

continued to be endemic for several decades thereafter.[12] It appears, therefore, that smallpox was not viewed as a significant medical problem until an epidemic took place.

TRADITIONAL METHODS OF TREATMENT AND PREVENTION

Over time, several methods of preventing and treating smallpox developed into traditional practices in Ethiopia. Most of these methods were fairly conventional in nature, while other approaches could be considered literally criminal in nature.

The most common type of traditional prevention was variolation, which was practiced in virtually all parts of the country. The practice of variolation has been defined and/or described countless times by dozens of experts. Dr. D.A. Henderson traced its introduction to before the 10th century, when it was the only procedure available to protect against high smallpox fatality rates.[13]

The scratch method of variolation is believed to have originated in Asia and then spread to other continents.[14] Dr. Henderson describes the practice as follows: "It consisted of deliberately infecting an individual with the smallpox virus by inserting or rubbing pulverized smallpox scabs or pus into superficial scratches in the skin."[15] Although the person who had been variolated usually developed a milder and less dangerous form of smallpox than when contracted naturally, the variolated person became contagious and could spread the disease to others who were not already immune.

In the best case scenario, the variolation resulted in a localized smallpox infection in the person inoculated, causing the formation of a pustule on the third day, with a scab formed on the twelfth day, at which

---

12 Ibid.

13 D. A. Henderson, Smallpox, *The Death of a Disease: The Inside Story of Eradicating a Worldwide Killer* (Amherst, New York: Prometheus Books, 2009), 44 [hereinafter, Henderson, *Smallpox, The Death of a Disease*].

14 Ibid. 45.

15 Ibid. 44.

time the patient would be fully recovered and protected from smallpox.[16] In some cases, however, pustules would form on the arm and elsewhere on the body and the fever and malaise would be much more severe, like a typical smallpox infection.[17] The practice of variolation spread across the world, eventually becoming prohibited by law in England and elsewhere near the mid nineteenth century. Nevertheless, in most parts of Ethiopia the tradition continued unabated until the disease was eradicated and the supply of infected materials was eliminated.

A simpler method of preventing the spread of smallpox was isolation, which was performed by either prohibiting or controlling the movement of people, or running away from an outbreak by escaping to the mountains in order to separate oneself from those who had contracted the disease.[18]

Forms of magic and superstition were also used by monks and others in an attempt to ward off or cure smallpox, but, not surprisingly, they were ineffective.

Sudorific treatment was more complicated, requiring the infected person to "be confined to his room without the smallest breath of air, and would be given hot drinks, extra bed clothing, and a fire, the door being securely closed to keep the room in darkness."[19] In early nineteenth century in the province of Tigray, "the patient would be placed on ashes or river sand and kept in his house, which would be closed to both air and light, with visitors rigidly excluded."[20] Of course, such isolation measures could only be successful if there was actually no contact with non–immune people.

Finally, there was the ruthless practice called purification by fire. This method is known to have been carried out by the Gallas, who were reportedly fearful of the prospects of the spread of smallpox in their communities.[21] As described by Bruce and other foreigners who witnessed it in the nineteenth century, when the disease "broke out in a household,

---

16 Ibid.
17 Ibid. 44–45.
18 Pankhurst, *Medical History of Ethiopia*, 28.
19 Ibid. 29.
20 Ibid.
21 Ibid. 28.

the neighbors, knowing it would spread to the whole area if unchecked, surrounded the house in the night and set fire to it. They then thrust the [patients] back into the burning dwelling at spear point even though they were their neighbors or relatives."[22]

As recently as the 1930s, it was revealed that the Somalis also practiced "rigid isolation of smallpox victims, as well as burning houses and personal effects to prevent the spread of the infection."[23] While the murder of one's neighbors may have been viewed at that time as a necessary solution that was required in order to protect the rest of the village, it clearly constituted abhorrent and criminal behavior by today's standards.

SMALLPOX IN ETHIOPIA PRIOR TO THE ONSET OF THE SMALLPOX ERADICATION PROGRAM

In pre–World War II Ethiopia, from 1916 to 1935, which included the reign of *Ras* Tafari Makonnen and the early years of Emperor Haile Selassie's rule, the process of modernization was enhanced, thereby allowing "significant developments in the governmental, missionary, and commercial fields, resulting in the increasing popularization and availability of foreign medical cures."[24]

In fact, there was an increase in the prevalence of smallpox vaccination services during this period.[25] The "Phelps Stokes mission reported that vaccination was gaining ground, while a decade or so later Rey noted that it was popularly recognized and appreciated," and it was estimated that 50,000 smallpox vaccinations had been given between 1924 and 1935.[26] These were positive developments, but it appears that no one really knew at that time how widespread smallpox had become.

In the post–World War II era, the variola minor strain of smallpox in Ethiopia was found to have a much lower mortality rate (one to two

---

22 Ibid.

23 Ibid. 29

24 Ibid. 205.

25 Ibid. 216.

26 Ibid. The Phelps–Stokes Fund was established in 1911 by a bequest of Miss Caroline Phelps Stokes, a New York philanthropist. The fund was set up principally for the education of blacks in Africa and in the United States. See more at: http://www.worldhistory.biz/sundries/42422–phelps–stokes–commissions.html

percent) than variola major, so the government considered smallpox to be a lesser priority than the fight against malaria.[27] In fact, in the late 1960s it was extremely clear that the USAID–supported malaria eradication program was the top priority and the Ethiopian government "was convinced that it could not undertake a second eradication program." [28]

IMPORTANT DEVELOPMENTS IN SMALLPOX ERADICATION

There were two important developments affecting smallpox eradication on an international level that occurred at about this time.

First, in May 1966, the World Health Assembly approved a 10–year intensified smallpox eradication plan that was "2–pronged:

- mass vaccination campaigns in which freeze–dried vaccine of assured quality were employed, and which were assessed by special teams, and
- the development of a surveillance system for the detection and investigation of cases and the containment of outbreaks."[29]

In 1967 this new approach of "surveillance and containment" was first implemented by the CDC program in Eastern Nigeria, and it achieved the interruption of smallpox transmission.[30]

This new strategy from the late 1960s was described by Dr. Henderson as containing two elements, as set forth below.

The basic inputs for surveillance were weekly reports from all health centers and hospitals, indicating the number of cases of smallpox. This information was to be compiled concurrently and analyzed, and the reports disseminated widely . . .. To strengthen this component, two or three–person containment teams were created. They would respond quickly to investigate reported outbreaks, verify cases, search for additional cases, and vaccinate contacts and others in the immediate area — creating

27 Henderson, Smallpox, *The Death of a Disease*, 216.
28 Ibid. 217.
29 Fenner et al., *Smallpox and Its Eradication*, 424.
30 Henderson, Smallpox, *The Death of a Disease*, 91.

a barrier that would block further transmission of the virus. Once the surveillance–containment methodology was put into operation, the effect in stopping smallpox transmission was often dramatic, even in poorly vaccinated areas.[31]

Since there weren't many health centers and hospitals on which to rely in Ethiopia, active surveillance became a major component of the SEP's surveillance and containment operations in Ethiopia in the early 1970s. The surveillance teams utilized several active techniques, such as searching for cases by talking to village leaders and visiting health centers and schools.

For example, Vince Radke, one of the PCVs working in Ethiopia, reported that "In the first classroom I visited, I obtained so many reports of cases in so many different villages that I went immediately to start investigating."[32]

This new strategy would eventually prove to be the most effective method of controlling the spread of smallpox, and, ultimately, the most essential in eradicating the disease.

The second important development occurred in 1965 when Dr. Benjamin Rubin invented the bifurcated vaccination needle, which was significant because it "was efficient using very little vaccine to get the job done. And the bifurcated needle was inexpensive . . . each needle cost a quarter of a cent."[33]

These changes set the stage for the beginning of the worldwide SEP effort starting in 1967, when it was "estimated that there were between ten and fifteen million cases with two million deaths occurring in forty–three countries," of which 31 were determined to be endemic.[34]

Ethiopia was, of course, one of the endemic countries, but, as mentioned above, a resource-intensive malaria eradication program was already underway there with the support of the USAID.

---

31 Ibid. 91–92
32 Ibid. 220
33 Ibid. 13–14.
34 D. A. Henderson, "The Global Eradication of Smallpox: Historical Perspectives and Future Prospects," chapter 1, in *The Global Eradication of Smallpox*, edited by S. Bhattacharya and S Messenger, (Hyderabad, India: Orient BlackSwan, 2010), 19.

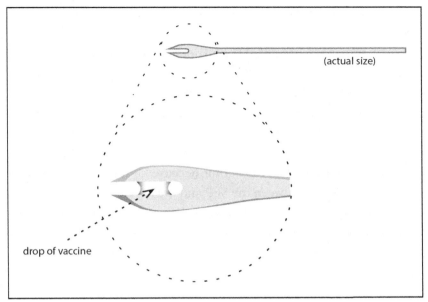

(actual size)

drop of vaccine

Bifurcated needle. A vaccinator would dip the tip of a needle in a vial of vaccine and a single drop would adhere between the prongs; then the vaccinator turned the needle at a right angle to the surface of the skin and made many rapid punctures. If vaccinators made fifteen punctures rapidly, vaccinations were nearly always successful, thus fifteen punctures became the standard. (Henderson, *Smallpox, The Death of a Disease, 294*)

In 1968 and 1969, two attempts were made by the WHO to arrange meetings with the Ethiopian government officials to develop a national plan for eradicating smallpox, but the meetings fell through.[35] It was not until Dr. D.A. Henderson, the WHO's chief of the worldwide SEP, met Dr. Kurt Weithaler, the director of the Emperor's Imperial Guard Hospital, that any progress was made.[36] Dr. Weithaler offered to serve as Ethiopia's principal adviser if the program was approved, then met with the Emperor and two days later the Minister of Health signed the WHO's agreement.[37] That series of events constituted the breakthrough that the WHO needed in order to implement the plan for the SEP in Ethiopia.

---

35 Henderson, *Smallpox, The Death of a Disease*, 217.
36 Ibid. 218.
37 Ibid.

THE ASSIGNMENT OF PCVS TO THE SEP IN ETHIOPIA AND ELSEWHERE

Although the author attempted to find documentary evidence of the first group of PCVs to serve with the WHO's SEP, it became apparent that the Peace Corps had not kept any specific records of such things. The questions that the author wanted to answer were, how did the WHO gain the agreement of the Peace Corps to allow PCVs to work in the SEP, and what country was the first to use the services of PCVs in its SEP? These matters were important to the author because he wanted to be able to trace the connection between the SEP and the PCVs.

Upon inquiry, Dr. D.A. Henderson informed the author that the original problems with securing the approval of the Peace Corps to permit PCVs to work in the WHO's program were related to Zaire, now the Democratic Republic of the Congo (DRC). Dr. Henderson stated,

> We needed personnel badly — huge country and few Congolese trained beyond the 8th grade. My appeal for PCVs was turned down because it was PC policy to have assignees based full–time in the community so that they could interact and so that they could get to know the people and vice versa. We needed them for mobile teams. During a short visit to D.C., I stayed with a college roommate, Peter Craig, and his wife, Sally, and she just happened to be responsible for the Congo desk, i.e., she was the policy maker. Very soon, the request to assign PCVs to mobile teams in the Congo was approved. We would never have succeeded without them. It seems to me that the approval to have PCVs for Ethiopia must have come at the same time or within a year of the approval for DRC.[38]

Therefore, it appears that those working behind the scenes in the U.S. government and the WHO were responsible for finding a way to get PCVs involved on a full–time basis in the SEP in Ethiopia. This was

---

38 Email message from D. A. Henderson to the author, dated January 18, 2016.

yet another development that would ultimately be a critical factor in the effort to eradicate smallpox in Ethiopia.

But what was the first country to use the services of PCVs in the SEP? In connection with that inquiry, Dr. Henderson provided the author with some information about the SEP and PCVs in Afghanistan. In a candid remark he stated,

> As I recall, my first visit to Afghanistan was in 1968. The program was a total disaster as is described in the Big Red Book. WHO had been providing vehicles and an adviser since 1963, plus 2 nurses. He [the adviser] shared one large office room with the 2 nurses, but would only communicate with them in writing (I can't make this stuff up). The program had gone badly and I think it was this adviser who persuaded the U.S. Peace Corps to send a contingent of nurses. He insisted that unless the mothers accepted vaccination, the children could not be vaccinated, and since (according to him) the male vaccinators could not vaccinate women, nothing could be done.[39]

Further inquiries about Afghanistan led to the acquisition of a book written by Carol Beecher, a former PCV from Afghanistan. The book revealed that 42 Peace Corps trainees were recruited for Afghanistan Group XI in March 1967.[40] All of these trainees were females, and they were trained in Brattleboro, Vermont to be smallpox vaccinators who would participate in a mass vaccination program in Afghanistan, where they were only supposed to vaccinate women and children. This limitation on their vaccination responsibilities was necessary due to what is called "purdah," an Afghan cultural phenomenon whereby women were effectively secluded in their homes and their husbands refused to allow them to leave the house to be vaccinated or to be vaccinated by male

---

39 Ibid.
40 C. Beecher, K. M. Alami, *Echoes Across Afghanistan, Choi, Choi, Naan,* (Indianapolis, Indiana, Dog Ear Publishing 2014), 1 [hereinafter, Beecher, *Echoes Across* Afghanistan].

vaccinators.[41] "Thus male vaccinators had been unable to enter village homes to vaccinate the women and children; also female Afghans were not allowed to be trained as vaccinators as this type of work would have required them to work outside homes of their extended families."[42]

Another all–female group of 36 Peace Corps trainees met for a 3–month training session in Tucson, Arizona near the end of 1968, but only 17 of those trainees ended up working as vaccinators in Afghanistan in 1969.[43]

Fourteen of those PCVs, plus their Peace Corps training director, were interviewed for the documentary entitled "Once in Afghanistan." The documentary shows that their work continued until 1970, when, incredibly, it was eventually discovered that the underlying reason for the all–female–vaccinator corps was not correct, as described below.

> It became apparent during this period that, contrary to previous ideas, the 30 United States women volunteers were not essential to the work of vaccination. It was found that when village leaders were properly informed about the nature of the programme, women were usually permitted to be vaccinated by male vaccinators, although sometimes on the forearm or wrist rather than on the upper arm, the customary site of vaccination. From the investigation of outbreaks, it also became apparent that few cases occurred among women, most of whom by the age of puberty had experienced smallpox or had been variolated or vaccinated. Thus, even if some were missed during the vaccination campaign, only a small proportion would remain susceptible. Accordingly, the volunteers were reassigned to assessment and surveillance teams and some helped to establish the necessary administrative and support structure at headquarters and zone offices.[44]

---

41 Fenner et al., *Smallpox and Its Eradication*, 661.
42 Beecher, *Echoes Across Afghanistan*, 1.
43 J. Vickers and J. Bergedick, *Once in Afghanistan*, (Dirt Road Documentaries, 2008).
44 Fenner et al., *Smallpox and Its Eradication*, 667.

A new report by the Peace Corps about PCVs working in the world-wide SEP gives some examples of experimental groups of PCVs who were used in Tanzania in 1967 and 1968 and in Afghanistan in 1966 on a temporary basis to see if they would be a useful resource in the SEP's work.[45] Nevertheless, it was Group XI of Afghanistan that was the first formal group of PCVs to be recruited and trained to work on a full-time basis with the WHO in connection with the worldwide SEP.

As for Ethiopia, the first Peace Corps group to include PCVs for the SEP work was Group XIV, which arrived in Addis Ababa on October 30, 1970.[46] There were 30 trainees in Group XIV, 18 of whom[47] were assigned to the Smallpox section, while 12 were assigned to the Rural Development section. When the two groups completed their separate, 3-month training programs, 17 Smallpox trainees and 11 RD trainees were sworn in as full-fledged PCVs on February 1, 1971.[48] The SEP PCVs were Jay Anderson, Gene Bartley, Clyde Emerson, Russ Handzus, Lee Heckman, Graham Holmboe, Charlie Kilmer, Phil Kneller, Dan Kraushaar, Leo and Joan Landkamer, Jim Lepkowski, Vince Radke, Stan Ratoff, Jim Siemon, Marc Strassburg and Gary Urquhart (the author transferred from a US-AID-sponsored food-for-work project, to the SEP in June 1971).

The SEP project officially began shortly thereafter, and the 17 Smallpox PCVs were assigned to work with 25 Ethiopian personnel, concentrating on the provinces of Kaffa, Illubabor, Welega and Gemu Gofa.[49]

Ultimately, six other Peace Corps groups, Groups XV, XVI, XVII, XVIII, XIX and XX included Smallpox trainees who participated in the SEP.[50] There was also at least one transfer from each of Groups X and XIII

---

45 K. Van Roekel, "The Peace Corps' Contribution to the Global Smallpox Eradication Program," Peace Corps December 2016, http://www.peacecorps.gov/contributionto-theglobalsmallpoxeradicationprogram, 19 and 32 [hereinafter Van Roekel, Peace Corps Smallpox Eradication Report].

46 J. Skelton, Volunteering in Ethiopia: A Peace Corps Odyssey, Beaumont Books, 1991, 19.

47 Ibid. 13.

48 Ibid. 49.

49 C. de Quadros, "Experiences with Smallpox Eradication in Ethiopia," D31 Vaccine 29 – S4 (2011) [hereinafter De Quadros, Smallpox Eradication in Ethiopia]

50 Ethiopia & Eritrea RPCVs, http://eerpcv.org/pages/rpcvs/training_groups.html

who worked in the SEP.[51] Although the Peace Corps' "Smallpox Eradication Report" arrived at a total of 72 Ethiopia PCVs who worked in the SEP from 1970 to 1975,[52] the author prepared an additional list (see table below) that shows some differences in names and a total of 73 PCVs. "When the groups overlapped, there were as many as 40 Peace Corps Volunteers working in the country's smallpox program in any given year."[53]

SEP/ETHIOPIA PCVS LISTED ALPHABETICALLY WITHIN PC TRAINING GROUP*

Name	PC Training Group	PC Service	SEP/Ethiopia Service
Timothy Williams	X	1968–72	1971–72
Michael A. Santarelli	XIII	1970–73	1972–73
Jay L. Anderson	XIV	1970–72	1970–72
Gene L. Bartley	XIV	1970–72, 1974–76	1970–72
Clyde S. Emerson	XIV	1970–72	1970–72
Russell J. Handzus	XIV	1970–72	1970–72
Lee Heckman	XIV	1970–72	1970–72
Graham Holmboe	XIV	1970–71	1970–71
Charles J. Kilmer	XIV	1970–72	1970–72
Phillip B. Kneller	XIV	1970–72	1970–72
Daniel L. Kraushaar	XIV	1970–72	1970–72
Leo J. Landkamer	XIV	1970–73	1970–73
James M. Lepkowski	XIV	1970–72	1970–72
Vincent J. Radke	XIV	1970–74	1970–74
Stanley H. Ratoff	XIV	1970–73	1970–73
James R. Siemon	XIV	1970–72	1970–72
James W. Skelton, Jr.	XIV	1970–72	1971–72
Marc A. Strassburg	XIV	1970–72	1970–72
Gary A. Urquhart	XIV	1970–72	1970–72
John Scott Porterfield	XV	1971–73	1971–73
William P. Anderson	XVI	1971–73	1971–73

51 Van Roekel, Peace Corps Smallpox Eradication Report, Table 3, 50.
52 Ibid. 50
53 Ibid. 50.

Name	PC Training Group	PC Service	SEP/Ethiopia Service
William Bailey	XVI	1971–73	1971–73
Larry Clark	XVI	1971–73	1971–73
Thomas Duffy	XVI	1971–72	1971–72
Gregory Hoffman	XVI	1971–73	1971–73
Scott D. Holmberg	XVI	1971–73	1971–73
Jack Howard	XVI	1971–73	1971–73
Paul Mongeau	XVI	1971–74	1971–74
Alan Schnur	XVI	1971–74	1971–74
Joseph Sina	XVI	1971–72	1971–72
Peter Squyer	XVI	1971–74	1971–74
David Bourne	XVII	1972–74	1972–74
Dexter Fairbank, III	XVII	1972–73	1972–73
Michael Felton	XVII	1972–74	1972–74
Pamela Noble	XVII	1972–74	1972–74
Steve Reiber	XVII	1972–73	1972–73
E.J. (Jay) Rowland	XVII	1972–74	1972–74
R. Mark Weeks	XVII	1972–74	1972–74
Dennis Weibel	XVII	1972–74	1972–74
Peter Carrasco	XVIII	1972–74	1972–74
John DeVleming	XVIII	1972–74	1972–74
Keith Heldenbrand	XVIII	1972–75	1972–75
Clayton Pape	XVIII	1972–74	1972–74
Donald Piburn	XVIII	1972–74	1972–74
Richard Poole	XVIII	1972–74	1972–74
Gerald Sulat	XVIII	1972–74	1972–74
Thomas Syre (né Syrewicz)	XVIII	1972–74	1972–74
Doug Arbuckle	XIX	1973–74	1973–74
Warren Barrash	XIX	1970–74	1973–74
Robert Bolan	XIX	1973–74	1973–74
Raymond Bridges	XIX	1973–74	1973–74
James Brown	XIX	1973–74	1973–74
Robert Cole	XIX	1973–74	1973–74
Stuart Gold	XIX	1973–74	1973–74

Name	PC Training Group	PC Service	SEP /Ethiopia Service
Tabo Mack	XIX	1973–74	1973–74
William Martin	XIX	1973–74	1973–74
Elmer Moore	XIX	1973–74	1973–74
Thomas Ridgik	XIX	1973–75	1973–75
Robert Steinglass	XIX	1973–75	1973–74
Theodore Tyson	XIX	1973–74	1973–74
Terry Brahmsteadt	XX	1974–75	1974–75
Vincent R. Campbell	XX	1974–76	1974–75
Kevin P. Carey	XX	1974–75	1974–75
Benjamin F. Crabtree	XX	1974–75	1974–75
Richard Godderz	XX	1974–75	1974–75
Gene Johnson	XX	1974–75	1974–75
Steven Lunde	XX	1974–75	1974–75
Donald Martin	XX	1974–75	1974–75
Ronald Mills	XX	1974–75	1974–75
Robert C. Ogden	XX	1974–75	1974–75
Clifford Pulaski	XX	1974–75	1974–75
Edward M. Ruppert	XX	1974–75	1974–75
Paul Weissleder	XX	1974–76	1974–75

*The sources for this listing of SEP Ethiopia PCVs are as follows:
(1) The Ethiopia and Eritrea Returned Peace Corps Volunteers website, http://www.ethiopiaeritrearpcvs.org/pages/rpcvs/training_groups/70-13to74-20.html;
(2) K. Van Roekel, "The Peace Corps' Contribution to the Global Smallpox Eradication Program," Peace Corps December 2016, 19 and 32, https://s3.amazonaws.com/files.peacecorps.gov/documents/open-government/Peace_Corps_Global_Smallpox.pdf;
(3) The Editors' files, documents and email messages among the authors regarding this topic; and
(4) The Freedom of Information Act report requested by the author and received from the Peace Corps, dated October 3, 2019, which confirmed the accuracy of this listing. [Due to a lack of certainty about the Group numbers for a few of the PCVs on the list, some Group numbers were estimated based on the years of service.]

THE SEP IN ETHIOPIA

Those of us who were fortunate enough to work in the SEP in Ethiopia quickly learned that there was a remarkably high level of leadership in the program.

Dr. Kurt Weithaler, Dr. D. A. Henderson, and
Dr. Ciro de Quadros seen here in Washington,
D.C. in1980. *Photo by Michael Santarelli*

Dr. D.A. Henderson led the WHO's global program with tireless skill, dedication and determination that inspired the managers and epidemiologists in the host countries. He was stationed in Geneva, but made countless trips to the countries in which the SEP was active.

In Ethiopia, Dr. Kurt Weithaler served as the Director and WHO Senior Advisor, and Dr. Ciro de Quadros was the WHO Chief Epidemiologist who was responsible for all of the work in the field. These men motivated the PCVs and their Ethiopian counterparts through their indefatigable work and commitment to the program.

"Ethiopia was the first country in the world to start its national smallpox eradication programme from day one with the strategy of 'surveillance and containment,' instead of mass vaccination."[54] That approach was followed religiously by the PCVs and the sanitarians and was constantly

---

54 De Quadros, Experiences with Smallpox in Ethiopia, D31.

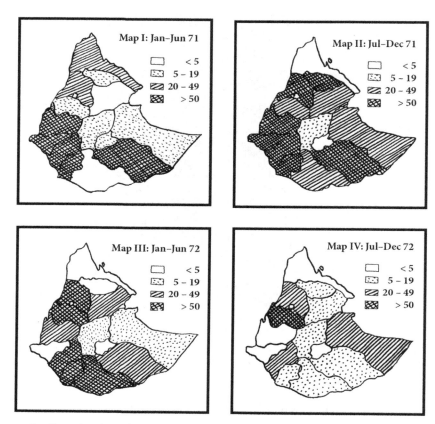

Smallpox incidence by 100,000 inhabitants. Ethiopia, 1971 and 1972

reinforced by Ciro de Quadros during his innumerable trips into the field. A mere 197 cases of smallpox had been reported by the Ethiopian Ministry of Health in 1969 and only 722 in 1970.[55] In 1971, everything changed dramatically with the onset of the SEP, and, "By the end of the year, a field staff of only thirty–nine people had recorded and contained outbreaks with a total of 26,000 cases."[56] This staggering number of cases of smallpox was the highest recorded of any country in the world.[57] Fewer cases were reported in the two succeeding years, with 16,999 cases in 1972,

55 Henderson, Smallpox, The Death of a Disease, 219.
56 Ibid. 220.
57 Van Roekel, Peace Corps Smallpox Eradication Report, 61.

whereas only 5,414 were found in 1973.[58] By September 1973, five of the fourteen provinces were declared smallpox–free.[59]

The maps above of Ethiopia, delineated by province, were published in the "Smallpox Surveillance Report" from January 1973, page 6.

The number of vaccinations performed in Ethiopia in this period of time was also astonishing. In 1971 there were 3,162,000 vaccinations and in 1972 a total of 3,222,000 vaccinations were performed, for a two–year total of 6,384,000 vaccinations.[60] This was an amazing, unforeseen accomplishment, attributable to the dedication and hard work of the SEP staff. From 1973 to 1977, 10,981,000 vaccinations were performed, for a seven–year total of 17,365,000 vaccinations just in Ethiopia.[61]

These herculean efforts were somewhat interrupted by the over-throw of Emperor Haile Selassie in September 1974 and the installation of a military dictatorship called the Derg. Despite the uncertainty and disorder that occurred as a result of the coup d'etat, the program contin-ued to function thereafter thanks in no small part to the perseverance of Ciro de Quadros, his counterpart, *Ato* Tamiru Debeya, and the fearless, dedicated SEP staff.[62] However, the Peace Corps withdrew the PCVs from the country in 1975 for security reasons.[63]

This was a very difficult transition period for the SEP in Ethiopia. Dr. de Quadros reported, "All UN operations except our programme stopped. Stopping the programme at that time would have been disas-trous. We received permission to stay in the country . . . .. However, with additional WHO resources we were able to deploy more nationals. In each province we started hiring more senior Ethiopians. The programme was 'nationalized.'"[64]

The number of cases discovered in 1974 and 1975 decreased to 4,439 and 3,935, respectively, despite improved surveillance. The number fell

58 Fenner et al., *Smallpox and Its Eradication*, Table 21.8, 1016.
59 Henderson, *Smallpox, The Death of a Disease*, 222.
60 Fenner et al., *Smallpox and Its Eradication*, Table 21.8, 1016.
61 Ibid.
62 Henderson, *Smallpox, The Death of a Disease*, 218 and 225, (also see, Van Roekel, Peace Corps Smallpox Eradication Report, 60.)
63 Ibid. 225.
64 De Quadros, Smallpox Eradication in Ethiopia, D32–33.

dramatically in 1976 to 915 cases as the number of infected areas continued to be reduced. In total, 58,031 cases were reported during the six–year period from 1971 to 1976.[65] "During this last phase, we monitored the programme by tracking the number of affected districts or villages. Affected locations were searched for ten weeks after the last detected case. If no further cases were detected during that period, the village or district was taken off the list of affected areas."[66]

Finally, on August 9, 1976, the last case of smallpox in Ethiopia was discovered in the nomad village of Dimo in the Ogaden desert, where a three-year-old girl, named Amina Salat, fell ill.[67] It was ascertained that during the incubation period she had been both variolated and vaccinated, but her recovery was uneventful.[68] Ten weeks elapsed thereafter without the report of another case of smallpox in Ethiopia or elsewhere, during which time Amina Salat became quite famous as potentially the last case of smallpox in the world. Before victory could be declared, however, another case was reported in Somalia, thus postponing the celebration of the worldwide eradication of smallpox.

CONCLUSION

Ciro de Quadros wrote the most succinct and accurate summary of the SEP in Ethiopia that one could hope to find, as follows:

> Over the course of the seven year campaign to eradicate smallpox in Ethiopia many challenges were overcome. Beginning with the overall lack of medical infrastructure and a variety of competing interests for the limited resources available to the Ministry of Health, smallpox was all but ignored for a long time. With the hard work of dedicated staff, a successful surveillance and containment strategy made great strides toward the goal, but government instability, harsh working conditions and nomadic

---

65 Fenner et al., *Smallpox and Its Eradication*, Table 21.8, 1016
66 De Quadros, Smallpox Eradication in Ethiopia, D35.
67 Henderson, Smallpox, *The Death of a Disease*, 228.
68 Ibid.

populations continued to present roadblocks. In the end the mission was accomplished through innovative interventions and continued persistence.[69]

Following centuries of sporadic and devastating epidemics of smallpox in Ethiopia, the disease was eliminated as a result of the dedicated efforts of those who worked in the SEP, and the government officials and community members who supported them. The PCVs and the Ethiopian sanitarians who labored in the program made significant contributions and helped achieve the success of the campaign through their hard work, fearlessness, single–minded commitment and their refusal to consider the possibility of failure, all of which were required to accomplish such a lofty goal as the eradication of smallpox in a country as complex and difficult to work in as Ethiopia.

Overall, the SEP improved the lives and the health of the Ethiopian people and provided the PCVs and sanitarians with such heroic experiences that many of them devoted their entire professional lives to public health service.

The recent losses of Drs. Henderson and de Quadros dealt a devastating blow to the public health community. Both men were honored by large, heartfelt and well–attended memorial services. They were respected as innovative pioneers, heroes and giants in the health field, particularly their roles in the successful campaign to eradicate smallpox. They will always be remembered as the guiding intellectual and emotional forces at the global level, and in Ethiopia, behind what many consider to be the single most significant accomplishment in the history of the fight against disease.

·

Acknowledgments — The author is very grateful to Alan Schnur, Gene Bartley and James Siemon for their timely and helpful comments and suggestions regarding the contents of this chapter.

---

69 De Quadros, Smallpox Eradication in Ethiopia, D35.

3

A Tale of Two Provinces

Smallpox Eradication Experiences
in Welega and Gojam Provinces

by Alan Schnur

After checking a smallpox report in a remote village in Ethiopia, I found myself walking for several hours after dark with local guides I barely knew, through fields and then along a ledge with a steep drop-off, without a light, and with no moon to light the way. I trusted the guides to get me back to the place we would sleep that night, and was not afraid or uncomfortable. Reflecting on this episode recorded in my notebook, with the entry expressing some amazement at how routine this travel felt, I have to wonder about how I had arrived at this extraordinary situation in Ethiopia, a long way from where I grew up in New York City.

I had started my college studies as a pre-med student, with the intention of applying to medical school. But along the way, I found the laboratory courses tedious, and dissection of animals too grisly, so I switched majors to history, also taking courses on journalism. I had always been interested in geography, and had even written a paper on Ethiopia, so I was interested in the Peace Corps, and applied after completing college. When they proposed to assign me to a program on smallpox eradication in Ethiopia, I was very interested. I found the preliminary introductory whether the patient was suffering from smallpox, chickenpox, measles, scabies or something else. We had to convince people to accept vaccination, and devise strategies for most efficiently and effectively vaccinating the necessary people, often in a population hostile to taking vaccination. We also had to interact with a wide range of government officials at all levels, health workers, teachers, religious leaders, village leaders, students, and ordinary people going about their business, to inform and educate them about the program, and, as far as possible, to get their support.

I estimate that, overall, my smallpox eradication work in Ethiopia (excluding driving time to reach an area) was 25% walking and riding to check rumors and outbreaks, 25% vaccination activities, 25% epidemiology (surveillance activities, finding and investigating outbreaks), 5% health education (explaining the program at schools, markets, government offices), 5% differential diagnosis of smallpox and other rash with fever cases, and 15% administrative/management/diplomatic (interacting with provincial and local government and health officials, and community members, and administration including preparing reports and accounts).

The above time estimate does not include the many hours spent waiting at *woreda* and *awraja* offices to get official letters to expedite the work in the areas to which we were traveling. Even after letters were obtained, there could be long waits at local level for the *mikitil woreda* governor, *balabat* (landlord), *atbia danya* (local community leader and judge), *chikashume* (elected village chief), or *netch libosh* (member of the local people's militia) to return home, or to turn up at the appointed meeting place. It was not unusual to spend almost an entire day waiting for a letter, or an afternoon waiting for the *balabat* to keep an appointment.

Occasionally, I would organize a show with my counterpart (*Ato Tefera Galleta*, a sanitarian in Welega province, was very good at this), where I acted like I lost my temper because of the long wait. My counterpart would then apologize profusely for the uncivilized behavior of the foreigner, and request that the *woreda* secretary please help to calm the situation by expediting the letter. This strategy worked occasionally, but it had to be applied carefully so as not to unduly upset people.

The author vaccinating in rural Welega. A smallpox poster is on the right. *Photo provided by author.*

The diplomatic aspect of the work was very important because we always had to interact with *awraja* and *woreda* governors to get letters, and to get local officials to accompany us. Without the support and involvement of local officials, the work went very slowly, or not at all, particularly in Gojam. The exact nature of the work depended on the area involved, and whether smallpox cases were present. We would routinely go out for two to four weeks of field work in Welega, and two to three weeks in Gojam, and then return to the provincial capital for a week to prepare reports, restock vaccine and supplies, receive mail, take a shower, and generally "recharge" our batteries. The photo[1] above shows an example of a vaccination session in a rural area of Welega province.

In Welega, I traveled by Land Rover from Nekemte, the provincial capital, with a counterpart sanitarian or dresser (a health worker trained to dress wounds, but with expanded nursing responsibilities

1 Photo was originally published in chapter 5 of *The Global Eradication of Smallpox*, edited by Sanjoy Bhattacharya and Sharon Messenger, (Hyderabad, India: Orient BlackSwan, 2010), p. 143.

in health centers and clinics), working as a team. We would split up in the field, with a local dresser, pharmacist, or student interpreter, accompanying me. As my Amharic became better, if necessary when there was no dresser or other suitable interpreter available, and a co-operative government official accompanied me, I sometimes went by myself on short trips. With the support of the government official, I could use the letter from the *woreda* or *awraja* governor to identify myself and confirm that I was a health worker and the purpose of my visit was to eradicate smallpox.

SMALLPOX CASE REPORTS FROM SUDAN TAKEN VERY SERIOUSLY

SEP HQ took reports of exported smallpox cases to Sudan very seriously. We spent much time on the Welega border with Sudan vaccinating and checking for cases.

Following the report of smallpox cases in the semi-desert area of Asosa *awraja*, along the Sudanese border, by the Sudan smallpox program to the SEP HQ office in Addis Ababa, I was sent to investigate with Tefera. The people in this area along the border were more closely linked to Sudan than the highlands of Ethiopia, with Sudanese currency more widely used than Ethiopian. People spoke Wotowit, a Semitic language, similar to Arabic, and not understandable for Amharic and Oromo speakers, so a "translation chain" was often required to interview people. We worked for 19 days in Asosa *awraja* in February-March 1972, driving along the few roads in the area, stopping at markets and villages and carefully interviewing villagers and village leaders, and also walking to some villages. We found a fresh smallpox case and five old cases, no longer infective, and vaccinated in the area. No one reported any other cases. We didn't walk to every village because this would have been impractical due to the size of the area, and it had been shown to be unnecessary since interviewing people at collection points (like schools and markets, and along the road) would uncover cases in the villages from which people were coming. We returned to Nekemte and reported to Addis that we had found a smallpox case, but there was not a serious outbreak.

When the reports of cases continued to arrive from Sudan, Ciro de Quadros flew to Asosa on March 13, 1972 for two weeks to join the search himself, so Tefera and I returned again to Asosa after three days in Nekemte. After my Land Rover broke down right on the Sudanese border, we had to wait for a car to bring spare parts from Addis.

While waiting for the car driven by Scott Porterfield and Leo Land-kamer (as mentioned in Porterfield's chapter, "My Adventures in Welo and on the Sudan Border"), Ciro and our team continued the work, travelling on foot and by mule or donkey, for seven days through villages near the border. With information about specific village names that had been received from Sudan, Ciro led the group, either walking or riding on a mule or donkey, for seven days to visit villages we had not visited previously. We discovered that our previous visit interviewees had not come from these villages, and that the smallpox cases had occurred between the areas from where our informants had come. So, the missed cases did not represent a failure of market/collection point surveillance, but, rather, was an example of the need to better map where people were coming from (not always an easy job in view of the lack of good maps).

This field trip with Ciro turned out to be one of my most memorable in Ethiopia, as we walked in the very hot sun every day, and then got to talk with village people and relax in the "cooler" evening air. We covered all the villages in the area and discovered about 100 smallpox cases (including older, unreported cases and active cases) and also vaccinated in each village.

One night, during this trip, while walking from village to village, we bought a chicken and Ciro treated everyone to his excellent Brazilian chicken stew. This stew went very well with the Sudanese style flat breads made in the village. In the evening, Ciro and I sometimes had an opportunity to play chess on the set he had brought, as we did from time to time in Addis. We found many smallpox cases, and I got to watch and learn from Ciro's incredible ability in the field. We also met with Anazir Ashafi, an important local official, who helped us a lot, but who was in such a rush to join our team that he reportedly left his home so quickly that he forgot his shoes — and had to go back to get them.

We eventually got to visit his home, and meet his many wives and children. Afterwards, whenever Ciro and I met, we always joked about those shoes.

ARRESTED IN SUDAN

Ciro returned to Asosa in April 1972 and we went farther north, along the Blue Nile River, vaccinating rather primitive tribal people and looking for cases. During this trip, on April 20, 1972, we drove on a very rough dirt trail from Ethiopia into Sudan at a non-official border crossing site to try and visit a Sudanese health facility in a small town and inform the health workers there about the smallpox situation on the Ethiopian side. Immediately after arriving, we were arrested, and the keys to Ciro's Toyota Land Cruiser were taken by the police. The police chief said he had to inquire from his superiors in Blue Nile province about what to do and we needed to remain in custody until he had an answer.

Ciro had his UN Laissez Passer, but I had no identification besides my official Ethiopia SEP identity booklet. I wasn't overly concerned about being sent to Sennar or Khartoum for crossing the border without a passport, but it was definitely a possibility. We were detained for three hours, sitting on cots under a thatched roofed pavilion, without any food. The teacher in the village was very concerned by this and came to speak with the Sudanese policeman and to offer us bread and canned cheese. Ciro announced that we were on a hunger strike until we were released, and we refused to eat the very tempting flat breads and cheese. Ciro looked like he would slap my hand if I reached for the breads.

Eventually, after three hours, we were released to return to Ethiopia at the insistence of the teacher, with the hunger strike probably also contributing to our release. We were able to exchange information on smallpox during our "detention," so we achieved our objective. As we were driving back into Ethiopia, we met Omar (who was very tall, about 6 feet 5 inches), one of the tribal leaders in the Wotowit community on the Ethiopian side, coming to rescue us, riding on one of the large, highly prized, and very fast, local donkeys. He was glad to see us, and we were glad to see him.

During this trip we also learned some new Arabic words like "*Azo ma'afish*," which we understood to mean "there are no crocodiles." We learned these words while swimming in the evening in the Blue Nile River. Ciro would say *"Azo fi!"* (there are crocodiles), and the response would come back "*azo ma'afish.*" But Ciro then asked why there were guards with rifles standing at the water's edge while we were swimming?

On another occasion, in January 1972, Gary Urquhart (PCV) and *Ato* Tamiru Dibeya (sanitarian), members of the central assessment team, met us in Dembidolo (in the *awraja* south of Asosa), not far from the Sudanese border, when they came to investigate a rumor of smallpox cases reported by the Sudan SEP.

When a Sudanese surveillance team under Abdel Gadir Hamad El Sid, a Public Health Inspector with the Sudan SEP, traveled into Metekel *awraja* of Gojam in February 1974 to search for smallpox cases and vaccinate, I was ordered to travel immediately from Debre Markos to the Metekel *awraja* capital to meet the Sudanese team and support them as needed. I believe this was also intended to demonstrate the presence of the Ethiopia smallpox eradication team. SEP HQ in Addis arranged visas (retroactively) for the Sudanese team members and organized a meeting with senior SEP staff in Bahir Dar to receive the report of the Sudanese team, and also to recognize their work. The team returned to Sudan the way they had come, through Metekel *awraja*, after being resupplied by the Ethiopia SEP.

WORKING WITH HEALTH CENTER & HEALTH STATION STAFF

We worked closely with the staff in the health centers and health stations (clinics), as far as possible. We would sleep in the health centers and health stations when they were available, setting up our folding cots in the most suitable place. In many cases, the health center chief would assign a dresser to work with us, if one was available. Similarly, one of the two dressers at a health station might accompany us, if there was not too much work at the health station. Later, I would realize that the dressers, and health center staff, were often more concerned about curative services than preventive vaccination since these were more remunerative, with people ready to pay or give gifts for treatment services. We would sometimes take high school students as interpreters, but they could prove less effective in relations with the local people than health workers. In the areas I worked, I did not hire any full-time vaccinators to work independently, although we did use the services of teachers, pharmacists and high school students when needed. In Welega, we could complete the work mainly using local health workers. In Gojam there were hired vaccinators from the cities working in rural areas, some of whom I had to supervise, but I found their work largely inadequate. I felt that they took a lot of time and effort to supervise, and were often not well accepted by local people.

LIFE IN THE FIELD – CHALLENGING CONDITIONS

It always seemed too inconvenient, and too much of a bother, to bring along a tent when traveling in the field. I preferred to travel light, with a folding cot and a sleeping bag. The standard SEP issue "Safari" brand folding cot, with legs that had to be bent and attached onto the frame each night, was actually quite comfortable, although too close to the ground so fleas could jump up on it, and any baby goats kept in the houses could nibble on my sleeping bag. I got to be quite expert in assembling the cot and could do it even when half asleep after a long day. Gear was often carried by a porter that I hired, or else tied onto the back of a donkey, that accompanied me when traveling on foot. Some of the benefits of not carrying a tent were that I could travel lighter, and thus often avoid the hassle of renting donkeys, and also could sleep in people's houses, setting up my folding cot in an open spot on the floor.

After arriving in a village in the countryside, if there was no accommodation at a health station, school or other suitable government building, the village *balabat* or other village leader would look after me, or assign someone to put me up. I, therefore, got involved in evening discussions after dinner, while drinking coffee, about smallpox, life in the United States, life in Ethiopia, and life in general. During these discussions, I was also able to give further information about smallpox eradication and the reason for my coming to the village. I believe these talks made a big difference in expediting the work as people could better understand what I was coming to do, and, also, that I didn't mean any harm. It also enabled me to get involved in some interesting discussions. I quickly understood that people living in villages were very intelligent, sophisticated, cultured, and human, although very poor and some living not very differently from pre-metal societies. We normally did not pay for sleeping or the food, but I would bring along candles, coffee and sugar to share with my host during my stay. Sugar was a delicacy for most village people, as it was expensive, so they would normally add salt to the coffee. On many occasions I would ask my host "do you like sugar in the coffee?" The response would invariably come back "yes, yes, if we can get it."

We worked in the most remote areas during the dry season, and in the towns and along the all-weather roads during the rainy season. If I was working in some distant *awrajas* accessible only by dry-weather roads (such as Kelem *awraja* in Welega, which was a famous coffee growing area, and Asosa *awraja*), I had to get my Land Rover back to the all-weather roads before the rains became too heavy and made the roads impassable due to the mud and rivers without bridges. The Land Rover, even in four-wheel drive, could slide on the mud off the road into fields, or become stuck in mud holes, or be unable to cross dangerous rushing rivers that had been quiet, fordable streams during the dry season. If I delayed too long, the vehicle might be lost to the program for the three months of the rainy season if it got stuck in an area far from the all-weather road. I would try to work as long as possible in the areas without all-weather roads to cover as many *woreda*s as possible for surveillance and vaccination. It often became a high stakes game to see if I would be able to get out before the roads were shut down.

The rains would start at first for a few hours at night, with the length and intensity of the rain showers at night becoming longer and stronger, and then finally starting to rain during the day as well as at night, before it started raining heavily all day. Once the daytime rain started, driving on the dry-weather roads became very difficult. Since the exact start of the heavy rains was not known, I would sleep at night in a health center, or in a local leader's house, listening to the pounding of heavy rain on the tin roof, wondering whether this would be the day that the rain started falling heavily during the day as well as at night. As long as the rain was only at night, there was time for the sun to dry the road during the day. But once the rain fell heavily during the day as well, the game was up and the road could become impassable.

Driving on the dry-weather roads could be very challenging due to the heavily laden trucks (lorries) carrying sacks of coffee beans or other goods. Their tires would dig out deep ruts and large holes in the road, which could fill with water when the heavy rains arrived. Before the rains, these trucks also played the same game of getting out before the downpours closed the roads. Our SEP Land Rovers, with four-wheel drive, could negotiate the roads better than the trucks, although it could be challenging if a truck was bogged down in the middle of the road, or at a river crossing, with very limited options to go around. It was remarkable that travel between towns on some roads in Welega that took eight hours to drive through the mud and across swollen rivers after heavy rainfall, might take only one and a half hours during the dry season.

Getting stuck in river crossings was especially dangerous since the rivers could rapidly rise during heavy rain. In some cases, there were flimsy bridges built high above the rivers as a way for small vehicles to continue crossing even after the rivers had risen. These bridges, particularly one memorable bridge on the main road to Dembidolo town, the capital of Kelem *awraja*, Welega were often really scary, with the thin branches, laid across two not very sturdy logs, crackling and bending as the Land Rover inched across it. I avoided taking the bridge to Dembidolo if at all possible.

One time, in Dembidolo, I was driving to visit a mission school when it started to rain heavily. I didn't think much of it since I had four-wheel drive, but as the rain continued, the road made of red clay became extremely slippery. I wasn't concerned because after more than a year in Ethiopia I had experienced slippery roads, and getting stuck in the mud. However, as I was driving along a ridge, using four-wheel drive, the wheels of my Land Rover started to slide on the red clay, going off the road toward a steep drop-off. I tried to steer the vehicle back to the road, but the wheels slowly continued to slide towards the edge and the drop-off. I was going slowly, and finally brought the Land Rover to a stop, with two of the wheels off the road and very close to the edge of the cliff. I looked down into the abyss, and thought that if the vehicle had stopped a few inches later, I might be down in the abyss, looking up, or, more likely, requiring medical evacuation. Some people came up to help and we pushed the Land Rover back onto the road again. After this close escape, I gave up my trip and slowly returned to the town, sliding all over the muddy roads, even in Dembidolo town. I had been stuck in mud many times before, and also got stuck several times in the sand of dry riverbeds, but it was much more harrowing to be sliding out of control near a cliff edge.

I found many of the truck drivers to be very good guys — the law of the road was that you helped someone in trouble as much as possible. On one of my first trips, in November 1971, after heavy rains, while still learning to drive in Ethiopia conditions, my Land Rover got stuck several times, and *Ato* Gematchew, a friendly, jovial truck driver, helped to pull me out each time. On one occasion, after his truck got stuck, my Land Rover got stuck farther along the road. I walked back about half a kilometer to his truck and he lent me shovels and wood planks to free the Land Rover. When my counterpart and I walked back to return the equipment, after freeing the Land Rover, his laborers (trucks always carried one or two young laborers to help out, and also to dig the truck out if it got stuck) had still not yet freed the truck and Gematchew was preparing a meal of pasta and tomato sauce before settling in for the night. Gematchew invited us to join him for the meal, and we later continued on to the next town. I promised to buy Gematchew several beers when we next met in town!

I also made a note to buy a pick, shovels and rope for the Land Rover for my next trip, and wondered why these items were not standard issue with the vehicle.

WELEGA PROVINCE BACKGROUND

Welega province was culturally and linguistically diverse, with an estimated population of 1,768,000 in 1971.[2] The main ethnic group was Oromo, with some tribal groups living in the lowlands near the border with Sudan. The province was due west of Addis Ababa, bordering Gojam (across the Blue Nile River), Shoa, Ilubabor and Kaffa provinces, and Sudan in the west. Welega was roughly about 350 kilometers from east to west and about 200 kilometers from north to south (about 70,000 square kilometers, or 27,000 square miles).

Welega had a relatively better developed health network in comparison to the other provinces of Ethiopia. When I worked there, Dr. Erik Nordberg, a Swedish expert assigned by the Swedish International Development Agency (SIDA) to work in the province, was the Provincial Medical Officer of Health (PMOH), in charge of the Provincial Health Department (PHD). There were three hospitals for the entire province, and a health center (HC) in five of the six *awrajas*. HCs mainly treated outpatients, and usually had a few inpatient beds, but were also responsible for public health outreach work, such as providing smallpox vaccinations. Each HC also supervised several health stations (roughly one health station in each of the 49 *woredas*), staffed by one or two dressers, which provided simple outpatient curative services and might also carry out public health outreach activities, including smallpox vaccination. Several mission groups, mainly from Europe, supported a mission hospital and several mission and church health units or clinics in rural areas, at *woreda* level or below. Accordingly, Welega had more health facilities per population than most other provinces.

Amharic was the national language in Ethiopia, with the school lessons and government business conducted in this language. However, the Oromo language (called Gallinya in Amharic) was spoken by most of the rural people living in the highlands. Amharic and Oromo come from two very different language families, with Amharic a Semitic language (related

2 Source: F. Fenner, D.A. Henderson, I. Arita, Z. Jezek, I.D. Ladnyi, *Smallpox and Its Eradication* (Geneva: World Health Organization, 1988), Table 21.7, p. 1011 [hereinafter Fenner et al., *Smallpox and Its Eradication*].

to Arabic and Hebrew), while Oromo is a Cushitic language (related to sub-Saharan languages). In the far west of the province there were many other languages spoken, with some of them related to Arabic.

The large number of languages could present translation problems, and sometimes a "translation chain" from the local language to Oromo to Amharic to English, and then back again was required for interviews! I noted that many of the people in Welega were very proud of their Oromo heritage and spoke only Oromo; even if they could speak Amharic, they preferred to speak Oromo.

The provincial capital, Nekemte, was about 320 kilometers (about 200 miles) due west from Addis Ababa on an all-weather road. The first 125 kilometers of the road from Addis Ababa to the famous mineral hot springs town of Ambo was a good asphalt road. Immediately after Ambo, the asphalt ended and a rather rough, rock-based, all-weather road continued for the remaining distance, becoming very winding after crossing the border from Shoa province into Welega. This road had been built in the late 1930s by the Italians during their occupation of Ethiopia, and reportedly not repaired since then. The travel from Addis Ababa to Nekemte took about seven to eight hours by Land Rover (depending on who was driving), but longer by bus. Consequently it was a long trip to come in from Nekemte to Addis Ababa, and not frequently undertaken.

There was an Ethiopian Airlines flight from Addis Ababa to Nekemte airport, and another flight to Asosa, but the C-47 aircraft (freighter version of the DC-3), with canvas seats along the two sides of the plane, was not very comfortable, with flights often bumpy and crowded with people and animals that were not experienced air travelers. Accordingly, when travel to Addis was required, I would normally drive or take the bus.

The only other all-weather roads in Welega were a newly built 110 kilometer gravel road west from Nekemte to Gimbi town (the center of a coffee producing area), and another gravel road of about 50 kilometers to the Finchaa hydroelectric power generation dam project in Shambu *awraja*. The only paved asphalt road in the entire province, was about one kilometer of road up to a palace of Emperor Haile Selassie, near the

Finchaa dam. All the other roads were dirt roads, which could become slippery and impassable during the rainy season from June to August, and also at times during the "short rains" from November to January. Although there were no asphalt roads, Welega had a relatively good road network (compared to the other provinces), with all-weather or seasonal dry-weather roads reaching to each of the 49 *woredas*. Two of the six *awrajas* had all-weather roads to the *awraja* capital, but the other four *awraja* capitals were only reachable on dry-weather roads, and thus easily accessible only during the dry season.

Nekemte, with a population of about 13,000, was the largest town in the province, although it was one of the smallest provincial capitals in the country. The second largest town was Gimbi with about 5,000 people during the height of the coffee season. Nekemte was the only town in the province with 24-hour electricity supply, and contained the provincial government offices, a post office, a Commercial Bank of Ethiopia branch and the provincial hospital. There were a few small shops selling limited dry goods and canned foods, and two *buna bets* near the main crossroad in town. There was a weekly market a bit out of town, reached via a rock-strewn road, where one could buy fruits, vegetables, some other food items and simple dry goods. This road had a sign saying "speed limit 25 kmph," and I was always surprised that a sign was necessary since a vehicle driven faster than 15 kilometers per hour would have been shaken into pieces by the rocks and bumps in the road.

Welega had several attributes that made it a more welcoming place for health services and foreigners than the northern provinces. The mission health facilities in the province, with foreign doctors and nurses providing health services to the people, were highly appreciated. The people in Welega were accustomed to foreigners providing medical services, and this contributed to a favorable attitude towards foreigners, including the PCV smallpox workers. People also had a very favorable impression of injections and vaccination. The mission health facilities, such as the Aira German mission hospital and other clinics, had large catchment areas (places where patients came from), with people travelling for days to visit the outpatient and inpatient facilities, which made them good smallpox surveillance sites.

Dr. Nordberg, the PMOH, actively tried to improve the health services in the province, and increase outreach to underserved communities. He was, therefore, very supportive of smallpox eradication, which was often the only government health service that reached to remote areas. Only after transferring to Gojam was I able to appreciate what a big difference the support of the PMOH could make for the success of the eradication effort. On a personal level, the PMOH and his staff made me feel welcome in Welega, and provided valuable assistance to the smallpox eradication work.

GOJAM PROVINCE BACKGROUND

The population of Gojam province was about 1,784,000 in 1971,[3] with Amharas the main ethnic group, and Amharic the predominant language. Gojam was northwest of Addis Ababa, bordering Begemdir, Welo, Shoa and Welega provinces, and Sudan in the west. The Blue Nile River marked the boundary with Shoa, Welo and Welega, and part of Begemdir.

Gojam had seven *awrajas*, but only 35 *woreda*s, for a population about the same size as Welega. This meant that the population of each *woreda* was quite large, and the *woreda* was further divided into *mikitil woreda*s. The *mikitil woreda* was an important level of government administration for smallpox eradication as the *mikitil woreda* governor was the one who could send directives ordering the village and local leaders to cooperate with the smallpox eradication workers.

The capital, Debre Markos, was about 310 kilometers (about 195 miles) northwest from Addis, on a paved all-weather road, reached after crossing the Blue Nile Bridge. The travel from Addis to Debre Markos took about six or seven hours by Land Rover or Toyota, but longer by bus. There was an Ethiopian Airlines flight from Addis Ababa to Debre Markos, continuing on to Mota, once or twice a week, and daily flights from Addis Ababa to Bahir Dar, a large town on Lake Tana, near the Blue Nile Falls, a famous tourist attraction.

---

3 Ibid.

Farmer and family threshing grain on a Gojam hillside at about 3000 meters above sea level, 1974. *Photo by author.*

The road from Addis Ababa to Debre Markos continued on through three more *awrajas*, to Bahir Dar, and then to Gondar (in Begemdir province) and Asmara. There was another all-weather gravel road that branched off the main Addis Ababa-Debre Markos road to Bichena *awraja*. There were only very rough dry-weather roads to the other two *awrajas*, Mota and Metekel (a large *awraja* that bordered Sudan). The road to Mota town, the *awraja* capital, was very difficult, with the road rutted by large trucks, which made driving difficult for smaller vehicles. Anyway, there was little point in driving to Mota with a smallpox vehicle as the highest risk areas in the *awraja* could not be reached by car. From Mota town, the only way to reach Bibugn *woreda*, where I did much of my work, was to walk for eight hours. The best ways to reach Mota were to pay a truck driver for a seat during the dry season, or take the Ethiopian Airlines flight.

Most of the *woreda*s in Gojam that were not on the main road to Bahir Dar could only be reached by rough dry-weather roads. Some *woreda*s were devoid of any vehicle access, and the only way to reach these *woreda*s was on foot, or horse or mule. Similar to Welega, dry-weather roads were only passable during the dry season, and could become impassable mud holes in places during the rainy season. The topography of Gojam was rugged, with many steep river valleys. The altitude was higher than Welega, with much of the province ranging between 2500 to 3500 meters above sea level. The rugged mountainous terrain, as illustrated in the photo at left, was one of the reasons for the lack of roads to many *woreda*s.

Gojam had two large towns: Debre Markos with a population of about 22,000, and Bahir Dar with about 12,000. Calling them towns might be an exaggeration, as they were more like large villages, with a few shops along the main road in the "downtown" area. These two towns were the only ones in the province with 24-hour electricity. There were more shops and better facilities in Debre Markos than in Nekemte, since Debre Markos had two larger grocery stores with a small selection of imported goods. Bahir Dar had more facilities and imported foods than Debre Markos, related to its status as an important tourist center. Due to the scarcity of imported goods, we often brought back food (e.g. cookies, chocolate, and cans of butter, cheese and juices) after visiting Addis Ababa.

There was a government hospital in Debre Markos, and health centers in each of the seven *awrajas*. During my work in Gojam, the PMOH was not very supportive of the program, and while the smallpox team could occasionally meet with him, it was not a dynamic, problem solving relationship. There were no mission clinics in Gojam, and many people associated foreigners with the Italian soldiers and administrators who oppressed the population during the occupation. Accordingly, there was a much less favorable attitude towards western medicine, and foreigners, in Gojam than in Welega. People were suspicious of western medicine, and had to be convinced about smallpox vaccination.

SMALLPOX ERADICATION WORK IN WELEGA

I traveled extensively in Welega province by vehicle and on foot during two years, from 1971 to 1973, and worked in all six *awrajas*. The provincial smallpox team was free to make its own monthly program of work. Following the guidelines from SEP HQ about using surveillance and containment vaccination as the strategy, we were free to decide how, where and when to implement the SEP policies within the province. The final say on the plans normally rested with the Ethiopian sanitarians. This could result in give and take, and some friction, if there was not agreement on the plan of work, particularly the work at local level. We would then present our plans to the PMOH, and only after returning from the field inform SEP HQ in Addis of the results of our work. SEP HQ did closely follow up on reports, and at times, as mentioned above, if there were problems, or to follow up on a rumor, Ciro de Quadros, or a Central Assessment Team, would come to visit. However, while there was a supervisory component to the Central Assessment Team work, it was not perceived as a "supervision visit," at least by the Welega provincial team PCVs.

While the main ethnic group in Welega was Oromo, with the majority of people speaking Oromo, the agricultural lands were mainly controlled by *balabats*, descendents of Amhara conquerors. The society in the highlands was feudal, with the landowners controlling the land and the lives of the peasants farming their land. The peasants were dependent on the landowners for their living, including judicial oversight, giving a very large proportion of their harvest to the landowner. So the *balabat* could order the peasants to be vaccinated and they would accept his order. This hierarchical order made people more inclined to follow orders of the government authorities and the landowners, and made vaccinating much easier. If the smallpox team came with a letter from the *woreda* governor to a large landowner, he would readily accept and help.

I was not fully aware of how the sanitarians were assigned to the individual provinces. But I noted that *Ato* Tadela Getahun (a sanitarian in Welega), who did not speak Oromo, often did not receive as much information as *Ato* Tefera, who was Oromo and from Welega. At times, there were some disagreements with Tadela about work programs, and I later thought that this might be due to his discomfort at not being able to understand what people were saying in the villages. I noted that in rural areas, people routinely spoke Oromo in the evening, even if there was an Amharic-speaking person present, and understood that people were proud of their language and their heritage. They didn't mind so much if a

PCV did not speak Oromo, but seemed less forgiving of Ethiopians who spoke only Amharic. After observing this, I commented in my notebook about the need for SEP HQ to assign sanitarians who could speak the local languages.

Welega had entered the attack phase in February 1971, with huge efforts to vaccinate in a large outbreak area in Asosa made by Tadela and PCVs Charlie Kilmer and Gene Bartley. I arrived in the province in October 1971, after Kilmer and Bartley had been reassigned to other provinces, at the same time that Tefera was added to the team to join Tadela. Later on, Steve Reiber and Peter Carrasco replaced Tim Williams. The new SEP team recognized quite early that there were still smallpox cases occurring in much of the western part of the province. The previous efforts had greatly slowed transmission of smallpox cases, but had not stopped it. The cases continued to spread eastward, toward the coffee-producing areas of Gimbi and Dembidolo, where there were large influxes of temporary workers during the coffee harvesting season. The smallpox team decided that rather than vaccinate in the middle of the outbreaks, we should start first at the eastern edges of transmission and try to build a wall of vaccinated people to contain the spread before moving our vaccination efforts into the center of transmission. And this we did. We moved westward on two fronts, checking for cases along the roads in Gimbi and Kelem *awrajas*, until we encountered reports of cases and then stopped and began to vaccinate there. This strategy proved successful as the cases did not break through our "walls" of vaccinated people. As we progressed westward, the cases were much reduced and we could mop them up, vaccinating the remaining unvaccinated people at collection points, or house to house, in affected villages.

It was not a problem to vaccinate since people liked injections and readily accepted vaccination. We could vaccinate many hundreds, and even more than 1000, people in a day by vaccinating in the main market towns and at strategic collection points in villages where *balabats* would bring people. We found it easier, and usually more successful, to have the *balabat* order people to a central vaccination point rather than going house to house.

People praying in unison at a religious festival near Begi, Welega, 1973. *Photo by author.*

We would often receive reports of smallpox cases in "the next village," which in Amharic is reported as "*madow*," which means "over that hill," although, unfortunately, this word isn't specific about over how many hills. A reported "short walk just over that hill" to investigate a case could turn into a full day's walk over several hills to arrive and, after finding the case was not smallpox and spending the night in the village, a full day's walk back to the Land Rover.

Large gatherings, like markets and religious festivals, as well as schools, were used to ask about smallpox cases and to vaccinate. By determining the catchment area, from where people were coming to these events, we could get a good idea of the smallpox situation in the surrounding area, thus avoiding the need to go village to village. Local people often suggested that we should attend markets and religious events because we would find many people to vaccinate. However, I found that while these events could be good for surveillance, they were not optimal for vaccination as people were busy, with their thoughts elsewhere, and thus many were not interested in vaccination. We sometimes vaccinated students at schools,

A smiling woman making bread at religious festival near Begi, Welega, 1973. *Photo by author.*

which was easy because the students could be ordered by the teachers and lined up. However, often the students had already been vaccinated, and we were merely giving revaccinations, which was not as powerful as giving primary vaccinations. Therefore, we usually left the vaccination of school children to the local health facility, if one was nearby.

My team attended an annual Moslem festival near Begi, Asosa *awraja*, close to the border with Sudan. Several thousand men came to pray at the tomb of a saint, some with wives and children, as shown in the photos at the left and above.

We set up a vaccination station at the festival, using a jet injector, but the jet injector kept malfunctioning, and needed constant cleaning. In the end, we gave up and used bifurcated needles. We did not vaccinate as many people as we expected, since people had other things on their minds, although we managed to vaccinate several hundred people, including people coming from Sudan.

People in Welega had a very favorable view of injections. When visiting clinics, they would often demand an injection from health staff, even if the condition did not warrant one, because they thought that the most effective medicines were given by injections. If the patient was not given a *murfi*, or needle (injection), they would be upset and think that the health worker at the health facility was not very good. We heard that this belief in injections originated when penicillin was used to cure many formerly fatal diseases, apparently bringing patients back from the brink of death. This favorable impression of injections helped the smallpox eradication vaccination effort because people in Welega readily accepted smallpox vaccination and occasionally even required crowd control to keep people from pushing and overwhelming the vaccination station. This contrasted markedly with some other provinces, like Gojam, where people did not accept vaccination.

I found that people readily accepting vaccination in Welega, especially if smallpox was present in the area, could sometimes be too much of a good thing when crowds chaotically surged forward to get vaccinated. At times, creative crowd control was required to prevent injury to the vaccinators and people surging forward for vaccination, and to allow vaccination of everyone. If the *balabat* called people to come to a collection point, we would try to estimate how many would show up, but sometimes we seriously underestimated. With several hundred people waiting, some would fear that the vaccine would run out and push forward to get the vaccination first. There was often a silence, like the quiet before a storm, as we opened vaccine vials and diluents and mixed the vaccine at the start of a vaccination session. But once we started, things could rapidly get out of control.

One time, at a market, I was pushed against a wall, and my arm scraped by people pushing for vaccination. Eventually, with the help of the *balabat*, order was restored, but only after I moved my Land Rover one foot away from the wall of a building, and then filtered people through one at a time, vaccinating from the door of the building, with the *balabat* making sure there was a one-way flow of traffic. Once the crowd was reduced, and people saw that there would be enough vaccine, things eased up. But it could be very stressful, and tiring to do non-stop vaccinating for several hours. Needless to say, this sort of situation never happened

The author standing in front of the large Welega map in the PMOH's office showing places visited, 1973. *Photo provided by author.*

to me in Gojam. This example of "on-the-spot problem solving" under stressful conditions, illustrates the creativity needed by PCVs to carry out the smallpox eradication work. Situations and conditions were often quite different, and creative work solutions needed to be continually crafted.

As part of our cooperation with the PHD, we would routinely take medicines and other supplies for health facilities when visiting their areas. This helped the credibility of the SEP, and also gave us a favorable opening with the health facility staff. We tried as much as possible not to overload, and possibly damage, the vehicles, and we were often, if not always, able to accomplish this. We also used to help the PMOH to update a large map of Welega in his office by putting in the names of villages, and indicating the location of local roads in the areas we visited, as shown in the photo above.

The PHD prepared a periodic newsletter, with practical and useful health, medical and administrative information, for all health personnel in the province. The smallpox eradication team would normally provide an article reporting on the status of smallpox eradication efforts, and urging support from all health personnel. I wrote some of these articles, including an article in the September 1973 issue, detailing the number of smallpox vaccinations performed by each reporting health facility, and urging each health facility to routinely provide smallpox vaccinations in order to maintain Welega's smallpox-free status.

Welega was the second province after Ilubabor to become small-pox-free, and the first province with more than 1 million population to achieve the goal. The last endemic case in the province had onset of rash in December 1972, with the last imported case (from Gojam), near the border with Gojam, having onset of rash in June 1973.[4]

SMALLPOX ERADICATION WORK IN GOJAM

During almost one year in Gojam province, from November 1973 to September 1974, I worked in four of seven *awrajas*: Debre Markos, Bichena, Mota and Metekel. Although the work was always challenging in Gojam, I found that the degree of difficulty varied, depending on the *awraja*, with Mota *awraja* by far the most difficult. However, everywhere I worked in Gojam was much more difficult than in Welega.

Many of the Gojam provincial health authorities, and government officials, were not very interested in smallpox eradication. Often, *woreda* government officials would not travel with the smallpox teams, and many lower level local officials would not work with the team even when presented with introduction letters from the *woreda* governor. It appeared to me that the government officials did not have very much authority over the local village leaders. The provincial governor (*enderassie*) also did not show much interest in the smallpox eradication effort, although he provided a letter that the SEP team members took with them in the field. This was quite different than Welega, where the government officials, from the provincial governor and PMOH to the *woreda* governors and *balabats*, were strongly supportive of the program and would help the smallpox teams.

---

4 Sources: *Smallpox Surveillance in Ethiopia No. 24*, Monthly Report January 1973 and Summary 1972, *Smallpox Surveillance in Ethiopia No. 35*, Monthly Report December 1973 and Summary 1973" and *Wollega Health, Newsletter for Health Personnel in Wollega Province*, No. 6, September 1973.

An entry from my notebook discusses this issue:

Wednesday, February 13, 1974
The biggest difficulty is the lack of helping people in positions of authority. If I have difficulty with the awraja governor there is no one to fall back on and seek support. No one at Provincial Health Department, no one at Provincial government and no one at WHO [in Debre Markos]. And this is the main problem.

On one occasion, after a frustrating meeting with the governor of Mota *awraja* to request support for the program, I made the following entry in my notebook as a draft letter to the governor (*Kenyazmatch* Ademasu Tariku). I did not actually send this letter, but it was therapeutic to write my thoughts down, and useful to prepare me for future discussions. I think it provides useful insights into the tone of the work in Gojam, and interactions with officials.

Letter to Kenyaz. Ademasu —

Sunday, February 24, 1974
As I tried to explain to you, but did not have enough time, you are correct that Wollega Province is different than Gojjam. Yes, the people are more cooperative, but so are the government officials. The government officials that I met in Wollega were enthusiastic about eradicating smallpox. They helped us in every way they could. But in Mota [*awraja*] you were so suspicious that even a letter signed by the *enderassie*, and a proper identification card from the Ministry of Health, signed by Yohannes Woldemariam, was not enough to convince you that these workers had come to eradicate smallpox. So you had to call Debre Markos to verify their letters, even though all their identification was in order. And in a small town like Mota news that the *awraja* governor had called [Debre] Markos for such and such a reason spreads fast. I hope that you have considered that this phone call may have indirectly led to the incident where someone from the town asked one of our workers from the USA for his passport. Also, as I did not have enough time to explain, our program is not a mass vaccination campaign. We cannot vaccinate everyone in Mota *awraja*. Our program is surveillance and containment. Asking where there are cases of smallpox and knowing this is as import-

ant as giving vaccinations. So we will work only in areas where there are active smallpox cases, passing quickly over areas that have no active smallpox. But even when we find cases, we cannot do many vaccinations. Partially because the people do not want vaccination, but also partially because we get little cooperation from the government officials. Maybe they are suspicious of the program though, as the officials above them seem to be.

I think it is unfortunate that you think the smallpox workers in Mota *awraja* are lazy. The SEP workers throughout Ethiopia have a history of going by mule, foot, or any means possible to reach infected areas. Many times SEP workers have been the first Ethiopian government health workers to reach an area. I am sure that many of the areas we have visited, and tried to vaccinate, in Mota have not been visited by any other health worker. I believe you will get corroboration of this fact if you ask some of the *atbia danyas* or *mikitil woreda* governors about the SEP work because they know how much we are walking, or going by mule, and thus are afraid to go with us, or if they start the work of trying to educate the people they become tired after a short time and beg off. But if you ask people like *Grazmatch* Wolele Bito, MW governor of Siltan Haile in Hulet Ij Enese *woreda*, he will tell you that we have been sitting in the towns doing nothing. Which would be true because we sat for two days in Rob Gabeya waiting for him to give us a guide to an area we wanted to go to.

I also find it hard to believe that you can think I am staying in Mota for my own pleasure. Because I like the towns and am afraid of the countryside. I realize that Mota is a very big, beautiful and advanced town, but I don't think a place where I sometimes cannot find any other food except 10 cent *shuro wot* from the *shai bet* would excite me and cause me to want to stop the work and relax in Mota.

The following entry from my notebook illustrates a situation where an *atbia danya* (local village leader and judge) refused a direct order from a *woreda* official:

> "He [a *woreda* official in Bibugn, Mota *awraja*] orders *Atbia Danya* to go with us to Babicha. The *atbia danya* refuses and asks the *woreda* official why he doesn't go."

Work in Mota *awraja*, in the highlands of Gojam, about 3,000 meters (about 10,000 feet) above sea level, was very challenging. The terrain was mountainous, with river valleys and steep ravines, and cold temperatures at night. The people living there were independent farmers, owning small parcels of land. They were very independent-minded, so one could not order them, but had to convince them of the value of vaccination. Even a letter from the governor might not convince them to accept vaccination. Most of the farmers had guns (many of them old rifles from World War II), so they could be a formidable force if they did not agree. The farmers in Mota *awraja* were reported to have fought back against the national army at one time, after refusing to pay taxes following a rumor that Haile Selassie had been deposed. They did well against the army ground forces sent against them, until airplanes were brought in. In the end, a truce and an amnesty were declared and Haile Selassie flew up to the area in a helicopter to show that he was still in command. So, these were very independent farmers, and there were no large landowners to order anyone to take vaccination. The smallpox teams had to go village by village explaining about the program and vaccination, and often could vaccinate only a few people per day. A visit to a village required sitting with people to explain the program, showing them the letter from the *woreda* governor and explaining the benefits of vaccination. One rumor that circulated quite widely was that we were really collecting blood, rather than vaccinating, with the blood used to power the airplanes that people could see flying overhead. These rumors had to be discussed and countered.

My notebook entries below reflect some of my thoughts about vaccination refusals in Gojam.

Monday, January 14, 1974

. . . 2) Unless we are going to use police or force, must put the vaccine to the people as a "take it or leave it" decision. If they don't want it, it was for their own good. 3) Must have medicine to give to the smallpox patients, or else we have no wedge to make people show us cases. 4) Cases do not go in waves in Gojjam. They go in circles. Maybe because of people only letting family in to visit, or because people are not as communal. But the smallpox pattern is different than in the south. 5) Threshold vaccination technique seems OK. Vaccinate enough people to let the others see that the vaccine works, and the rest of the people will take vaccine in the future.

Saturday, May 18, 1974

. . . the PC training courses should include a visit to a *tukul-shai bet, tella bet,* in Dangla [town]. I'll have to arrange for some old woman to prepare some *shuro wot.* Can demonstrate to the PC trainees what an average *tukul* looks like and point out how independent from outside forces the people are. Only some metal pots, and maybe coffee and kerosene for their [simple wick] lamps, but all these can be bought at the local market. Also people up in Choke [mountainous area in Mota *awraja*] are well off. They have plenty of cows, donkeys and sheep, plenty of grain, fertile land and not too many diseases. And the diseases they have, they become accustomed to. The man works in the field, comes home to some 'gebskolo', some *tella,* coffee, conversation, supper and then sex. How different are our lives? So why should they want to change? To accept something from the outside world that is going to change their way of life . . . .. So the Gojjamis seem to be pretty shrewd customers who know that they're well off and know that the government won't help them for the foreseeable future. But they're intelligent and will know that the vaccine will help them. And eventually, if the government gets itself together, they'll accept it also.

DANGEROUS SITUATION IN MOTA *AWRAJA*

The Gojam provincial SEP team made its own work program, like in Welega, but in Gojam there was a WHO SEP Epidemiologist who closely supervised the work and helped prepare the monthly work schedules. However, once the team reached an *awraja,* the field work planning and implementation was the responsibility of the individual teams. I traveled to Mota twice, both times by airplane, and both times without a counterpart sanitarian because the sanitarians were working in other *awrajas.* It was planned that I would work with a dresser from the Mota health center or one of the health stations, but as described below this did not always work out as planned.

On one of my field trips to Mota *awraja* in Gojam, I wound up working alone high up in the mountains at above 3000 meters altitude. At the Bibugn *woreda* office, I had met an interested *atbia danya* (who was also a *netch libosh,* with the title of *hamsa-alika* in the local militia — equivalent rank to a sergeant), who informed me that there were smallpox cases in his village and requested the team to join him.

The *woreda* governor had said he would accompany a team to the place, and arrange for a mule. But, as explained below in my notebook entry, at the given time to depart, the governor was not available. The smallpox vaccinator, *Ato* Solomon, hired before I arrived in Gojam, refused to go, preferring to remain in the *woreda* capital. Since the *atbia danya* was interested, and cooperative, I decided to go with him alone, and eventually left at 8:05 a.m.

> *Friday, February 15, 1974*
> Fantastic, my head must be getting soft. We are now on the 4-hour road to Wabir, with no guide, no letter, no mule for me to ride on. The *woreda* gov. says he will come at 7:00 to help us and to make sure the mule I have arranged for comes. At 7:45 the mule has not come and the gov's house is locked tight, still asleep. So I say screw them and head off by myself with no guide or letter. My chances for success are 2%. And the gov. says he will come at 14:00 but do I really believe this after he left Mota without us. Either I'm using reflexes from Wollega or I'm stupid. Or more probably tired. You can't walk 4 or 5 hours a day for 3 weeks . . . [and not get tired].

The *atbia danya* (*hamsa-alika*) I went with from Bibugn *woreda* was one of several very helpful people I met in Mota. During the visit to the village under his responsibility, high up in the mountains, he tried his best to convince people to take vaccination, but with only limited success, although I eventually recorded five active smallpox cases. I estimated that we had vaccinated about 5-10% of the people, and this in a village with active smallpox cases. However, during this four-day trip, while trying to vaccinate in a village outside of his responsibility, he rather abruptly told me to sit down in one place while he went off to discuss some things. I was rather upset that we were wasting an entire morning when we could have been vaccinating. Early in the afternoon, he came back and said we needed to leave quickly, which we did. He later explained that there were some elements in this village who thought that the smallpox vaccination was just a ruse, and they should just rob and dispose of this *ferengi* who had the audacity to visit their village.

The *woreda* governor was upset that I had gone off without a letter to visit the village with the *hamsa-alika*, but the next week I was able to return to the area with a dresser from the *woreda* health station, plus a letter from the *woreda* governor. During this visit, I was able to vaccinate several hundred more people, and in a few villages managed to vaccinate almost everyone. I never found out if the *hamsa-alika*, or my previous visit where people had a chance to see that the vaccine was not dangerous, had played a role in the better than expected success on the second visit. During my visit to Bibugn *woreda*, I had received credible reports of a smallpox outbreak in a neighboring *woreda* (*Feres bet*) in the next *awra-ja* (Kola Dega Damot). I took great satisfaction from the fact that later, when this outbreak was finally investigated, and controlled in 1975-1976 by many teams transported by helicopter, there was no spread into the neighboring areas of Mota where I had worked. I considered this result partially due to the sincere efforts of the capable *hamsa-alika*. He was aware of the smallpox cases in his village and the neighboring *awraja* and understood that the vaccination would protect his people. But he could not order the people to line up for vaccination. They had to first understand what we were doing.

AN EXAMPLE OF SEP HQ SUPPORT FOR PCVs

The smallpox eradication team worked hard at the provincial level to involve the provincial health officials in the smallpox eradication work, and actively tried to interest them in the program. I had tried for a few months to involve the Gojam Provincial Health Officer, *Ato* Bono Hora (the senior sanitarian in the province, whose responsibilities also included infectious disease control) in smallpox activities, with some success. I remember talking with Bono about the attributes of successful HCs. He told me that when he worked in Ilubabor (one of the more remote and difficult provinces) as a HC chief, despite limited resources from the government, he would get the outreach programs done one way or another, borrowing Land Rovers from other government agencies, mission clinics or business people to reach distant areas. We agreed that, if the health officer was interested and capable, he would find the resources to run successful programs; but if the health officer was not interested, and not ready to work hard, even if resources were available, programs would not run well. Bono was one of those who worked hard and well.

I did not get along well with the new WHO SEP Epidemiologist-advisor assigned to Gojam. I noted that he was not spending much time in the field, and felt that he did not fully comprehend how difficult the field work was, and did not properly guide and support the field staff when they ran into problems.

One time, after returning from a difficult field trip where everything seemed to go wrong, I found that the WHO SEP Epidemiologist had told Bono not to get involved in smallpox work, after I had been trying my best to involve him. I was really angry and later confronted the WHO SEP Epidemiologist. He replied that he was in charge. I was so upset that I telephoned to SEP HQ in Addis while still angry to complain and, shouting into the phone, asked them to come up and sort out the problems between the WHO SEP Epidemiologist and the provincial health office. I think it was a sign of the respect and trust that the SEP HQ staff in Addis had for the PCVs, that they listened carefully to my views and complaints and advised me that they would look into the matter. Ciro de Quadros arrived some days after this to investigate and to calm things down. Shortly after this, the WHO SEP Epidemiologist in question was transferred to another province, and Ciro took over responsibility for Gojam. After this, Bono became an important contributor to the successful eradication effort in the province, and later went on to work with the SEP in other provinces as well. He eventually went on to work with WHO programs in other countries.

This story illustrates that senior SEP staff in Addis were very supportive of the PCVs, and respected their judgment. In the case of a disagreement between an experienced PCV and a WHO SEP Epidemiologist, the PCV's position was considered and an investigation done. This resulted in PCVs having the confidence to bring problems to the attention of SEP HQ since they knew their views would be taken seriously. I found that this support of field staff by the headquarters smallpox eradication staff (in Addis as well as Geneva) reflected a constant, integral feature of the smallpox eradication effort, in Ethiopia, as well as all the countries in which I later worked.

COMPARISON OF THE SMALLPOX ERADICATION WORK IN WELEGA AND GOJAM

In Welega, the cooperation of the people, and government officials, carried the SEP teams along when they got tired. One could see the progress daily, with large numbers vaccinated, and the reduction in smallpox cases. In contrast, the lack of cooperation at all levels in Gojam, and constant struggle to explain the program, get letters, get people to accompany you, find and investigate cases, and argue with people to be vaccinated, caused stress and frustration, and sapped morale. As a consequence, the work in Gojam went much slower than in Welega, was more tiring, and gave less feeling of accomplishment. Some illustrative notebook entries reflecting on the differences between Welega and Gojam are shown below.

> *Monday, December 24, 1973*
> Work in Gojjam must be labor intensive. In Wollega you can work in a *woreda* for 2 weeks, vaccinate 60% or more of the people and be 90% sure it is free of smallpox. But in Gojjam you can work in a *mikitil woreda* for four weeks, vaccinate not more than 20% of the people and can't be more than 50% sure that there is no smallpox. So it seems the ratio of workers should be at least 12:1 [12 Gojjam workers for 1 Wollega worker]. Can also cover more ground in Wollega. Gojjam work is slow and inconclusive.

> *Wednesday, December 26, 1973*
> If SEP/Ethiopia expects the same tactics that worked in the south to work in the north, they are mistaken. People here [in the north] are much more suspicious, much more serious and in their own way more intelligent. People are more democratic here than in Wollega also. In Wollega are some rich people and many poor. Here, all the people are poor although better off than the poor people in Wollega. But I have to wonder how poor they are when I count the cattle. Are hundreds of cattle for each village and if each cow is worth Eth$100 then they have some money. But the cattle are wealth, so they won't sell them for cash . . . they are afraid of change. So they like their thatched *tukuls*, and think their health

is not so bad that they have to sell cattle to improve it . . . no one can force anyone else to do something. He can only ask.

Tuesday, February 26, 1974
In Wollega, *balabat* says "sit down and have some *buna* while I send letters to call the people," when you come. Here *Atbia* [*danya*] or *chikashume* says "so what?" "What do you want?" "Why don't you go away?" In south can give appointment for area or market. Here in Gojjam, impossible.

I feel that one of the very important factors for the success in Welega was the full support of the provincial government for the smallpox work. In Gojam, there was only very limited support, without good access to the *enderassie* to seek his support to more closely involve the *awraja* governors. The PMOH in Gojam would occasionally meet with the smallpox team members, but was not very supportive of the program. In contrast, the PMOH in Welega fully supported the program, and let the HC chiefs at the *awraja* level know that he saw the smallpox eradication program as very important. While the HC chiefs I worked with in Gojam were usually friendly and sympathetic, because of their own staff constraints they could not always provide personnel to travel with me, possibly reflecting the lack of priority at provincial level. In Gojam, government officials at lower levels (*woreda*, *mikitil woreda*, village and sub-village levels) also were often not cooperative, with official letters sometimes rejected by local officials, or pushed off to less powerful local figures, who could disappear during an SEP team field visit.

In Welega, transportation was much easier than Gojam, with more places accessible to a vehicle. Porters to carry bags would be assigned by the *balabat*, or could be hired. Since the Land Rover could go more places, walking trips were shorter, so a small bag and a field cot that could be carried by a porter was often sufficient for a field trip. Gojam was often the opposite of Welega. Travel was more difficult over the mountainous terrain, and since fewer places were accessible by Land Rover, one had to pack supplies for longer trips. In addition, since the temperature was colder high up in the mountains, one needed more clothing and supplies. In Gojam, porters, even when payment was offered, were often not available, and we found few people with the interest or authority to assign porters. Instead, one had to hire donkeys to carry the bags, with all the complications of negotiating with the owner of the donkeys and then dealing with his schedule and the donkeys. So travel in Gojam was much more complicated, frustrating and tiring than in Welega.

ADVENTURE STORIES AND ANECDOTES

While on the whole, I think I was very safe during my stay in Ethiopia, every smallpox eradication PCV has stories and anecdotes about adventures, near misses, dangerous situations, as well as lessons learned. Below I share some of my adventures, insights gained, lessons learned, and also some descriptions of lighter moments. Reflecting back on my life in Ethiopia during this period, and comparing it to smallpox eradication during later periods in Ethiopia, I have to admit that we were much better off during my period of work. One didn't have much concern about personal safety in terms of being killed or robbed. The safety situation changed later on in the program, with some smallpox workers killed (including two Ethiopian workers in Gojam in 1975–1976),[5] or kidnapped during the eradication effort. However, two of the sanitarians I worked with in Welega province took pistols with them to the field.

Bitten by a dog in a Gojam village where the owner went mad

On one occasion, in Dembecha *woreda* of Debre Markos *awraja*, Gojam, I was bitten by a dog while investigating a smallpox case. As the text below from my notebook indicates, since the dog appeared in good health I decided to continue the work in the area and go back to check that the dog remained healthy for the next week or so.

> *Thursday, April 25, 1974*
> Is quite a day. Get bitten by a dog and now have to call PC to see about rabies shots. Then have a windshield wiper stolen off the car. Then find 3 cases that I can trace and get no leads on the

5 Fenner et al., *Smallpox and Its Eradication*, p. 1026.

case in Dembecha town. Yet do 150 secondary vaccinations. A long day, but I 'm not sure if I accomplished too much. The dog incident was pretty frustrating. The dog came up behind me while I was looking at an old case. He came up slowly and seemed to be sniffing until everyone noticed him and got excited. He then nipped at me, almost as an afterthought (I wonder what would have happened if he came up on the run looking to chew up someone). He bit through the pants and didn't tear the pants, but did draw blood. I washed it with soap and water and added iodine, but it was bleeding pretty well. It would seem to not be dangerous since he bit through the pants, but I'd rather check with the experts (Doc Ey). But it makes me think of all the times I was so nonchalant with dogs, figuring they don't bite. But this one took me completely by surprise. The people, of course all said the dog was OK and not to worry. But they also said they were all OK. That all the children had had smallpox and didn't need the vaccination.

Sunday, May 5, 1974
Meet *netch libosh* of Yeworeda Mikael. He says is no SP and every-one vaxed. See the dog for the last time, and he still seems healthy and tries to bite Getinet [a dresser] and Kaesa Laku [local official]. However, *Ato* Walli [the dog's owner] has become mad. As he tells Kaesa Laku not to come back or he'll kill him.

Unrest in Addis Ababa affects the smallpox work in the countryside

The news of the army mobilization in Addis Ababa in late February 1974 was an important, and potentially serious, event. I was working high up in the mountains of Mota *awraja* when I heard the news on the radio, as detailed below in my notebook. I considered it best to return to Debre Markos, and debated the best way to do this. Since I had flown to Mota, and didn't have a vehicle to return to, I could decide whether to walk for two days back to Debre Markos, or for four and a half hours to Dembecha town (capital of one of the *woreda*s in Debre Markos *awraja*, on the main road from Debre Markos to Bahir Dar) and take a bus to Debre Markos. After reaching Dembecha, and taking the bus to Debre Markos, I found that things were more peaceful than expected. I stayed in Debre Markos for one week, and left again for the field on March 9, 1974.

Friday, March 1, 1974
Last night heard the army has taken over Addis Abeba, and put up barricades on entrances to the city. Hard to decide whether we should try to get a bus in Dembecha, or go back to Markos by two day walk. Finally choose to try Dembecha, although I have my doubts. But all is peace in the countryside. Nothing has changed. Life goes on the same, with people eating *shuro wot*, driving out the cows and sheep in the morning and herding them back at night. The same rural routine, except that the radio the *ferengi* brought is mentioning something about a curfew in that far off place called Addis Abeba . . . Arrive in Dembecha. All is quiet and peaceful. As if nothing was happening in Addis Abeba . . . Although no one can hear English [news] in this town so I doubt if they know that Addis Abeba and Asmara have been taken over by the army since it has not been announced on Radio Ethiopia yet.

Knowledge of local language important

As PCVs, we received very useful language training in Amharic and Oromo, along with cultural sensitivity training. Speaking even a little of the language made a big difference in our effectiveness and understanding of local customs.

One time I was driving to Debre Markos with two newly arrived PCVs on a training mission. Some kilometers after crossing the Blue Nile Bridge into Gojam, we were flagged down on the road by people waving their arms. When I stopped, a person quickly came up to the Land Rover and very politely informed us in Amharic that there had been a motor vehicle accident and asked if we could please take someone to the hospital in Debre Markos. This was a very reasonable, and urgent, request and I immediately agreed to give the injured person a ride. During the discussion, the two newly arrived PCVs were very frightened, almost cowering in the corner of the Land Rover, afraid that we were being carjacked. Understanding the language enabled one to get a totally different understanding of a situation.

Informative conversations after dinner at night in village houses

I remember many times sitting at night in someone's house drinking coffee, with the clay coffee pot (*jabena*) on a charcoal fire, with ears of corn roasting alongside the pot. There was always some snack served with coffee, either roasted corn, barley or wheat. There is a saying in Amharic, *"Bado shai mon yitetal?"* which translates as "who would be so inconsiderate as to serve only tea without a snack?" This custom was observed everywhere in Ethiopia, where tea or coffee would always be served with a snack — roasted grains in the countryside, or bread or cake in cities. I found this quite a pleasant and suitable custom, and ever since have always served some cakes or cookies with tea or coffee at my house, or at work meetings I hosted.

Being invited into people's homes gave a unique opportunity to appreciate the sophistication of the people, and I was always amazed that the concerns of the village people I talked with, who were among the poorest in the world, had a foundation similar to people anywhere: things like the children's welfare, family matters, neighbors, work and health. One time, while sitting and talking after dinner around the charcoal brazier-like stove, used to give warmth and for roasting coffee beans and ears of corn, someone asked me and my interpreter, "who is watching your wife while you are here in the countryside working?" The response was that there was a *zebanya* (watchman) at the house in the city. One of the persons sitting around the stove immediately shot back: "And who is watching the *zebanya*?" We all laughed. I was always impressed by the intelligence and sophistication of many of the village people with whom I interacted. They might not have shoes, only very basic clothes, and be very poor in material goods, but they had a very sophisticated outlook, and good reasons for behaving as they did. I grew to understand that "clothes do NOT necessarily make a man."

I noted that sometimes very poor people, with not much food, would invite us to a simple meal. Looking at the amount of food they had left in their storage bins, which had to last until the next harvest, I recognized that a simple invitation from a poor person might be showing much more hospitality than a rich person inviting someone to a large meal. It certainly represented a larger proportion of their income and available food. It was at times a delicate balance to decide when to offer to pay for food we ate in the evening when staying in people's houses and when to accept the food as a heart-felt invitation. I feared that it might be taken as an insult if someone was inviting a guest to a meal, and then the guest thought that this person was merely carrying out a business transaction to get some money for preparing the meal. Certainly, when I invited people to eat at my house I would have felt surprised if they offered to pay for the meal. Of course, at times we were forced upon people by the government letter as we needed a place to stay in areas where there were no hotels. I usually offered to pay if the person in the house where we stayed was very poor. If it was a rich *balabat*, then I would not offer to pay, although I suspected that often the *balabat* later required his tenants to contribute to my food, in exchange for the vaccinations received.

I also learned that village people did not necessarily go to sleep when it got dark. Many times we would stay up talking until late at night around a charcoal stove, with a small wick lamp to light up the *tukul*. On some occasions, at 11:30 pm, or even later, I had to excuse myself and say I had to go to sleep after a long day to get up early the next morning to continue work.

Debating, and Amharic play on words, as a "national sport"

In Amhara areas like Gojam, sophisticated plays-on-words, with double meanings, were often used, and taken very seriously. Ethiopia is famous for the *k'nay*, a type of poem with hidden, often critical, meanings underneath a surface, inoffensive meaning. Words with double meanings were used in court cases, as well as in *k'nay* poetry. One such *k'nay* was about Mota Keraniyo where the author writes that he didn't see any oxen plowing the fields during his visit, but the hidden meaning noted that the king had come through some time before and killed many people while putting down a rebellion. Mota has historically been a problem for the central government.

I had the impression that debating was in some ways the "national sport," particularly in Gojam, as reflected in my notebook entry below. On weekends, after church, or before the planting season started, the men would gather at selected places to present or listen to court cases and the local judge (*atbia danya*) would hear the case and make his ruling. Word plays were often used. For example, one litigant might tell his opponent "*argitay menager alibih*," which literally means "you should be certain when you speak;" but if one splits the words differently and reads the same Amharic letters of the first word as "*ar-gitay*," the meaning can be interpreted as "eat shit."

> *Friday, January 11, 1974*
> People here love their courts and litigation. The courthouse has been jammed for the three days I've been here in Bibugn [*woreda* in Mota *awraja*, Gojjam]. They seem to leave their work and come to the *woreda* office to argue with their neighbors and *atbia danyas*. The *atbia danyas* are now holding court in the square in front of the office. Are 4 or more *atbia danyas* with their secretaries and people standing and arguing their cases in front of them. Too bad there's no way to change these people's attention to smallpox. A poster of *fantata* [smallpox] would be nice in the courtroom . . ..
> If he [*woreda* chief judge] could speak to the people and convince them to help us we could finish quickly as the men have no work now — or will leave it for some playing at the courts.

An uncomfortable "guest house"

During a visit to Mota, in January 1974, in one village where we had to stay the night after doing some vaccination work in the village, the *atbia danya* put me up in his "guest house." This was quite a special guest house at more than 3,000 meters above sea level: one was unable to close the door so the freezing wind blew through the room for the whole night. That night I nearly froze in my feather-depleted sleeping bag, even after piling all my spare clothing on top. I didn't stay a second night in this guest house, and I suspect that not many people did!

Skilled village shoemaker saves the day

During the work in Asosa *awraja* in February 1972, the front of the sole of my American-made shoe came unglued and started flapping as I walked. I stopped at a small local market that had a shoemaker sitting on the ground, with his wares placed on a cloth, and inquired whether he would be able to repair the shoe. This middle-aged, simple man took the shoe in his hand, turned it over once to look at the bottom, and immediately took out his knife and proceeded to cut a groove in the rubber sole. I was quite concerned that he was going to totally ruin the shoe, but held my tongue to see what would happen. After cutting the groove in the sole, he then took out his needle and some thick cord and proceeded to sew the sole to the upper part of the shoe using many strong stitches. The stitches remained in the groove so the cord would not be cut while walking. This repair lasted for many months, until I could buy a new pair of shoes. I was very impressed that this workman, living in a very remote part of the country, seeing an American type shoe probably for the first time in his life, could very quickly analyze the shoe and the problem and design and implement an excellent solution. I profusely thanked the man, and paid him the fair price that he asked for. He seemed to take this unusual assignment in stride. This craftsman's intelligence, ability and integrity, was far beyond what one would expect simply by looking at his very simple clothes and appearance.

Some comic interludes

Although the work could be taxing, and conditions quite primitive, with the availability of the next meal not always certain, there were also some lighter situations that eased the workload and provided comic interludes. Two examples from my notebooks are shown below, including the following story of an event on a dry-weather road while driving back to Nekemte from Asosa *awraja*.

Tuesday, March 7, 1972
One incident bears recording. Just before Mendi, we [riding in a Wollega SEP Land Rover] met these two donkeys standing right in the middle of the road facing us. [Totally overwhelmed by the combined stupidity of two donkeys] I slowed down to a stop [right in front of them] and honked my horn. [After five seconds of staring directly at the car, and being blasted by the horn] they both [finally] got the idea I wanted to go through at the same time and [simultaneously] they turned into each other, bunking heads. They then retreated in complete disarray. Needless to say, Tefera and I had to sit a few minutes to stop laughing before we could continue. A classic. It greatly brightened the drive.

Wednesday, December 8, 1971
One good line from Alem Teferi. When a guy asked if there was a
fast or any restrictions for the vaccine [after he was vaccinated].
The people standing around said he couldn't sleep with his wife
for 30 days.

EPILOGUE

The northern, Amhara-majority provinces were among the last in the
country to become smallpox free, with the last case in Gojam occurring in
March 1976. The outbreaks in Gojam were finally controlled using many
teams, and helicopters. The helicopters addressed the travel problems and
indicated the importance of the program to the people, and the large teams
ensured enough manpower. I was amazed to hear that travel from Mota
to Bibugn *woreda* was only a few minutes by helicopter, as compared to
my eight hour walks. So in the end, the shortcomings we faced in Gojam
in 1973 and 1974 were addressed, and the program was successful. The
Ethiopia SEP report to the Smallpox Eradication Certification Commission
notes that, "In Gojam, the most difficult *awraja*, often closed for security
reasons, was Mota. In September 1976, this *awraja* was re-opened and
a special search was made using helicopter backup. Three Surveillance
Officers supervised 89 local searchers and 23 SEP vaccinators."[6] No cases
were found. While the very large number of workers for this search reflected the need to rapidly confirm that there was no ongoing smallpox
transmission in Mota, the scale and method of working were similar to the
helicopter operations carried out in the Gojam highlands in 1975–1976,
and provides some idea of the staffing and operations that were eventually
needed to stop transmission in the Gojam highlands.

PCVs were given responsibility for planning and implementation of
important public health activities at a very young age. I learned responsibility, cultural sensitivity, the benefit of a focused, simple and achievable
strategy, and to appreciate simple pleasures like drinking clean, cold water,
taking a hot (or any!) shower, and reading a newspaper after four weeks

6 Yemane Tekeste, Alebachew Hailu, C. do Amaral, P.R. Arbani, O. Ismail, L. N. Kho-
dakevich and N.A. Ward, *Smallpox Eradication in Ethiopia* (Brazzaville: World Health
Organization, 1984), p. 88.

in the field with little contact with the outside world. My experiences in Ethiopia also taught me many lessons about life. Seeing how people living in poverty conditions were so sophisticated, and very worthy of respect, made a lasting impression that I have carried throughout life. I learned that one always needs to go below the surface appearance and appreciate and understand what is inside.

After Ethiopia, I went on to work with the smallpox eradication effort in India, Bangladesh and Somalia, applying the lessons learned in Ethiopia. To this I owe a debt of gratitude to SEP senior management. People like Ciro de Quadros and Kurt Weithaler trained us, supported us, believed in us, and instilled a belief that even the most difficult task was possible with good strategies, good policies, careful planning and hard work. Even something as seemingly impossible as eradicating smallpox in a country as challenging as Ethiopia could be achieved.

A FINAL ACKNOWLEDGMENT

For all the lessons I learned during my stay in Ethiopia, I have to be grateful to the people of Ethiopia, the Peace Corps and all of the SEP team members. One final acknowledgment is required, in keeping with the theme of this book. In 1978, after finishing my smallpox eradication work, I returned to the United States without a clear idea of what to do next, but knowing that I needed to start on a new endeavor. I went directly to my aunt's house in New York City from the airport and found a cryptic message there to call a telephone number in Washington, D.C. Not sure what the message was about, I dialed the number. Ciro answered the phone and, in his memorable, cheerful voice, said "What are you doing in New York? You start work here on Monday!" This was the start of a consultancy working with Ciro at the Pan American Health Organization (PAHO), which again gave me the opportunity to watch and learn from his guiding, supportive, encouraging, cheerful, visionary and passionate leadership style as he started up the Expanded Program on Immunization in the Americas, achieving the same extraordinary successes that had marked his work in Ethiopia and Brazil. Working with Ciro in Ethiopia and at PAHO, and his support after I completed an MPH degree and was looking for positions with WHO, were crucial contributors to my eventual career in international health.

•

4

A Lesson Relearned in Welega

by Gene L. Bartley

I never thought about or considered the continent of Africa, or even the world outside my home in Denver, Colorado, until entering undergraduate school at Westmar College, a small religious school located in the corn fields of Iowa. There I met many foreign students from far away countries with unusual names like Ghana, Kenya, Nigeria and Sierra Leone, which could only be found on a map and not in my conscious mind. Eventually, my intrigue with Africa was further developed when I joined the International Relations Club on campus and eventually became the club's president. This experience planted a seed in my mind that would never leave me.

After graduating from college in December 1968, with a major in biology and minors in education and psychology, I began to pursue a career teaching high school students in Simla, a small cow town in eastern Colorado. At that time, Africa was temporarily pushed back into my unconscious mind, but never totally forgotten. Teaching was my minor in college, so while it was not necessarily my favorite line of work, I enjoyed it, but I was not really interested in continuing in education because I wanted to apply what I had learned in a practical way. It was also about this time that I began thinking about Africa again as I recalled my days in undergraduate school. I wondered, could I find a way of helping those who may need my skills? In my discussions with friends and teachers at the high school, I was informed and actually reminded about John F. Kennedy's Peace Corps, which had already been in operation since 1961.

Prior to the end of my first full-time year of teaching, I sent an application to the Peace Corps (PC) office in Washington, DC. In the application I stated my preference to work in the countries of Africa and Asia, the two continents that were seeking manpower in the fields of science and teaching. One month later, I received a reply letter informing me of the availability of a position to teach science in a technical college in India. I appreciated the offer, but I turned it down because I wanted to apply my skills and qualifications in a hands-on environment rather than teach. Finally, in August 1970, a letter arrived informing me about a newly formed program for the eradication of smallpox in Ethiopia. Peace Corps Volunteers (PCVs) were being assigned as manpower for the World Health Organization (WHO) to implement the Smallpox Eradication Program (SEP). I immediately sent back a positive response since this program would give me the opportunity to work in Africa.

The offer reminded me of the Peace Corps motto at that time, which expressed the kind of job I was about to undertake, "The hardest job that you will ever love." I did not understand or anticipate the full impact of my decision at the time, but that decision would change my life forever.

PEACE CORPS ORIENTATION AND TRAINING

The Peace Corps set in motion administrative procedures starting with a pre-orientation workshop with the objective . . . I believed . . . to scare and weed out those who were only looking for a cheap way to visit a foreign country, as well those with weak stomachs or minds. I would not be fooled into bowing out so easily because I wanted to know what this faraway place in Africa had in store for me.

On the technical side, the PC trainees who passed the first stage of the orientation received technical training for one week (October 20-28,

1970) at the Centers for Disease Control (CDC) in Atlanta, Georgia. The briefing included the use of Ped-O-Jet injection equipment for mass vaccination, designed mainly for use in urban settings, as well as the useful bifurcated needle, which turned out to be much more portable and practical for giving smallpox vaccinations in rural Ethiopia.

In 1970, at the start of the SEP, the Ethiopian population was mostly rural, with around 90% of the population living and working in the countryside. This statistic alone should have alerted us to the fact that we would face significant challenges when carrying out surveillance and containment operations in remote villages.

After completing both the administrative and technical training state-side, the Group XIV PCVs hopped on board a plane to Ethiopia. Since I had never traveled outside the United States before, even though I was curious, I was also a bit apprehensive and worried about what was waiting for me in Ethiopia.

We arrived in Ethiopia on October 30, 1970, and one of my first memories after exiting the airplane in Addis Ababa was throwing a Frisbee on the grounds of the Bel Air hotel, which was where we stayed for the first couple of weeks. We were trying to reconnect to what we left in the States. We would eventually find out that some of the luxuries we left behind could only be found in Addis Ababa, the capital of Ethiopia.

We continued with the PC in-country orientation that was led by an Ethiopian training company called Alem, which provided our cultural and language training for the next three months.

The training also provided us with a feel for the terrain and transport in Ethiopia by organizing trips by bus, Land Rover four-wheel drive vehicles, and train to the towns of Bahir Dar, Dire Dawa, Gonder, and Addis Ababa.

Learning the language was the most challenging part of the training program. We were trained to speak the Amharic language, the national language of Ethiopia, but we were also informed that Ethiopia had a diversity of ethnic groups and languages, with over 80 ethnic groups/tribes and 83 different languages with up to 200 different dialects spoken. Alem Company utilized the "immersion technique" of Amharic language training, which meant that there was very little or no use of English in the classroom. My final language tests results were passable . . . I received a total Foreign Service Institute (F.S.I.) score of 1+ out of 3. Fortunately, I became much more fluent when I started using Amharic in the field. It was ironic, however, that my first posting in Ethiopia was in Welega province in Western Ethiopia, where the main language was Oromo!

In early November of 1970, at the request of the Ethiopian Ministry of Health (MOH), the PC smallpox trainee group had their first experience in the field when we assisted in a cholera vaccination campaign using Ped-O-Jet injectors to administer cholera vaccine to large populations in specific areas of the country. I was stationed in Shoa Province, in the town of Butajera and surrounding areas, for the cholera campaign. The bright side of this unfortunate epidemic was that it provided an opportunity for the PC trainees to get vital, hands-on experience for the upcoming SEP activities and vaccination campaigns, including operating and servicing the Ped-O-Jet injectors.

Our practical training in the culture was found each evening in the *buna bets*, which were local restaurants/bars that served up drinks and food, among other things. This environment provided a place to use and develop our rudimentary Amharic language skills.

In addition, interspersed between our cultural and language training was technical training provided by WHO/PC as well as MOH staff members. The technical briefings included PC policy and administrative information, SEP strategy, history and etiology of the smallpox disease, and practical use of Ped-O-Jets, as well as the mechanical operations of a Land Rover . . . and especially how to use 4-wheel drive and the winch.

Looking back on my experience, the most challenging barrier to our work was the transport and lack of mobility in the rugged terrain of Ethiopia that included roads in high mountains, wide and deep valleys, deserts (some of which was below sea level) and semi-deserts, and thick, wet tropical forests. Furthermore, very few paved or all-weather roads existed, except for the main roads from Addis Ababa to the provincial capitals . . . and the majority of those being gravel/dirt roads. In reality, the teams mostly drove their vehicles on roads built by villagers, which could actually be considered to be more like broadened footpaths, and more often than not, PCVs would accomplish their surveillance and containment activities traveling by mule, donkey and, of course, on foot.

A second barrier that we faced was infections and diseases that affected our personal condition and activities in the field. The health of the PCVs in-country was the responsibility of the PC country office in Addis. We were given vaccinations and medication to combat all sorts of common parasites, bacteria and other infectious elements and illnesses that we were exposed to during our work in the field. This took a real toll physically on those who had not been exposed to these types of invisible enemies, which in turn slowed down field-work. This constituted a definite barrier to our work, especially for the PCVs and surveillance teams in general.

GOING OUR SEPARATE WAYS AND SETTLING IN

At the conclusion of PCV training, we were given a farewell party hosted by the PC country office and the U.S. Embassy. It was quite a relief to have completed the intensive 12-week in-country training program. The smallpox trainees of Group XIV were officially enrolled in the Peace Corps as PCVs on February 1, 1971 and this meant that we would be leaving for our various posts around the country.

The SEP assigned two PCVs to each of the provinces that were initiating the program, which were mostly in the southwest part of the country. Later, we would be assigned to different provinces, as the program was replicated in the northern provinces, using the experience gained in the south.

Charlie Kilmer and I were assigned to Welega province in western Ethiopia as a surveillance team. Since the majority of the population there was of the Oromo tribe, we were required to learn simple phrases in the Oromo language.

By mid-February 1971, we were on our way to take up our duties, transporting our equipment and personal household goods to "set up camp" in Nekemte, the capital of Welega — about 320km (200mi) from Addis Ababa. The SEP provided each team with a Land Rover and equipment to implement the program in their respective provinces.

Ethiopia's first PCV Smallpox Eradication group (number XIV) prior to departure to their respective provinces of assignment. Left to right: Clyde Emerson, Dan Kraushaar, Marc Strassburg, Gary Urquhart, Phil Kneller, Graham Holmboe, Jay Anderson, Charlie Kilmer, Russ Handzus, Vince Radke, James Siemon, Gene Bartley, Jim Lepkowski, and Stan Ratoff. Addis Ababa, February 1971. *Photo provided by the author*

As predicted, settling into the assigned post was not an easy process. It was especially difficult to find a suitable house to rent (with luxuries like running water and an indoor toilet), although, due to our heavy load of field-work, we did not use our the house very much during the early months of our assignment.

To get back and forth between Addis and Nekemte, Charlie and I were permitted to fly the Ethiopian Airlines DC-3s. The DC-3s were the workhorses of the domestic airline service and were very dependable. But before a plane took off or landed, the airstrip had to be cleared of cattle, sheep, goats and people. Once we were in the plane we had to share the space with goats, sheep and chickens, and the ever-present strong smell of butter and the lavatory in the back of the plane.

Our basic initial strategy prior to starting our work was to make contact with key institutions and officials in the provincial capital to introduce ourselves briefly and obtain introductory letters from the government, which would enable us to seek the necessary cooperation in the *woreda* (similar to county) administrative offices. The relevant provincial government administrative offices that we contacted included the Provincial Health Department (PHD), and representatives of the ministers of education, and water resources. In addition, we organized meetings with bilateral government agencies, such as the Swedish International Development Agency (SIDA), which was heavily involved in the building of schools and health clinics, as well as other development activities. Furthermore, we contacted relevant organizations that were described as Non-government Organizations (NGOs), and Faith-based Organizations (FBOs), which included the Ethiopian Orthodox Church, missionary groups and Islamic center, all of whom turned out to be important collaborative institutions in the rural areas.

We also found it most helpful to contact the Sudan Interior Mission (SIM), which was involved in extensive work and activities in rural communities in Welega. SIM was an important contact group and collaborative partner in the field, especially to gain the cooperation of those who worshiped in the SIM built churches.

And finally, we received a detailed briefing regarding the smallpox situation in Welega from *Ato* Tadela Getahun, the MOH sanitarian who was assigned to work with us in the SEP in Welega. The sanitarians "played an exceptionally important role; they were graduates of a recently established 4-year course of study in the health sciences which was designed for students who had completed secondary school."[1] The sanitarians' training and responsibilities included communicable disease surveillance and control. All of the SEP sanitarians in Ethiopia received additional training on smallpox eradication from the SEP before starting work.

As a result of our meetings, we were able to prepare a detailed plan of action and timetable for implementation.

Ato Tadela was a peaceful and quiet man who had very traditional beliefs about how things should be done, and he was not afraid to speak his mind. Due to his very strict approach to carrying out the work, we

---

1 F. Fenner, D. A. Henderson, I. Arita, Z. Jezek, I. D. Ladnyi, *Smallpox and Its Eradication* (Geneva: World Health Organization, 1988), 1009.

had many heated discussions, but the outcome of those discussions was always a compromise that allowed the team to move forward.

A side benefit of our discussions was the collection of previously unreported provincial data regarding smallpox that we forwarded to the SEP/HQ Office in Addis Ababa. The office then updated their records with more accurate information as baseline data, which would allow our team to monitor and evaluate program implementation in the future.

THE FIRST AND MOST CHALLENGING SMALLPOX OUTBREAK – BEGI AREA

In coordination with the PHD, we agreed to start our surveillance work in the Begi area, which was in the far western part of Welega province, near the border with Sudan, where there was an ongoing smallpox outbreak that the PHD believed had not been properly contained.

In our outbreak investigation, we would utilize the surveillance and containment strategy developed by WHO for detecting, investigating and containing smallpox outbreaks in the field, which was utilized from the start of the SEP in Ethiopia. The components included: a) active search for smallpox cases; b) immediate response to any report of suspected cases of smallpox; c) investigate and trace the chain of transmission; d) identify source of disease and detect all cases; e) ring vaccinate in the area around the cases to stop transmission; and f) follow-up of the area vaccinated to detect any fresh cases. The strategy also called for improving smallpox surveillance and routine reporting of cases, and for obtaining the cooperation of all public health facilities in routine vaccination. This strategy was used with success by the team in the Begi outbreak.

In retrospect, the Begi outbreak turned out to be the largest smallpox outbreak discovered in Welega during the SEP, in terms of the geographic area affected and the sheer number of cases.

After two weeks of orientation and fact-finding with groups in Nekemte, we set out with *Ato* Tadela to investigate the outbreak.

We looked at a map and located Begi about 367 kilometers (228 miles) west of the provincial capital.

Through my recent researching Online, I discovered that the road conditions in Welega in 2015 would allow one to reach Begi from Nekemte in approximately five hours . . . but that was definitely not the case back in February 1971. It was a totally different situation during our time there, and making that trip was a story in itself.

THE ROAD TO BEGI

We travelled from Nekemte on an all-weather, gravel road going west-northwest to the town of Gimbi. An all-weather gravel road is considered a road that is not affected by seasonal climatic conditions and permits year-round vehicle use.

The roads beyond Gimbi were classified as dry-weather roads, and were not usually passable in the rainy seasons which are typically from June to September — the "big rains," and February to May — the "small rains."

Our investigation of the outbreak took place in February, which is a time for some small rains, and the streams and rivers were either completely or partially filled with water, which caused problems when passing over the locally-made bridges. These conditions made our journey from Gimbi through Nejo, Mendi, Bambesi, and finally to Begi much more challenging.

One situation we encountered along that section of the road was quite remarkable.

Before reaching Begi, we diverted to Asosa (the *awraja* capital) where we picked up a health officer and a dresser from the Asosa Health Center. They would help us with travel routes, investigation, language and, most importantly, obtaining cooperation from the local population through local government officials, NGOs and the religious institutions in the area.

After a day of rest and discussions, we left Asosa with our two new team members, drove back to Bambesi and turned south toward Begi.

I had never driven a 4-wheel drive vehicle in low gear before, and likewise never used a winch, and was only trained in the use of each during the in-country training and orientation. As luck would have it, I had to use both during our travel to Begi that day . . . and subsequently many times afterwards during the remaining days I spent in Ethiopia.

The area south of the town of Bambesi is known for slow moving rivers, standing water flow and swamps during the big rainy season, which makes it almost impossible to travel by car on the dry weather roads through this area. The trip we made was during the small rains, which, while somewhat better than during the big rains, still presented many problems. The road that day was passable up to Bambesi, but after that the road narrowed and the rivers, streams, and brooks became more frequent, as did the "bridges" over these water obstacles.

The term "bridge" is used loosely here, and in my estimation none of these qualified as one compared to any I was familiar with in the States. There were basically two kinds of bridges, one having several logs laid side by side simply thrown across the stream, while other bridges we encountered had two large logs put across the stream and then smaller filler branches/trees placed across and in between the two larger logs.

We could not forge the streams because they were too muddy and had very steep banks, which made it impossible to cross, so we were forced to use the bridges. Despite our serious concerns about whether the bridges could support the weight of the long-wheel base Land Rover, we all agreed to continue using the bridges as our only alternative. Our national hosts assured us that using them was normal procedure for this area.

Well, it did not seem normal to my mind, but we had no other choice. What made me more scared was the fact that the others decided to get out of the Land Rover, and move to the other side of the stream, leaving only me to drive the vehicle across.

I held my breath, put the vehicle in 4-wheel drive low gear — sometimes referred to as the "grannie gear" because the speed was so slow — and opened all the windows because I had heard that was a good idea in case the bridge collapsed and the car was submerged in the water I could escape much more easily. I started across the first bridge very slowly and heard the smaller branches beginning to bend and crack under the weight of the Land Rover. This seemed to be normal to the Ethiopians standing watching on the other side of the river, but I did not concur with this observation.

The author digging out his Land Rover when it was stuck on a local bridge made of tree limbs. Bambesi, Welega, February 1971. *Photo by Charlie Kilmer*

I made it across the first bridge and was applauded. I looked down and saw my knuckles had turned white because I had gripped the steering wheel so tightly.

I was then labeled as an "expert bridge-crosser," so everyone said that I should drive across the next bridge.

Unfortunately, the next bridge was one of those that had much smaller trees filling the distance between the larger logs, which made it a much more difficult challenge than the first bridge. Through the spaces between the smaller tree trunks on that bridge we could see the water moving below, which meant trouble. Under these circumstances, if the car slipped or moved off the larger logs, the vehicle would end up resting high-centered on an axle or crankshaft.

My luck ran out on that second bridge, and the worst happened. The wheels slipped off the large logs, and the vehicle fell between the smaller logs, causing the chassis to come to rest on the smaller logs that provided no traction. Basically this meant that the tires were not getting

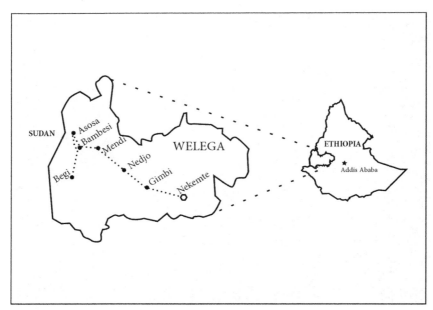

The 368 kilometers Nekemte/Begi route with a side stop in Asosa.

any traction and we could not move forward . . . or backward in 4-wheel drive. Therefore, we had to use the winch to get across that bridge.

Fortunately, we pulled it across that bridge and the other bridges, which varied in length from five to ten meters, and were found almost every fifteen kilometers along the road between Bambesi and Begi. Even though the road was only 60 kilometers (37 miles) long, it took us several hours to travel, which delayed our arrival significantly.

Luckily, there was a bright side to the slow travel caused by the bridges . . . it provided time for the team to begin interviewing people along the road about possible smallpox cases. We found and identified many old cases that day along the road and learned that the current outbreak had been ongoing for several months. When we finally reached Begi, we realized that the outbreak was quite large in terms of the area affected and number of cases. With this initial information, we understood that it would probably take quite some time to trace the chain of transmission and vaccinate those areas around the active cases. And as it turned out,

Charlie Kilmer leads meeting to plan next steps to control outbreak with priest, sanitarian & health worker. Begi, Welega, February 1971. *Photo by the author.*

we had to work in the outbreak area for over two months to complete the containment process.

The total distance from Nekemte to Begi is 368 kilometers (228 miles), and presently it takes a little more than 5 hours to drive. I recall that in 1971 the drive took at least twice that amount of time.

BEGI

Upon arrival in Begi, we were grateful to be invited to stay at the Begi Health Unit, and proceeded to set up our operational base there, which was basically in the center of the outbreak area. The Health Unit provided us a place to sleep on our cots with a roof over our heads and a semi-nice latrine. Normally, Charlie and I would set up a two-man tent in the field. For our meals, we were introduced to the local restaurants in town for dinner while breakfast usually consisted of oatmeal, tea and bread that we prepared over a one-burner kerosene stove.

In the following days, we met with local health officials and planned a strategy to start investigating recently reported cases and decided on the areas on which each team would concentrate. As we suspected, there were old cases everywhere, which required a lot of time and manpower to complete case reporting forms that would eventually give us an accurate indication of the total number of cases in this outbreak and the chain of transmission.

IN THE FIELD

We also met with local government officials to make an official appeal for permission to perform vaccinations in their areas, and requested guides and letters of introduction with, of course, an official stamp.

Our best source of information and assistance came from valued local, government-appointed officials called *chikashumes,* as well as the respected priests in the local Ethiopian Orthodox church.

The Begi area also had a large Muslim population, especially near the Sudan border. Their leaders also provided us with excellent cooperation and support in mobilizing communities to accept vaccination in the rural areas.

During this time we discovered the importance of our meetings with the local leaders who gave us much needed cooperation. These meetings were extremely valuable and without them we could not have given nearly 50,000 vaccinations during the Begi outbreak.

On many occasions, the vaccination team and I were provided lunch by one of the important figures in the community . . . it is always nice to tell your neighbors and friends that you hosted a foreigner, known locally as *ferengi,* in your home. The typical lunch was bean or lentil sauce with *injera,* followed by coffee flavored with salt or butter. Begi was known for producing and exporting coffee, mangoes and butter to the capital and beyond, and the coffee was excellent.

Often during the investigation we were invited to sit down to experience the traditional coffee ceremony, which involves roasting of raw, green coffee beans, grinding them, boiling the grounds and serving the coffee three times, burning of incense and eating locally baked bread.

Ciro de Quadros (second from the right in straw hat) advising team on surveillance with village leaders and SEP health workers. Begi, Welega, February
1971. *Photo by the author.*

OVER THE NEXT VALLEY AND HILL

The extent of the outbreak in Begi was larger than anticipated and required a large team to record cases and give vaccinations in the outbreak
area. We spent over two months there, and were fortunate to have the
assistance of Dr. Ciro de Quadros, WHO Epidemiologist from Addis
Ababa, who made a visit to advise and monitor the surveillance team on
implementation of the strategy, especially since it was the first outbreak
investigation for our team.

In this context, there is a special story to tell about Ciro during the Begi
outbreak. When we were driving back to our camp after a long, hard
day of surveillance and vaccination work, Ciro turned to me and said
"It is still early so let's walk across the valley to the other side and meet
the vehicle in Begi!" I was surprised by this statement and said, "I am
tired and the health workers have already covered that area and found

Tadela leading the team from hut to hut in sparsely populated areas near the Sudan boarder. Welega, February 1971. *Photo by the author.*

no active cases." He replied, in his usual direct and sometimes humorous way, and in his Brazilian-accented English, "The walk will do you good, and besides it is a small valley." So, I agreed to go, and we jumped out of the vehicle with vaccine, needles and reporting forms in hand while another driver drove our vehicle back to base camp. We walked down one side of the valley, and then up the hill on the other side, showing the famous smallpox recognition picture to the residents and using our sign language to communicate.

I was very surprised when we discovered that there was an active case in the old outbreak area not far from our base camp in Begi! We convinced the leader of the area, who, fortunately, spoke Amharic, to have all of the immediate contacts and the people in the surrounding area vaccinated, and they complied. After he and I completed all of the inoculations, we continued on our way back to the camp in Begi before the sunset brought darkness.

It was then that I understood why Ciro had come to Begi . . . to teach us to go beyond what we thought we knew and do the unexpected.

That is exactly what we did that day, and I will never forget the lesson he taught me. It caused me to think about my own father's words when he was teaching me to fly fish as a young boy in the Colorado mountain streams. He advised that when I have not caught any fish, I should go back and look at the water again. He simply meant that I should not just fish in the deep holes where you normally expect to find fish, but other areas that I might have missed, such as the shallow riffles, the dark water under the overhanging bushes, and water behind the rocks or near a fallen tree. It was a lesson learned and well taken then, and, I had relearned that lesson as a result of Ciro's demonstration that it applied to my work in Ethiopia too! That is, to do your work thoroughly, check out all possibilities until you are positive there are no more cases, and carefully follow-up previously completed work.

This first smallpox outbreak with which I was involved was quite a challenge, but also a learning experience. Through our work, we were able to accurately document the scale of the outbreak, the number of cases found and the number of people vaccinated. The number of smallpox cases recorded from Asosa *Awraja* in 1971, including those that were reported during our February investigation, was 2,062.[2]

Almost all of these cases were from the Begi outbreak. A total of 51,618 vaccinations were performed in Asosa *Awraja* from 1971 to 1973 by the provincial SEP teams, with most of these performed while we were containing the Begi outbreak in 1971.[3]

With six months of experience, I felt more at ease when moving to my next assignment in Welo province in northern Ethiopia to implement the same program. There were different challenges, but my experiences

2 *Smallpox Eradication in Ethiopia* (based on the 1979 report to the International Commission for the Certification of Smallpox Eradication in Ethiopia), WHO AFRO/Ethiopia Ministry of Public Health, 1984, 133.

3 Source: Annual number of smallpox vaccinations reported to the Welega SEP Office for 1971, 1972 and 1973 (up to 28 April); included in the "Wollega Report to the Ethiopia Smallpox Conference, 17-20 September 1973" (presented by Alan Schnur).

in Welega made me confident that I was prepared for any situation that might develop.

CIRO'S LEGACY

When I reflect back on my life, especially my experience in Ethiopia, a question continues to bother me to this very day. I can only formulate this query as follows: "Is there any way of knowing where or what I will be doing tomorrow, in a month or even next year?" My life has been filled with wonderment and excitement and I believe the person I am today and where I have lived is in part due to those special persons surrounding me, who I call "kindred spirits," and who continue to this day to influence my life.

One of those special kindred spirits was my hero and mentor, Dr. Ciro de Quadros, who was the WHO Epidemiologist during the SEP in Ethiopia. He was a fighter and a champion for the health of the children of the world. In the Ethiopia that he loved and worked during those early years, the children were the most significant beneficiaries of the SEP because they were blessed to grow up in a smallpox-free world.

He loved the children who surrounded him in the field and he understood the importance of their future well-being, which was only possible if they had a chance to grow up as healthy children.

This was only a beginning of his legacy and, he later went on to work for global programs in the Expanded Program for Immunization (EPI) and GAVI, the Vaccine Alliance towards the eradication of polio and elimination of other vaccine-preventable diseases that targeted the children of the world.

I feel compelled to elaborate on my thoughts in terms of what Ciro meant to me. He was many things to many people. It is impossible to describe him in just a few words, but I view him not only as my hero and mentor, but also as my colleague, guide, teacher, and older brother. He was a force and strength for us young men working in the field in Ethiopia, and we believed he was sent to eradicate a disease that we only started to understand in those few short months after arriving in Ethiopia. He had

Ciro de Quadros, at his best, leading countries to increase funding for immunization through SABIN program. Dakar, Senegal, August 2013. *Photo by the author.*

so many extraordinary abilities, and among the most memorable were his optimism, great sense of humor, and the patience and ability he had to teach us in a relatively short time how to work effectively on the front lines against a disease that was the first to be eradicated in the history of mankind. His finest quality was the determination he exhibited in making heroic efforts to defeat diseases and attempt to improve the health of the world's children in a small way, starting in Brazil, then in Ethiopia, and later in the Americas, and indeed globally. He possessed an endless supply of energy to walk all day in the heat and sun without food and water in pursuit of the discovery of possible smallpox cases. I tried to emulate his characteristics and ability in the field because they held the key to our success, but nobody could match this giant of a man in the field.

Even after I departed from the SEP after two years of fighting the smallpox virus, Ciro continued to help and advise me over the years in so many ways. He was there when I needed a strong reference for entering graduate school for an Master of Public Health degree. He was my reference when I was hired as a Technical Officer in the WHO African Regional Office in Brazzaville, Republic of Congo. After my retirement, he asked me if I wanted to work in the polio program, and on his recommendation and reputation I was hired as senior polio consultant with the Bill and

Melinda Gates Foundation in Kenya during the period of the re-infection of polio from Somalia. Finally, I had the privilege and honor to work in two programs that were designed to achieve the global eradication of a disease, and Ciro was the person who made it happen.

While I was working in the polio program, I met Ciro for the last time at a conference in August, 2013 in Dakar, Senegal, prior to his untimely death on May 28, 2014. At that time, he was Executive Vice President and Director of the Sustainable Immunization Financing (SIF) program for the Sabin Vaccine Institute (SVI), a program that had been introduced and implemented in 18 countries globally. He gave a presentation that I will never forget, exhorting the importance of the work in each of those countries to increase domestic funding of immunization in innovative ways. The goal was to encourage countries to achieve financial sustainability for their immunization programs over time, in an environment of dwindling external funding.

Ciro will be remembered for many things by the global public health community, but for me I will remember him most of all for his wisdom, true kindness and endless and unselfish support.

·

ACKNOWLEDGMENTS

The author is very grateful to Alan Schnur, James Skelton and Scott Porterfield for their timely and helpful comments and suggestions regarding the contents of this chapter.

5

The Teppi Outbreak
An Introduction to Smallpox

by James Siemon

When I first saw Ciro De Quadros in Ethiopia during January of 1971, I had no idea who he was or what he would come to mean for me. He was a young doctor, seemingly in his late twenties, speaking to sixteen American Peace Corps Volunteers (PCVs) and a number of Ethiopian health workers in heavily-accented, and somewhat halting, English about smallpox transmission in Brazil.

Weeks later, I appreciated vividly just what Ciro had been trying to convey to us that day — the working basis, the simple principles and daily routines in the eradication effort that had already made him a respected figure in the global eradication of smallpox. The method, the working procedures of surveillance and record-keeping would eventually make all of us feel famous, too, in a much smaller way. He led, we followed, and those lectures laid out for us, clearly and memorably, step by step, what to do when and wherever we might encounter smallpox cases.

By that time reports already rumored that the southwestern province of Illubabor, where I had volunteered to go, was experiencing an outbreak of smallpox. I paid attention. What I couldn't have suspected at that time, however, was how much Ciro de Quadros would teach me about leadership and about friendship.

Before that day, we PCVs had, for assorted reasons of our own, signed up to pursue an abstract goal of eliminating a terrible disease we had never seen. The goal remained abstract that January day because none of us had even seen a case of smallpox, and according to the best World Health Organization (WHO) estimates, it wasn't certain that we would find much of it in Ethiopia. In the previous two years, all of Ethiopia had reported only 919 cases (197 in 1969 and 722 in 1970) in a population estimated at twenty-six million.

On the day we met Ciro, though, we weren't exactly brand-new to Ethiopia itself, nor to the other personnel of the Ethiopia Smallpox Eradication Program (SEP). Our Peace Corps Group XIV had stepped off the plane from America in late October 1970, and right into a national emergency that sent us scattering all over the country in a hastily-mounted anti-cholera campaign.

We had quickly gotten to know Kurt Weithaler, the hard-working and blustery Austrian physician who was the Executive Director of the Ethiopian Smallpox campaign. Dr. Weithaler drove us hard during the anti-cholera campaign, but worked closely with us and lavishly praised our work in rapid response and inoculations.

By contrast, all we knew about Ciro de Quadros was that he would be the Chief Epidemiologist of the SEP. Despite his evident youth and his struggles with English, the person speaking to us in front of the blackboards in that seminar room in Nazareth was impressive.

Though our cohort wasn't much on paying respect to authority figures, Ciro's serious demeanor commanded respect. He wasn't one for rhetoric, and he never would be, but that day he spoke with an intensity of commitment that quietly communicated the idea that what we were about to do was the most important task on the planet.

In retrospect, I realized (as he confirmed for me) that he must have had low expectations for a bunch of American kids like me, a recent college graduate with a degree in English Literature, who so far hadn't much in the way of prospects or achievements. To be honest, the only thing that I felt good about when it came to myself was being there — in Ethiopia — in the first place, and having already worked hard under difficult physical conditions to insure the success of the anti-cholera campaign. Traveling for weeks around the country, living in huts and tents while dispensing inoculations to a very frightened public was something I took pride in. Beyond that, there wasn't much, at least on my account.

I had initially applied to the Peace Corps and requested a medical assignment because I had vague ideas about doing something to make a positive difference in the world. President Kennedy's Peace Corps ideals were inspirational, but I also remember wanting to connect with America's better self the way that my father's World War II generation had been able to do.

But amid the gloomy anger that greeted Nixon's April 1970 Cambodia invasion, I had been drafted.

An early summer letter I received from the Peace Corps in 1970 offered me the chance to join a medical program in Africa. From then on it had been a race against time; I desperately wanted to go, but the draft board seemed determined to thwart my best efforts. In a comical conjunction, I was ordered to report for military service on the very day our flight was scheduled to leave for Ethiopia. I remember nervously sitting in the JFK transit lounge watching men in suits pull other young men out of the room. I'll never forget the relief as our plane lifted off the runway for Ethiopia.

Of course, none of this was evident to Ciro, neither my vague idealism, my lack of self-assurance, nor my immediate problems with the draft, as he stood before the room full of new PCVs come to work for SEP in Ethiopia, wearing his Paris-tailored suit, speaking passionately about the working details, the small, but brilliantly effective, techniques that would provide us with an unprecedented historic opportunity: we— the motley group of bearded twenty-something PCVs — could actually contribute to ending one of history's most destructive diseases. But from what he said, we needed to get it right. On that day, and several subsequent ones, I took notes when Ciro spoke. It's a good thing I did.

GOING TO TEPPI

Three weeks later, on February 3, 1971, Ciro's talk became suddenly very real as I read a pink phone-message slip that had been left at my downtown Addis Ababa hotel. In shaky spelling the note read, "Come to the office right away. Get vaccine and instructions. Flight to Teppi tomorrow." For a minute I failed to absorb what this meant.

I had, in fact, just come back from shopping for camp stoves and flashlights to get ready for provincial deployment. No one else in our Peace Corps SEP group was even imagining deployment to their provincial capitals for a week or so, let alone flying off to tackle an epidemic in an uncharted rural area.

I remember thinking that maybe this note was a mistake, or maybe the rumored epidemic was the result of a misdiagnosis and a subsequent panic. How could there even be a smallpox emergency in progress without anybody doing much about it till now? In any case, this message meant that I would be traveling on my own to a place that was more threatening based on what I knew about it. As events turned out, I would spend the most intense days and weeks of my life over the next month in southern Illubabor, which was about 600 kilometers from Addis.

By the time I climbed onto the Ethiopian Airlines DC-3 that was heading for Teppi via Jimma, Kaffa province, it was very early the next morning. I was carrying a backpack full of vaccine, a change of clothes, and smallpox reporting forms, and I believed that I knew four things.

First, Illubabor could be dangerous. Way back during the summer of 1970 Peace Corps pre-staging in Philadelphia, we had all heard about the Illubabor PCV who had been killed and partially eaten by a crocodile. (This narrative remains alive in Peace Corps oral history; sitting out a flight delay in Dulles airport in 2014, I listened to recently returned Zambia PCVs retelling the whole grisly account.)

Second, Illubabor was mostly dense rain forest, and largely inaccessible by vehicle. In November of 1970, PCV Dan Kraushaar had returned from two weeks of giving cholera vaccinations in Illubabor complaining loudly about extremely wet climate, dense vegetation, and lack of roads.

Third, there was Illubabor's cultural isolation, its mix of different ethnic groups who didn't speak Amharic, the one language in which we had been trained. Actually, this cultural isolation didn't sound so bad in theory, since my experience of Sidamo province's heavily-travelled gravel and paved roads during the cholera campaign had provided me more than enough exposure to the sort of truck-stop culture that flourished along Ethiopian highways.

Finally — and on the plus side — I had briefly visited Metu, Illubabor's capital, the week before, and there encountered a thriving Swedish hospital with a healthy mix of international and Ethiopian health workers, actively addressing illnesses of all sorts.

As it turned out, though, there was one crucial thing that I thought I knew, but that in fact did not turn out to be true about Illubabor. In his hurried instructions Ciro had told me, as he urged me to do a good job and prodded me to make haste: "You will find a Swedish hospital there. If you need anything, they will provide every assistance. We are notifying them."

In fact, there was a Swedish hospital in Illubabor; however, it was in Metu, and was scores of roadless kilometers — and worlds of cultural distance — removed from where the outbreak had occurred, and where I was going to be the next day.

While this is an extreme example, stunning misinformation about basic facts on the ground outside Ethiopia's urbanized areas was symptomatic of the confusion that initially confronted the SEP. We would have to establish the facts ourselves in everything from locating facilities and population centers, to mapping paths and hamlets, to establishing networks of communication.

On that day in February 1971, I was bound for Teppi, a spot on the Ethiopian Airlines map, a lengthy, anxious DC-3 flight west from Addis via Jimma, Kaffa. The final leg stretched over kilometers of roadless, unbroken and what looked to be, at least from the air, virtually uninhabited forest, as green as green could be imagined to be, laced with white cloud-like whisps of moisture, and dotted here and there with clusters of three or four round thatched *tukuls* in small clearings. Besides being ill and anxious, I don't remember more than that about the flight except for turning over in my mind the procedures Ciro taught us that should be followed.

But I'll never forget the rest of that day.

There was no hospital, no one to meet the flight, an airfield that turned out to be only a small clearing in the forest, with a windsock, a tin-roofed, mud-walled building, and a single man wearing an Ethiopian Airlines uniform seated behind a small table.

At some point, after waiting for an hour or so for someone from the "hospital," I asked the agent in my clumsy Amharic, if he could make a phone call for me. He responded that there was no hospital, but there was a health center. That would do, I replied. And it did. He called and began an animated conversation in Amharic in which I recognized the words for "foreigner" and smallpox.

I would be using Amharic — a lot of it, more than I ever thought I knew —in the next 48 hours, and over the next weeks, but only with officials and interpreters, not with the people who had smallpox or knew anything about those who did. They didn't speak or understand Amharic.

As a result of the agent's call, someone might show up to assist me. I had lived in Ethiopia long enough not to be certain how long it would take; after about an hour, a barefoot teen-aged boy arrived to lead me on the half-hour walk to the health center.

By 2:30 p.m., we had reached the clinic — a cluster of six to eight small, one-story, whitewashed adobe buildings, some rectangular with tin roofs, others round with thatch coverings, all set in a clearing bordered by a very tall forest interspersed with fruit-bearing lime and papaya trees.

Ato Shibberu, the Health Officer, was a man not much older than I, doing a good job in a difficult spot; I remember that his office wall displayed a painted quotation from JFK: "Ask not what your country can do for you, but what you can do for your country."

I was initially shocked that he was barely aware of cases of smallpox rumored to be nearby; but then, neither he nor we in the SEP suspected the size and the virulence of the epidemic then raging throughout Teppi *woreda*.

Proportionally, Shibberu was no more unaware of what was going on in Ethiopia's countryside than the SEP or the WHO, only the sheer magnitude of this epidemic had somehow registered its existence in the first place.

A reliable information network would only come months later. Furthermore, there was little reason the people of rural Teppi *woreda* should even bother to report smallpox in most instances, let alone report it to officials connected with a government many distrusted.

Ethiopians had lived with this disease for generations, and generally knew how to mitigate its most extreme perils. For millennia, the practice used in many parts of Ethiopia of variolation — taking live smallpox virus from active pustules and introducing it under the skin of the uninfected, especially children — had usually guaranteed variolated individuals a relatively mild infection along with lifelong immunity. Unfortunately, things did not work out so well for everyone else, since the variolated person could and often did give full-on, deadly smallpox to others.

Evidently, this outbreak in Teppi, if it really was an outbreak of smallpox and not some misdiagnosed epidemic of chicken pox or measles, was different, or so it seemed in those few days before we began to discover how many thousands of active cases of smallpox the country really had.

FINDING AND CONTAINING THE OUTBREAK

The small village rumored to be infected was some 10 kilometers by rough dirt road from Teppi itself.

The first imperative in Ciro's list of procedures was to get to the active case, to ring vaccinate around it, and to get evidence about transmission: where did the disease come from, and who might have gotten it from the infected person?

But the Health Center had no vehicles to get me to the village before dark. What it did have to offer, however, was a person who turned out to be the crucial asset: the energetic, dedicated and multi-lingual sanitarian, *Ato* Atenafu.

Atenafu began our weeks together that afternoon by quickly finding a man who knew how to get us in touch with the man who owned the only vehicle that could get us to the village — a large flat-bed truck. It cost a lot of money, but Atenafu bargained and we rented a one-way trip. It turned out that, as long as I was paying for it, lots of other people were eager to travel that route as well. As we rode out of Teppi, Atenafu and I stood in the truck bed, leaning forward onto the roof of the cabin with about 20 other passengers seated around us, most in a jovial mood. That mood changed abruptly as we approached the infected village and heard the keening of high-pitched women's voices in mourning. Everyone fell silent.

This was different. Ethiopia, we thought, had a form of smallpox called variola minor. Though the disease was gruesome, and could cause blindness and lifelong facial scarring, deaths were supposed to be rare, much rarer than with variola major.

Someone had just died, but there was commotion not just in one home, but in several *tukuls* and mud-walled houses. We stopped, almost at random, at the nearest one-room dwelling where we heard sounds of distress. When Atenafu and I entered the small thatched hut we saw by the waning light what was, for either of us, our first case of smallpox. The middle-aged woman we saw was alive, but covered with angry pustules, and was clearly dying; she too would be gone by morning . . . but the room was full of people.

This is where Ciro's emphasis on procedure paid off: we followed the drill. We vaccinated those standing around the dying woman and her immediate neighbors. Meanwhile, we recorded the names of others who may have given her the disease, and we enlisted volunteer guides to take us to their houses right away.

I quickly began vaccinating while showing Atenafu how to administer the vaccine, even while he interviewed the bystanders.

As the darkness fell and we walked house to house around the village, Atenafu pulled me aside and said, "This smallpox is really terrible. I had the Ethiopian vaccination myself as a child" (he showed me his variolation scar on his abdomen), then added, "Please, give me this vaccine right away. I'm afraid."

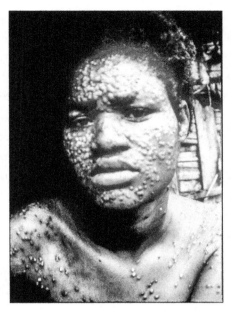

A smallpox victim in Teppi, 1971.
Photo by the author

I did, and right there I asked him to re-vaccinate me as well. What I had seen had frightened me, too.

We slept in a nearby *tukul*, and Atenafu's alarm clock joined the roosters who lived in the hut to get us up at 5:00 a.m.

Other cases were all about and in various stages of infection; we didn't know where to start, but we knew what to do and kept to the procedural steps, quizzing everyone about details as we vaccinated the rest of the village.

The fear of smallpox had united this small community, and as we vaccinated, we followed Ciro's investigative procedures by asking those who flocked into the village for marketing or for vaccinations the names and locations of other outlying cases.

At first this seemed superfluous, since those we vaccinated claimed to know of many cases of smallpox in every direction; later on, however, we would learn the wisdom of keeping careful notes, even though the effort seemed initially to slow us down. Atenafu did the quizzing, I did the recording, while we both vaccinated. I noticed he seemed to be switching between more than one or two languages.

By the afternoon of the second day, we had at least five different leads for more cases, and several of the members of the village alleged that there were cases among people who belonged to other distinct linguistic groups and spoke neither Amharic nor the regionally-dominant Oromo language, including people who spoke Kafa or Shekkacho, and nomadic peoples who spoke versions of Majang. I wasn't prepared for that, but Atenafu's linguistic skills provided the single most important key to our subsequent success.

Atenafu and I spent the next five days walking muddy paths and byways that led us to dozens of more cases in every direction and among every demographic group.

I learned to spot different ethnic identities by clothing and naked-ness, by body piercings and headgear (including the skins of the Colobus monkeys worn with tail to the rear of the wearer's head). I learned to use a compass and keep a rough map going as we walked. I knew I would be completely lost without Atenafu's help, but I was determined to learn how to navigate in the deep forest, even when we couldn't see the sun. I could hear Ciro's voice in my head telling me that we would need to be able to re-trace our steps to find these unmapped places, these hamlets and clearings again, to verify that the work of containment had been done right in the first place.

We didn't have tents in those early days, and so we slept where we could in local huts, buying fruit or a chicken from farmers when we could, but we managed to send news back to Addis Ababa by way of notes we paid to have walked back to *Ato* Shibberu at the Health Center in Teppi.

Then came help. First, on February 9th Marc Strassburg, another Group XIV PCV, reached Teppi, having come from Jimma in his Land Rover, bringing more vaccine and some C-rations . . . they were wonder-ful. Marc himself was a priceless lift to the spirits, with his characteristic energy and administrative skills, instantly taking on coordinated searches in neighboring areas.

Having the Land Rover meant that we could sometimes get to adjacent dirt roads, but almost as importantly, the car gave us a place to sleep at night if we could walk ourselves back to wherever we had left it. Some nights we even drove ourselves back to the Teppi Health Center to sleep; others we slept in the twelve-passenger Rover, depending on where the working day ended. It wasn't much for comfort or for privacy, since people eagerly looked in the windows night and day, and I remember being startled awake in my sleeping bag to find a face peering at me, but the car was blessedly free of fleas and lice.

We had been working together for several days when Ciro flew in from Addis.

We joined up that evening at the Teppi Health Center . . . Ciro would have driven to the site right away if he could have. He spent the first hour or so going over forms with Marc, Atenafu and me, pressing us for missing information, questioning our reports of deaths (there were more than expected) and our vaccination numbers (there were a lot by then), pressing us on the need to get back out and find active sites of infection.

First thing the next morning, we were back to the outbreak sites, and from then on, the next days were a constant round of investigation and vaccination.

MOMENTS REMEMBERED

Some moments stand out from that time, but among all of them pride of place goes to the end of the second day with Ciro, when he paid me the best compliment I'd ever had by congratulating us on doing an outstanding job in attacking the outbreak. I'm not sure what he had been expecting, but from remarks he made later, I am certain that he was skeptical about the abilities and commitment of the PCVs. From that moment on his trust and confidence in me never wavered, even when years later, I would turn down his appeal that I abandon graduate study to re-join him in working for the WHO.

Another moment with Ciro that stands out from those first days came during his own initial encounter with truly deep African rain forest. We would spend many days in the next years in similarly dense vine-draped forests, but this was a first for him.

We were well away from any road or even a broad path, walking single file over roots and broken, muddy terrain, and in what there was of late afternoon light filtered through the leaves. I could see him ahead of me in his bright yellow shirt and a straw hat as he negotiated the path. Atenafu was walking behind me. We were all tired and uneasy because we had been at it all day, and we were not far from where Atenafu and I had had an unsettling experience with one of the groups of leaf-skirted forest people three days earlier.

On that earlier occasion, Atenafu and I had managed to locate one of their temporary camps where it was rumored that there would be cases. As we approached the small clearing where four or five tiny huts were located, everyone, perhaps a dozen people, had simply disappeared, slipping with eerie silence out of sight among the trees, though a small fire was left still faintly smoking. I was astonished. How did they do it?

But Atenafu read their behavior — and worse still our utter isolation — as signifying danger. He pulled out a small pistol that he had been carrying unbeknownst to me, and cleared the safety, saying quietly but forcefully, "This is bad, very bad, get ready to run."

We paused, and nothing happened, so we very quietly retraced our steps, leaving by the path we had just used to approach the clearing.

Now, as Ciro, Atenafu and I walked through a nearby part of that same very wet forest late one afternoon, monkeys suddenly began howling high up on the branches that arched over our narrow path.

At first I was startled, thinking something was really wrong . . . Atenafu had his pistol out again. As we stood stock still, listening hard, all we could hear besides the howls were the leaves rustling with the monkeys' violent swinging movements. Ciro turned back to me, smiled broadly, threw out his arms, and with his wonderfully Brazilian-inflected English said, "Jim, it's just like something out of Edgar Rice Burroughs! Enjoy it!"

I did, I would. That was a lesson, and one that was to be every bit as important in the long haul as the procedures Ciro de Quadros taught and the values of dedication and perseverance he modeled for us all.

LOOKING BACK

There were many later high (and low) points in working with Ciro in provinces from north to south across Ethiopia, in deserts and on mountain sides, but Teppi was the first of what was, I think for both of us, a marvelous set of experiences and achievements — hard work, good work, but really exciting, shared among people who believed in what they were doing.

A picture of the Teppi experience is immortalized in the *Washington Post* image that reprints my photo of Marc Strassburg, Ciro, Shibberu, and the Teppi *woreda* governor standing in front of the truck that took Atenafu and me to the first cases. The photo was taken right before Ciro hosted a party for the community featuring an open-fire sheep roast that he took great pains in overseeing from the butchering through the grilling. (That photo is featured in Marc Strassburg's Chapter 17 of this book.)

By the 20th of February 1971, our team had reported 166 cases (eventually 228 for February), with ten deaths, and performed around 8,000 vaccinations in the Teppi area.

On the 20th, I was on a bus to Bedele, Illubabor to begin work with PCV Russ Handzus and Illubabor's smallpox health worker, *Ato* Haile Michael, on another outbreak that would cover a vast area. While riding, I wrote these sentences:

> We think the [Teppi] outbreak is under control. We hope. It will take time to sort out, but the things I've learned in just over two weeks and the places I've been have been fantastically interesting. This job is not only physically trying, but a real mental test, like detective work. The people in the forest areas have been wonderful; those who live a three-hour walk from a road or a village wouldn't let us leave without offering food, *tej*, coffee, bananas, or whatever they had. And well away from the settled hamlets, nomadic people, dressed in leaf skirts and wearing long metal nails through their lips, sometimes ran away, but other times invited us to watch them sing and dance. Here, health is life and

death, and there's virtually no health care to be had, but they dance anyway. In some areas, people had no idea who Haile Selassie might be, and local wizards exercised life and death powers over an entire area; in one case, the chief refused to be photographed or to be vaccinated, but encouraged his people to pose for us and carefully made all of them get vaccinated.

And finally, one other passage, not written from Teppi, but from Bedele in March, 1971:

No mules showed up today. De Quadros drove in from Addis Ababa with Dr. A. J. Hajian from the WHO Eastern Mediterranean Office in Alexandria to check on us and our efforts. I'm learning from Ciro how important it is to be appreciated, to be praised when you work hard. Somehow, I feel much less tired after he tells me that we are doing great work.

I have tried to remember that experience, too, as a teacher, an administrator, and a parent. I took notes.

Great work, Ciro. Thank you for letting us share some of it with you.

•

6

Smallpox Eradication in Gemu Gofa Province

by Dr. Scott Holmberg

The problem with memory is that, while there are islands of clarity, these exist in misty seas. So, while some memories from over 40 years ago are still pretty immediate, much has been lost. I am fortunate, though, that I can draw on two written records from the time when I was working for the Smallpox Eradication Program (SEP) as a Peace Corps Volunteer (PCV). One is a "journal" of my letters home that my sister typed up and had bound as a gift for me many years ago. The other helpful document is "A Report from Gemu-Gofa Province, Ethiopia (WHO/SE72.48)" — "the WHO Report," which I coauthored, and which described some of the challenges and successes in eradicating smallpox in that remote province between September 1971 and September 1972.

Reading these now, especially the journal, I am reminded again of how incredibly lonely I was during the many weeks I spent in the field, far from even a dry-weather road, among people who often didn't even speak Amharic. Looking back, I can only shake my head at how young and callow I was, but I suppose this is a common reaction for all of us looking at our 21-year-old selves.

The author and Ethiopian dresser Girma Tilahum after freeing their Land Rover from the mud in Gemu-Gofa, 1972. *Photo provided by the author.*

As background, I had filled out a Peace Corps application pretty much on a whim, just before I graduated from college with an English degree. I was negotiating to be hired as a high school teacher in Rhode Island, when the unexpected offer from Peace Corps came inviting me to join the SEP in Ethiopia. It turned out to be one of the luckiest twists in my life.

Also, as background, in terms of my assignment, Gemu-Gofa, was a province in the southern part of the country. Its capital, Arba Minch ("Forty Springs"), was the southernmost provincial capital in Ethiopia. The province was about the size of Connecticut and Rhode Island together, but it was filled with some of the steepest mountains and deepest ravines in Africa. In my opinion, it is one of the most beautiful places on the planet.

However, it was very difficult to get anywhere far from the small capital in the eastern edge of the province, as the unpaved all-weather road ended there. All other roads were impassable in the rainy season. Growing up in Boston, I really didn't understand what "rainy season" meant. Imagine trying to walk through a foot of loose gelatin laid atop a plain of glass, up a steep hillside, and you can imagine why most activities had to stop during the rains. Further, even in the dry season, our Land Rovers and Toyota Land Cruisers were frequently breaking their rear axles as we negotiated big boulders and ruts in the "dry-weather roads."

Thus, the most efficient way — well, really, almost the only way — of getting around was flying in a C-47, which was essentially a stripped-down freighter version of the DC-3, to one of the two other "airfields" in Gemu-Gofa. These planes, built in the 1930s, were converted from their use as transport planes in WW II . . . standing on the ground one could reach up and wiggle their aluminum wings.

Sitting in canvas benches bolted to the bulwark so we were facing inward, these trips were often wild rides as we swooped and circled, bucked and rolled around mountaintops until we came to another "airfield." These had to be buzzed once or twice to get the grazing livestock off them, so that then we could skid to a stop on the grassy, muddy and short "runway." However, Ethiopian Airlines had a remarkable safety record with these utility planes, and one always got to the destination in one piece, even if somewhat nauseated.

Once on the ground and armed with a letter from the governor, directing local officials and *chikashumes* (chieftains) or *balabats* (big landowners) to provide housing, food and support for our vaccination efforts, I would pick up an even younger Ethiopian assistant or "helper"— paid at the generous sum of one *birr* (Ethiopian dollar, worth about 40 US cents) per day — and start hiking up and down mountains for 2 to 3 weeks at a stretch, while the sun still shone.

I have heard that Addis Ababa is now a gleaming city with big modern buildings and traffic jams. I suspect that Arba Minch has been transformed, too, from an idyllic small town of a few thousand people, sitting on a plateau overlooking two large lakes filled with crocodiles and hippopotami, with green mountains rising up behind. When I lived there I could lay in bed at night and sometimes hear lions wheezing as they passed in the fields behind my house on their way down to the lakes. (But, lest I forget to mention, I would also frequently hear a mosquito buzzing near my ear.) I am sure that Arba Minch is far more developed now, and probably finally has phone service.

However, I am also sure that most of the places I walked to have not changed. For the most part these were clusters of *tukuls* (thatched-roof, round houses), sitting on the top of mountains. These villages were so far from roads or communication, and the people were essentially subsistence farmers and serfs, that I was convinced they could not have been touched much since medieval times. There was a reason I was often the only foreigner who had ever been to these mountain hamlets: they often had nothing, sometimes not even much metal. For example, on a few occasions in these places many days walk over mountains from even a dry-weather road, I could see men lined up and breaking soil — cultivating, if you will — with pointed sticks. I did not see metal plows. One of my still clear memories is of my bemusement at finding a Fanta grape soda can in a remote hut in a village where I had not seen any other metal, glass, or plastic. I don't know how it got there, but I deduced it was used for measuring.

I always carried a K-ration (now called MREs) with me to have for my "Sunday dinner." It was great to open a can and find peanut butter or spam or pasta (well, sort of pasta)! And, of course, since I smoked cigarettes at the time, those few American cigarettes were always a welcome condiment. One of the best parts, though, of those Sunday repasts was that when I was done with the cans, I would give them as a gift to the hostess of the house, who accepted them as a great luxury and with effusive gratitude. With them she could measure grain or coffee or whatever. Money would have been of far less use to her — at least in the short term — than a tin can.

THE WORK

Getting back to the actual work . . . our operations were based on the global SEP strategy of "surveillance and containment," which was the technique Dr. Ciro de Quadros had used so successfully in Brazil, and which he had brought to the Ethiopian program.

Dan Kraushaar vaccinating a woman at a market in Gemu, 1971. *Photo by the author.*

Sometimes we would walk for days, find fresh cases of smallpox, and then vaccinate everyone we could find in that hamlet and the surrounding ones. Then on to the next area. As we moved from one place to the next, this usually required hiking down steep escarpments then climbing the next ones, sometimes hand over hand, so some of these trails were not amenable to the use of horses or mules. Still, as we were usually only a few young people on foot, we could move good distances and so get to the next chieftain's house before nightfall.

From page 5 of the "WHO Report," I am reminded that:

The "army of young vaccinators" concept was more or less abandoned, as of last year. We found it difficult to check the work of large numbers of vaccinators, which was often slovenly when we could check, and they were expensive to maintain. Further, we could not guarantee them steady work.

As arduous as it could be at times, we found that a small, "light"-moving team could accomplish a lot more than large parties of vaccinators, reluctant as they were to move far from the roads and hard as it was to verify their work.

Although about 60% of the Ethiopians we met and vaccinated were members of the Gemu tribe and another 20% were Gofas, they were living so remotely from each other that as we moved from village to village, dialects would change. People would giggle at our translator who came from 25 miles away. Thus, one can imagine that most of these people had not seen someone from another race. On the one hand, it was good that I was a great draw — a "circus attraction"— I suppose, but on the other, people mainly came to gawk at me and not get vaccinated until the local leader ordered them do it.

Dan Kraushaar and I once tried to get people to line up, but the practice beggared the idea. They would stand unmoving in the line, so I had to call them up from greater and greater distances. This was my one experiment with a concept that we take for granted.

Not all of the terrain was mountainous, as Gemu-Gofa has extensive plains in the south, which are part of the Great Rift Valley.

For the longest trek I took there, my then-assistant, Legassay, and I set off from a town called Felege Newai (which loosely translates as "He made a wish here" in Amharic; but the town is called "The sh---y place" in the local language.)

We walked for 10 hours until in the gathering dusk we came upon an incredible site . . . a tin-roofed house with a kerosene lantern illuminating a few better-dressed Ethiopian men playing cards.

It turned out that this was a veterinary team that was traveling into the Great Rift Valley, which in Ethiopia is called the Danakil Depression. The enthusiastic leader of the party said, "This is great, we'll vaccinate the cattle against rinderpest and, when the people bring their cattle, you grab them and vaccinate them for smallpox." He continued: "We have everything — police, porters, assistants, refrigerators, and we have a cook, Zerayhoun, and he can make *ferengi* (foreign) food!"

It was an offer impossible to resist, and *Ato* (Mr.) Tseguy, the leader of the Rinderpest Program, was true to his word.

Looking like we were out of an old movie about safaris, instead of two or at most three of us scrambling up, down and over steep terrain, we were now in a long conga line of about 20 men carrying small refrigerators (necessary for the rinderpest vaccine) on their heads, a police escort, vaccinators, the local mayor, and others, as we snaked through the grasslands from pre-dawn until dusk.

The 10-hour walk the day before had been footsore enough, and this day I remember being so hot and tired that when we came to the one small river on our route, I just plopped in, clothes and all and luxuriated for a few minutes. Within 10 minutes of arising from the river, though, I was hot, completely dry and dusty again. The party meandered along. Finally, not having eaten all day, we came to the first hamlet at dusk. *Ato* Tseguy said that first night, the "foreign" food chef would just give us some light refreshment. This turned out to be flour (uncooked) with some *berbere* (hot pepper), salt and water, pressed by Zerayhoun's hand into small, dry, inedible grenades. Not inedible, strictly speaking, as I was too hungry not to eat a couple.

We vaccinated the next day, both the cattle and the people, and I was struck by two things. First, this was the poorest place I had ever seen in my life. I've worked in a fair number of developing countries since then and it still holds that distinction. Essentially semi-nomads, the people had no clothes but a slight thong, a bit of cowhide over their shoulders, and a walking stick.

Second, the flies were so thick that despite the great heat I kept my sleeves rolled down so that at least I would not have to have them clustering on my bare forearms, too. Any standing liquid immediately was filled with drowning or drowned flies.

Finally at the end of the day, *Ato* Tseguy assured me that, in honor of my presence, we would have "foreign food" that night —"spaghetti."

I wondered how Master Chef Zerayhoun would make pasta given the dearth of water, as we were already meting out clean drinking water.

My worries were misplaced.

After two hours of dinner preparation *Ato* Tseguy and I each got a bowl of fusilli pasta with a nice red sauce on it. We eagerly spooned into this, and, as I took my first mouthful, a few things struck me. The fusilli noodles were not cooked but crunchy, the dish was incredibly salty, and the red sauce contained no tomatoes — it was entirely ground red pepper. I looked up with a questioning look at the always genial *Ato* Tseguy who had broken into a broad smile. "Oh," he said, "that Zerayhoun, he sure knows how to make foreign food."

We continued on for days finding small collections of people, vaccinating them and their livestock and, to my relief, finding no cases of smallpox. While the hiking was made easier because of the flat terrain, the heat, dust, and lack of water made it just as difficult as scrabbling up and down the mountains.

At one point, we passed a smallish muddy hole filled with orange water that we could see the goats and cattle pissing in, and little children romping in. Hiking another two hours we came to a collection of *tukuls*. A young veterinary assistant and I asked for some water and we were given a glass with orange water in it. Hmmm. We poured the water through a handkerchief stretched over another cup and we could see small worms and maggots wiggling in the orange silt collected. This was the best we could do, so we strained some more water and boiled it extensively for disinfecting our used bifurcated needles, making tea, etc.

About two weeks in, *Ato* Tseguy, always affable and good-tempered, declared we were having a goat feast at his expense!

I was not prepared for what followed.

The first evening, the goat offal (innards) are eaten raw. A server brings a stick over which the intestines, liver, and spleen are draped, and each diner takes a sharp knife, cuts off what he wants, dips it in *berbere*, and eats it. By this time, I had been through some difficult conditions: I recall one time being so exhausted and hungry, that I ate some roasted wheat that the household dog had walked through. Did I eat this raw goat? You bet I did. And I almost enjoyed it.

Still, the funny thing is, we didn't get sick from Zerayhoun's cooking, or from the orange water, nor from the raw goat organs. As we were finally climbing out of the desert-like valley our party came across a wild apple tree. Because it was moist and tart, the little unripe apples tasted great going down, but many of us, myself and *Ato* Tseguy included, suffered bad abdominal cramps the last 15 miles of hiking.

Again though, at the end of the day, I'd vaccinated about every child I could find, and had been able to confirm the lack of smallpox in a wide area. (One thing I have learned as a professional epidemiologist is to declare success, whenever possible, whether one deserves it or not.)

I saw many diseases and since people mistook me for a doctor I was asked for a lot of advice or even for help I couldn't give. Aside from smallpox, people had some very obvious diseases: goiters, elephantiasis and jaundice come to mind. I was a poor biology student in college. I slept through and didn't attend most of my classes as they were held at the then unconscionable hour of 9 AM. (Though never credited, my C+ in that course is one of the great scientific achievements of all time.) Anyway, I wrote my parents and asked that they send me my biology book, and, reading it by candlelight, I discovered that I had a real interest, and even a passion, for what I had been missing in a classroom.

Still, even with knowing more biology, I was unable to dispense medical advice or treatments. I know this was a common problem for us PCV "eradicators."

Peter Squyer, a fellow smallpox program PCV, told me about the time he was called in to help with a breach birth in which the woman and the incompletely delivered infant, with its little arm sticking out from the woman's vaginal opening; both died. My experiences were less harrowing than that, thankfully, but the experience and interest did make me determined to take premedical courses and try to go to medical school when I got back to the States. I know many fellow PCV vaccinators also went into careers in public health.

What did not go into my reports — or the letters home that my mother would read — were the thankfully rare, dangerous episodes, such as when an old man thought I was part of the Italian army re-invading Ethiopia, and who aimed at us with what appeared to be a musket dating from the 17th century. We talked him down, and I went to great lengths to assure him that I was an American. Of course, so remote, so old and white-haired, he probably had no idea what the difference was between Italy and the United States.

Another time we were stumbling in the dark on a mountainside and had not yet arrived at the next *chikashume's tukul*. Apparently, one of the villagers had seen me in the dark and assumed I was part of an invading army. In any case, we started hearing horns blowing and drums beating up and down the mountainside in alarm about our small party. My Ethiopian assistant came running wide-eyed as a spear had whizzed by his head. There are no courses for this in college, but common sense dictated running as fast as we could to the next local leader's house.

Later, when doing fill-in work in other parts of Ethiopia, I was pressed by the local official to take a soldier with me, "for protection against the local bandits." My experience at that point was that when someone pointed a gun or a spear, he was far more afraid of me than I was of him, and could be reasoned with. Still, I reluctantly accepted an old, fat, uniformed guy in sandals as part of my small vaccinating party. On the route, he saw a monkey sitting on a rock that was curiously looking at us. Our protector leveled his old gun at the monkey who was only several paces away, fired . . . and missed. The monkey stayed sitting there, looking at us.

After walking a distance into a more remote area we came to a collection of small huts from which emerged a tall, very well-formed man — he reminded me of a dark Errol Flynn — dressed in black clothes rubbed with butter. This clothing is apparently some indication of the robber class (but why rubbed with butter?). He looked closely at me, the mule we had with us on that trip, and all our belongings, then leveled me a knowing smile. My assistant was terrified. About that time, the "soldier" came huffing up the trail and took one look at the bandit. The bandit stared stonily back . . . then the two fell into each other's arms . . . they were long lost brothers-in-law.

The next day, as we left the village with the tall bandit striding in front of our group, I saw him look up and signal to some men crouching with rifles on an overhanging hill. They stood up, waved back, and disappeared behind the hill.

This was not an episode I could include in my letters back home.

Other tense situations arose from completely unexpected sources.

One evening in remote Gemu-Gofa, after boiling our bifurcated needles for the next day, I poured the hot water down an ant hole in the *tukul* floor of a local chieftain's house. Apparently, our host was an animist who worshipped ants, and I had to remain still and silent as my assistant tried to defuse the situation.

Another time, a local *balabat* brought his 8-year-old daughter, dressed in a tattered "good" dress, for me to marry and take with me. We had the good sense to tell the father I was married and that our custom did not allow taking a second wife. Still, his disappointment at not getting what I would pay for his daughter was evident.

The problems and threats were usually more mundane and mild. As stated on page 5 of the "WHO Report," we wrote:

> The most difficult problem, as elsewhere, is getting local people to cooperate with the programme. Even in a province that is generally cooperative and friendly, there are a few large tribes which stubbornly refuse vaccination; for example, many workers were suffering at one time from human bites . . ..

Still, balanced against those rare moments of potential conflict and misunderstanding between persons from two sharply different cultures who knew next to nothing about one another, were many, many acts of hospitality and kindness.

One still-clear memory was when my assistant and I were temporarily lost, and we asked the occupants of an isolated *tukul* for directions. We were taken in at growing dusk, given some room on the floor to sleep and the few beans and *injera* (a round, sourdough flatbread) the family had to share.

The author wearing a *gabi* — a hand-spun, hand-woven, cotton wrap worn during cold weather by both men and women — in remote Gofa, 1972. *Photo provided by the author.*

I am hesitant to write about this single act of kindness because it suggests its rarity, when, in fact, high standards of hospitality and kindness were the norm. I think that the success of smallpox eradication in Gemu Gofa can justly be ascribed in greatest measure to the accepting and generous Gemus and Gofas.

On a more technical note, in the period between October 1971 and February 1972, looking at Gofa, one of four *awrajas* (districts) of Gemu -Gofa province, we saw 726 acute cases of smallpox and vaccinated over 118,000 people. Looking at the area, we figured that this *awraja*, with its population density of 27 persons per square kilometer, could support smallpox virus transmission. After vaccinating about half of the population of Gofa, combined with the effects of immunity to variola from prior infection, smallpox transmission ceased. In lesser populated *awrajas*, we had not seen any or many active cases, and in more populated areas, vaccinating the larger villages or towns seemed to be efficacious.

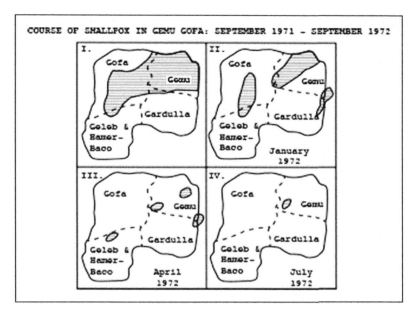

Course of smallpox in Gemu Gofa, September 1971 – September 1972.

Thus, by mid-1972, no further active cases of smallpox were seen in Gemu-Gofa. We declared victory!

Anyway, I smoked a lot of cigarettes in those days, and saw a lot of arms to vaccinate in "a lot of dusty, fly-ridden places," as D.A. Henderson once knowingly remarked to me. At the end of a year, we were able to circle back to the most populated areas of Gemu-Gofa and could not find any active cases of smallpox. Based on "active" surveillance — essentially, looking for cases rather than passively having them reported to us — we were able to describe the eventual elimination of smallpox in our province.

Looking over this short account again, yes, many hardships were endured, but even young (and callow) as I was, I always knew that I would be re-turning to the States someday and the hardships, and loneliness would end. So, almost anything is bearable. One has to think about the people left to work hard and sometimes face want in the places we have long left.

As I once read in another PCV's account from some other place, luxury is "a cold beer and a hot shower." That's right. I know that few people in the States enjoy their morning shower as much as I do.

•

Finding the Last Outbreak of Smallpox in Southwestern Ethiopia

by Stuart Gold

I felt like the "new kid on the block." I had finished eight weeks of in coun-try language and cross-cultural training in Awasa five months earlier and was set loose both as a Peace Corps Volunteer (PCV) and a Surveillance Officer working with the World Health Organization's (WHO) Smallpox Eradication Program (SEP) in Ethiopia. I was a kid of 23, who had barely been outside the middle-class confines of West Los Angeles. I had never been out of the United States, and being a health worker in Ethiopia, one of the poorest countries in the world, was a bit more than just a mind opener. It was much more like a shock to the sensibility in which I was raised. And in the parlance of the day, it was a "mind blower." To put it simply, I was not prepared for the reality of Ethiopia, a place where it appeared that only one person in 10,000 was lucky enough to own a pair of shoes; where a drought and subsequent famine had left thousands to die of starvation; and where in many places in the country, the odds of just surviving childhood could be bleak on a good day.

My only previous experience with anything Ethiopian occurred in the early 1960s in Los Angeles, California. While in middle school, I was one of thousands of students who were bused to the UCLA campus to see Haile Selassie, the then Emperor of Ethiopia, deliver a speech. He had just taken over as chairman for the newly established Organization of African Unity (OAU) that was headquartered in Addis Ababa, the capital of Ethiopia. I had no idea what to make of it all, and my only solid memory of that day relates to what happened after the speech when the Emperor took a few questions from the audience. Being the early 1960s, it was just the beginning of the youth movements and an era of protest in the United States and one of the groups that had formed was The Black Student Union (BSU). One of the questions was from the head of the BSU, who proudly asked the Emperor, "What is it like being a black leader in emerging black Africa?" I was quite taken aback when Selassie responded "I don't know, I'm not black." Like most there, I was mystified by his answer, but years later, as a resident of Ethiopia myself, I quickly found that because Ethiopia was shielded by geographic and cultural barriers from the rest of Africa, the people there for the most part saw themselves as Semitic and not so much African. This realization was an important piece of the puzzle for me, because many times the world-view of the Ethiopians that I met seemed to contradict what was going on in the rest of the African continent. It seemed very curious that the OAU was headquartered in a country that didn't seem to really relate to the rest of the continent.

ASSIGNMENT IN KAFFA PROVINCE

Somehow, I had truly lucked out being posted to Kaffa province. In a country dominated by majestic vistas, high plateaus surrounded by rugged mountains, steep ravines, blazing deserts and crocodile infested rivers, Kaffa was a paradise. It was located in the southwestern part of the country. It had lush deep forests of hardwood and coffee trees, a moderate climate and for the most part it was not affected by the famine affecting the country in the north. The word coffee was derived from the name of the province itself. In retrospect, it's ironic indeed that I didn't even drink coffee then. That was one of many things about me that would change as a result of my Ethiopian experience.

During college I had discovered that I lacked the ability to learn languages easily. I was again reminded of this during training. Unlike many of my fellow PCVs, learning the Amharic language was a daunting challenge for me. My language skills seemed to limit me to finding the bathroom, occasionally bargaining with the locals for food and transportation, and, for my vaccination-related work, saying, "Give me your left arm." Considering that I had Peace Corps friends in-country who were fluent in Amharic, and sometimes even one of the regional languages, it was a bit embarrassing to say the least. I suppose that it all relates to the Clint Eastwood quote, "A man's got to know his limitations," and language skills were mine.

Fortunately for me, I had Bekele Dega working with me as an assistant/translator. Bekele was a 16-year-old Ethiopian who was smart enough to parlay his most basic English-language skills into a full-time career translating and generally helping with the vaccinations for SEP workers like me. He was translator, helper, and for weeks at a time in the field, he was often the only person with whom I could converse. He helped navigate the cultural boundaries that I constantly ran into.

All this being said, Bekele was just the kind of assistant that I needed to get the job done. Without him, it would have been impossible.

The WHO and Peace Corps workers of the SEP are often given credit for the eradication of smallpox in Ethiopia. We did contribute to the management and help to implement the eventual demise of smallpox in Ethiopia, but in fact, it was the nationals on the ground, the translators, helpers, and sanitarians who worked alongside us who deserve most of the credit. Without them, we would have been unable to navigate the nuances of the Ethiopian culture and traditions. It was probably the most important factor in allowing us to achieve our goal.

I eased into my job in Kaffa province in the fall of 1973, living in its capital city of Jimma. There had not been a case of smallpox in my area for many months and I was told that the program had basically become one of routine maintenance . . . trying to vaccinate any people who had never been vaccinated. The concept was that if you could find and isolate any

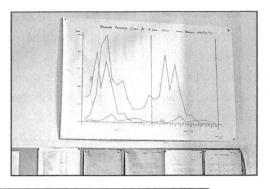

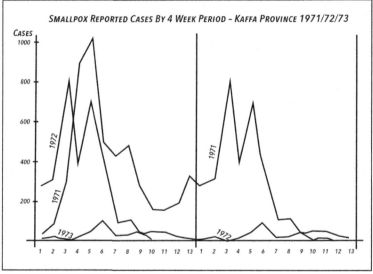

Upper right: Chart hanging in the Jimma SEP office showing decline in number of smallpox cases during 1971,1972 and 1973. *Photo by the author.* Lower left: The chart.

infected persons within a boundary of people who were already vaccinated, there would be no one to pass the infection to and any outbreak, or imported cases would be stopped cold.

The approach seemed to be working as evidenced by the fact there were no more cases of smallpox in Kaffa and several other provinces, and the disease was in serious decline in the rest of the country.

It's funny how some days seem so insignificant, so mundane, and so seemingly bland that their only purpose is to bridge those that might be seen as more important. I thought that Tuesday, January 29, 1974 was going to be one of those days! I was wrong, and it turned out to be much more interesting. The basic assumption that I would not find smallpox would be put to the ultimate test this particular day as I found myself with my translator Bekele "tooling up the road" in my WHO-issued, powder blue Toyota Land Cruiser.

After months of brutal three-week trips walking up and over mountain ranges, living in a tent, and hacking my way through dense jungles, I decided to take it a bit easier for a month. Rather than head for some exotic far away part of the province and be away for weeks living in my tent, I decided to take day trips between the provincial capital of Jimma and the main coffee center of Agaro to a place called Mana *woreda*, which was a little less than an hour or so leisurely drive from Jimma on one of the only paved roads in the province. "What could be easier?" I thought. I almost felt guilty. Well almost!

It was a typical late January day in Jimma. The temperature was in the mid-80s during the day and the 40s at night with moderate humidity, which meant great weather for an easy drive from my home base. The road was surprisingly good, only two lanes but with traffic mostly limited to an occasional commercial truck, someone's goat or a herd of cows.

Our first stop was the town of Yebu, the governmental headquarters for Mana *woreda*, and the office of the *woreda* governor, where I planned to pick up some letters of authorization.

Working for the SEP in Ethiopia gave me a lot of independence, but there were times when it was necessary to deal with the realities of the Ethiopian Government and its bureaucracy. It was all part of the job. My friends in the Peace Corps used to joke about "Ethiopian Time," which was calculated by adding six hours to any appointment time, and if it happened by then, you considered yourself lucky.

During training we were told that the local culture would not change for us, but it was a thing to behold when you had an appointment with a local governmental official or village leader and they would look at you

The author (center) with a *balabat* (right) who has just received a chicken as a gift, Kaffa 1973. *Photo by Bekele Dega.*

like you were crazy if you arrived on time . . .if they were there. I spent a great deal of time grumbling, waiting and being frustrated. You'd think that I would have learned quickly, but old habits die hard, and for me I guess it was easier to go with what I knew rather than a totally different way of looking at something. Eventually, I had to accept the reality of the situation and sort of learned to go with the flow. I did eventually learn to save my sanity by accepting the fact that, yes, things ran according to Ethiopian standards, not mine.

That day, we finally had our meetings, and I eventually came away from them with written letters from the governor authorizing the locals to work with me and assist with getting people vaccinated. These letters were mostly for the *balabats*, who were the local chiefs, or the *chickashumes*, who where local village-level leaders, and they were supposed to read the letters and cooperate. This generally resulted in getting help to gather people in a market or school for vaccination or to have them listen to a quick lecture on smallpox and to ask if they had seen any cases.

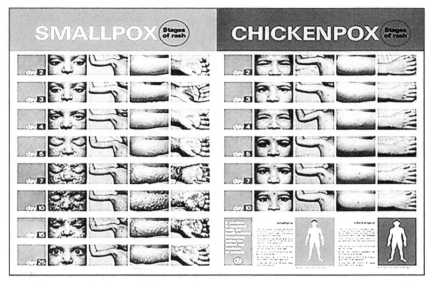

Poster showing the stages of rash for both smallpox and chickenpox. The poster was prepared in 1970 by WHO to help newly recruited staff to recognize the differences between the rashes for each disease. The text and drawings at the bottom give simple guidance to distinguish the signs and symptoms of smallpox from those of chickenpox.

After finally having received the letter from the governor, we performed vaccinations at a school with about a couple of hundred students.

The schools were a great source of information. The students came from small villages all around the area. They overheard discussions by the adults and heard all the local gossip about what was happening to everyone around them. The markets were great for getting hundreds of people in one place for vaccinations, but if you wanted information, the schools were the best place to get it and vaccinate at the same time. There was no need for parental approval because the governor's letters gave me the authority.

Most schools that I visited were similar in construction to the other buildings in town . . . that is, the walls were made with a thin lattice of wood covered with mud, and were protected by a tin roof.

Bekele and I had plenty of bifurcated needles and freeze-dried vaccine (about 250 doses per ampule), plus some visual aids in the way of

Left to right: Bekele – holding the poster, the author, and the school principal with students at the rear. School lecture, Kullu Konta, Kaffa province, 1974. *Photo provided by the author.*

photographs of people with smallpox, and a large green and red poster that showed the differences between smallpox and chickenpox. These posters were about four feet wide and three feet high. At the top, the red part was labeled "smallpox" and the green part was labeled "chickenpox," but it was written in English so the students couldn't read it. There were many individual photos giving diagnostic guides to differentiate the two diseases at various states. We commonly took these with us and they were often posted at schools and places where people might congregate. Since chickenpox was the most common disease mistaken for smallpox it was useful to have as many of these visual aids posted around as possible.

Generally at the schools I would lecture in English and Bekele would translate what I had said into Amharic, the national prescribed language. Then either one of the students or the teacher or the schoolmaster would hopefully translate what was said into whatever was the most commonly used local language. In this area around Jimma, it was mostly called Afan

Oromo (called Gallinya in Amharic), which was spoken by the Oromo or Galla (a term previously used for the tribe).

A month earlier, I was in an area called Kullu Konta where I lectured at a local school. There were so many children who spoke so many languages, that there were at least four or five iterations. I spoke in English, Bekele spoke in Amharic, the schoolmaster translated into Afan Oromo, one of the students translated into Kulu Kontin and a couple of other students translated into some of the other local languages. I often wondered if it was sometimes like that game we used to play at parties back in the States — the telephone game — where a bunch of people formed a line and the first one in line told the second one a story and so on down the line until it got to the last person in the line. By the time the story got to the end of the line, it rarely bore any resemblance to the original. I often wondered what the final version of my presentation sounded like.

Once my lecture ended, invariably I would ask if any of the students knew of or had heard of any smallpox cases. I can only imagine that in some cases the lecture was so twisted that some thought I was looking for a kid with festering acne, but it was not a surprise, however, when one or more of the children raised their hands and told me of a case they knew about that just happened to be in a nearby village or in the most extreme cases, over the next mountain range. Anyway, my job was to track down these rumors and make sure that there were no a cases of smallpox.

Most of the time, I discovered cases of chickenpox as well as scabies and many other dermatological skin issues that I didn't have a clue about, but I always remembered that my job was to vaccinate as many people as possible and make sure that it was not smallpox. This particular Tuesday in Yebu, depending on how you look at it, I either got very lucky or very unlucky.

We had just finished vaccinating at a school on the main road and went to another, a bit closer to the town of Agaro, the principal coffee center for Kaffa province. We pulled out all of our visual aids and I gave my usual speech about smallpox and chickenpox and again asked if anyone there knew of any cases. A student in the class raised his hand

First smallpox case found by the author in Kullu Konta, Kaffa, January 29, 1974.
Photo by the author.

and explained to Bekele that there was a boy across the street from the school, on the main road, who had smallpox.

I immediately thought, "Wow! That's easy, I can check it out and be home back in Jimma for a late lunch."

We walked across the street, being led by the kid from the school, went through a fence and entered a small, mud-walled building. There lying on a cot was a young man with what I immediately realized were classic smallpox pustules.

"So much for "the best laid plans . . .," I thought, then I immediately went into a state of shock. Smallpox was not supposed to be here! I was told specifically that there were not any active cases of smallpox around anymore! For a split second, it was a total disconnect.

Bekele looked down and casually remarked, "*Fentata*" (smallpox). He'd been working with the SEP since before my arrival and had seen many cases.

It was an instant game changer and I was in the middle of a total brain freeze. I guess that's when the training kicked in.

Inexplicably, the first thing that I did was re-vaccinate myself even though I had already been vaccinated twice in the last year. I had the "good stuff" with me . . . the Russian vaccine. During training, we had used three different vaccines: American, Kenyan and Russian. The American and Kenyan vaccines worked similarly such that a day or two after being vaccinated a person developed a slight reaction at the vaccination site, and if they didn't scratch the scab, it was over in a few days with no complications. The Russian vaccine was a way different animal. This stuff was BRUTAL. If you used the Russian vaccine, which we used most of the time, we vaccinated as many people as possible and then headed far away as fast as we could because we knew that by the next day, everyone that we had vaccinated would start getting headaches and fevers that lasted a day or so and would not necessarily be happy to see us again.

In full disclosure however, this is an example of my being caught in total hypocrisy. Up to this point, I had felt superior with my western medical knowledge. I had watched while Ethiopians in the field seemed to want medicine to hurt them as proof of its strength. In many cases, they seemed to prefer a dull, large needle to a pill because they thought that the more it hurt, the stronger the medicine. So, in retrospect, even though I had already been vaccinated with both the American and Kenya smallpox vaccines, I fell into the same exact pattern and grabbed the Russian vaccine because unconsciously I equated the harsh side effects with its strength. Either way, I wasn't about to take chances as I looked down at the young man in front of me with an active case of smallpox. Better safe and possibly sore, than sorry.

We found seven cases of smallpox in the small dwelling. A mother, a daughter and the son, whom we had seen first, were in the front room, and there were four other members of the family in another room. They had progressed about half way through the disease as there were open pustules covering much of their bodies. They were fairly listless and didn't appear to be suffering much, but I can't imagine that they were too

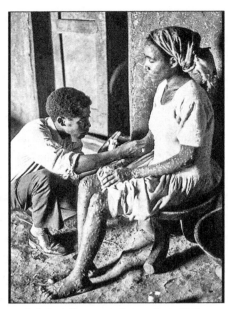

Bekele collecting scab samples in Kullu
Konta, Kaffa, January 29, 1974. *Photo
by the author.*

comfortable. I gathered as much information from them as I could for
the report forms (history of the cases and potential sources of infection)
and collected scab samples to send to the SEP. Unfortunately, the family
was not very cooperative and were quite distrusting. The amount of information that I could gather from them was minimal and did not add
much to determining the source of the outbreak.

There were other people in the same household and in the adjoining
one who did not show any symptoms, but they refused to be vaccinated.
Even seeing their friends or relatives with an active case of smallpox did
not convince them. It was very frustrating for me, and since I hadn't experienced this before, I decided that we should immediately head back
to Jimma to the office at the hospital and report what we had found to
the SEP in Addis and try to come up with a plan.

About an hour later we rolled up to the hospital in Jimma and told a
disbelieving Kaffa SEP sanitarian that I had found smallpox. He looked

at me like I was crazy. Only when Bekele confirmed my story, did he take it seriously and want to come out and look at the cases. I attempted to contact Dr. Ciro de Quadros at the SEP office in Addis, but was unable to get through. I decided to try to contact him again the next morning, as well as to take those doubting my diagnosis out to see the new cases.

The next few days were a whirlwind of activity. We gathered all the SEP resources in the Jimma SEP office and focused on the new outbreak. Once everyone agreed that I had discovered a smallpox outbreak, all available people and resources were assigned to multiple teams that would be designated to work in different parts of Mana *woreda* to do "ring vaccinations" around the cases, which is basically a methodical attempt to vaccinate every person in a wide circle around the case.

More trips to the field and some basic epidemiological sleuthing by other teams seemed to indicate that this "new" outbreak was actually left over from an older outbreak that had occurred a couple of years previously and was traced to a known Muslim population of a small village in Mana *woreda* who were associated with a previous outbreak. Not only was this particular group of people culturally resistant to being vaccinated, but they kept to themselves for the most part. On top of that, they embraced the Ethiopian custom of "keeping company with the sick." That is, when a family member is sick, the family gathers around to keep them company for extended periods of time. This, unfortunately, guarantees that many people will be exposed to whatever pathogen is causing the problem. The good news was that the area had been well vaccinated previously and, because most of the surrounding areas had been thoroughly vaccinated, it meant that the outbreak could be more easily contained since the disease would circulate slowly only through a very small community of people who did not want to be vaccinated.

WITNESSING POLITICAL UNREST

A few weeks went by during which Bekele and I focused our vaccination work in the Yebu and Haro areas of Mana *woreda*. We made some day trips from Jimma, but many times we ended up going into the back-country on mules for a day or two at a time to vaccinate at markets, and trace down more rumors of suspected cases. While I was focusing all my attention on this smallpox outbreak, what I didn't realize at the time was that something monumental was occurring that would reshape the entire country and history of Ethiopia and, within weeks, make it almost impossible for western health workers to do their jobs. What I did not realize was that the entire country was starting to come apart at the seams.

There were so many reasons for the unrest.

In the early 1970s, the feudal conglomerate known as the "Ethiopian Empire" was comprised of fourteen provinces, most of which were ruled by governors mostly chosen from members of the royal family. In turn, the country was ruled with an iron fist by its Emperor, Haile Selassie, who was from the Amhara ethnic group. During our training, we were told that the country was approximately 18% Amhara and 60% Galla. I had learned that the Galla (presently referred to as Oromo) ethnic group had been actively subjugated for years by the Amharas. The anger, frustration and resentment festering just under the surface meant that Ethiopia was a land held together only by force.

Other factors also played into the mix.

These were just some of the issues at hand that produced more instability and affected our ability to do our work:

- The 1973 famine, which spread mostly in the north, was killing thousands, but the government in Addis Ababa appeared to turn a blind eye and a deaf ear to the swelling international outcries for them to help.

- An international oil crisis had made fuel more expensive, negatively impacting the economy and causing both prices and unemployment to rise.

- What was characterized as unrelenting corruption caused the students to become radicalized and open to utopian Marxist ideology. They demanded curriculum changes in the schools and massive systemic reforms.

With all of these forces in play it was only a matter of time until there was an igniting event that would become a tipping point for the entire country. Unbeknownst to me, that event had occurred a couple weeks earlier on January 12, 1974, when non-commissioned junior officers at a military base in Sidamo province mutinied and took their commanding officer prisoner. They were protesting poor food and water conditions at the base. Word of this action spread rapidly and other military units followed suit. While the Emperor was unable to gain control over the situation, other discontented groups, including students, teachers, workers and basically most people who were not part of the very small minority elite controlling the country, joined with the breakaway military demanding changes and protesting for land reform and famine relief. Things began spiraling out of control. Before too long, there were riots in Addis Ababa itself and there was talk of a full scale civil war.

For the first few weeks of February 1974, I spent most of my time working on the smallpox outbreak. Since the area where I was working in Mana *woreda* was close, I was able to go back on occasion to Jimma to spend the night to get more vaccine or to file reports with SEP in Addis.

While there, I heard bits of gossip and news from both my roommates and the Voice of America and BBC shortwave radio broadcasts. The news was disjointed and confusing, but it was obvious that there was something important going on. I didn't realize the extent of it or if it was going to affect me and everyone that I knew. It seemed distant and the stories of riots in Addis did not relate to my existence as an SEP Surveillance Officer working out of Jimma in Kaffa province, but that was about to change.

On the afternoon of February 28th, after having spent a month fighting the smallpox outbreak, Bekele and I were taking a break.

So far, all the teams working the outbreak had reported over 60 cases of smallpox. I was especially looking forward to getting a warm meal and a hot bath.

That day, we walked out of the bush from Mana *woreda* into the town of Haro where I had parked my Land Cruiser. On the way to the car, we passed a large *tukul* (thatched circular house) that was filled with people. They were laughing and clapping excitedly as they listened to a small transistor radio. Bekele asked what was going on. They informed us that the Prime Minister in Addis Ababa was forced to resign and the government seemed to be collapsing. These Oromo people appeared to be very excited because, as I understood it, they disliked Haile Selassie and the government in Addis Ababa.

Back in Jimma things had started to get weird.

I did not realize just how significant this was until we found soldiers with machine guns on the street corners with very serious looks on their faces. After dropping off Bekele, I made it back to the house that I shared with my roommates. We spent the evening listening to the shortwave radio news broadcasts and watching troops marching down the street past our house. It was very confusing and a bit scary. What little news we could get related to what was happening in Addis. We had no idea what was happening in Jimma.

The next couple of weeks were bizarre. There were strikes and protests in the streets, and once when I needed to make a trip to the SEP office at the hospital, rocks were thrown at my car. It suddenly felt much safer to be in the field than in the provincial capital.

Then for days at a time, it seemed that everything had returned to normal and then something else would happen. My roommate, Vince Radke, was attacked and beaten by students. Luckily, he got away with minor bruises and a large bump on his head. Another roommate, Don Piburn, also had rocks thrown at him.

It seemed that many of the students were becoming radicalized and equated being a foreigner, especially an American, with working for the CIA. It was more than a bit irrational, but hysteria seemed to be ruling the day.

Between the riots and protest marches there were days of calm and with no news about what was happening, so it was easy to just go about our business vaccinating people like everything was normal. I guess that it became a revolution in slow motion for us; things slowly spiraling out of control, but not so dramatically as to cause a crisis.

The work in Mana *woreda* did wind down and we continued to vaccinate in and all around the area that recently had active cases and before long, there were only rumors and no active cases left. All rumors were checked, but it all went back to the pattern that I was familiar with, that is, more dermatological conditions and chickenpox. The last outbreak of smallpox in southwestern Ethiopia was contained.

IN CONCLUSION

By early spring of 1974, the U.S. government seemed to finally accept the fact that it was not safe to station PCVs in most of Ethiopia, and the PCVs who wanted to leave were given the option of either terminating their service or being relocated to another country.

The SEP in Ethiopia continued without the PCVs, and was led by its national Ethiopian smallpox workers in the field with support from WHO leaders such as Dr. Ciro de Quadros. It took two more years to eradicate the disease. The last smallpox outbreak in Ethiopia occurred in August of 1976.

During the time that I spent as an SEP Surveillance Officer in Ethiopia, I was personally involved with the vaccination of 15,227 people. So many years have gone by since those days. Sometimes it just seems like a dream. I feel honored and proud that I was able to play even a small part in this crusade against one of the world's great killers and the first disease to be eradicated by mankind. It was the experience of a lifetime for a kid who grew up in a sheltered, middle-class American home, and one I will always cherish.

•

8

Sharing an Office with Ciro
and
Reminiscing About Him

by James W. Skelton, Jr.

TRANSFER TO THE SMALLPOX ERADICATION PRO-GRAM

In mid-August 1970, I accepted an invitation to join the Peace Corps and become a trainee in the Rural Development section of Group XIV in Ethiopia. I was not aware that there would also be a Smallpox Eradication section of Peace Corps Volunteers (PCVs) included in the overall training group until we arrived in Atlanta for our orientation session on October 18, 1970. From there, we flew to Addis Ababa, Ethiopia for Group XIV's 3-month in-country language and culture training. Upon completing training, I traveled to Mekele, a small town in Tigre province by bus, and moved into the house I had agreed to rent during one of my on-site visits during training. I thought I was fully prepared to begin my assignment as the project accountant for the USAID's Food for Work Program, which was to be implemented and administered by the provincial office of the Ministry of Agriculture.

Unfortunately, the provincial Minister of Agriculture in Mekele made sure I was unable to have an active role within the provincial office by limiting the scope of the job to a one-day-a-month event in which I was supposed to approve the reports that someone in his office prepared. Although I wasn't even provided a desk, I tried to stay active by visiting the office and talking to some of the Ministry's employees who were sympathetic to my predicament. After four months of fruitless attempts by representatives of the USAID and the Peace Corps to rectify this situation, I returned to Addis Ababa in late May of 1971 in hopes of being given a second chance to make a contribution as a PCV.

On the morning of May 31, 1971, I met with Jes Portugill, the Peace Corps country director in Ethiopia, to discuss the possibility of transferring to a new position with the World Health Organization's (WHO) Smallpox Eradication Program (SEP). Jes was extremely pleasant, in his mid-40s, and always seemed to be even tempered and reasonable. I was very pleased when he told me that SEP Ethiopia needed someone to handle accounts and other administrative matters, so I told him I was interested and would like to give it a try. In anticipation of my positive reaction, Jes had already arranged a meeting with Dr. Kurt Weithaler, the Ethiopia program director of the SEP and WHO senior advisor, for later that morning in order to discuss details.

For the first time in months, I felt a bounce in my step when I left the Peace Corps office. I had been so disillusioned by my frustrating experience in Mekele that it was difficult for me to believe this new prospect would actually materialize. Nevertheless, I was feeling positive about it when I spotted Bob St. John, the jolly, spectacularly mustachioed fellow Group XIV PCV, driving past the bus stop where I was standing. He brought his green Land Rover to a quick stop when he spotted me, and I jumped in the passenger seat. I told Bob where I was going and he agreed to take me to the SEP offices in the large, rectangular Telecommunications Building on Churchill Street.

It was with some foreboding that I bade Bob farewell and jumped out of the Rover, walked to the front door and pushed my way through to the lobby. Upon alighting from the elevator on the 6th floor and finding suite 616, the SEP director's office, I hesitated in an attempt to gather myself in anticipation of the unknown.

In Teferi's office, Addis Ababa, 1971. Left to right, Teferi Seyoum, Kurt Weithaler, Abonesh and Yolanda. *Photo provided by the author.*

There was no way I could possibly have foreseen what awaited me on the other side of that door! In short order, I met one of the most energetic and fascinating men that I have ever known. As I entered the outer office, I immediately faced Dr. Kurt Weithaler, who was standing there giving directions to two young, female secretaries. Kurt, a big, slightly overweight man in his 50s, was clean-shaven, balding and blessed with an incredibly high level of energy. He shook my hand enthusiastically and, in his deep Austrian-accented English, introduced me to the secretaries, Abonesh and Yolanda. Then, he ushered me into his inner office, pointed to a chair across from his wide, paper-covered desk and flopped into the large, black desk chair.

His light blue eyes sparkled as he regaled me with stories about the guys in the field, both Americans and Ethiopians, who could not keep their accounts properly, or at all for that matter. I truly enjoyed Kurt's animated description, waving his arms around while characterizing his dedicated field workers as being great at vaccinating and reporting cases of smallpox, but seemingly hopeless at anything related to administrative work. I would learn later, of course, that the PCVs and sanitarians in the field were so overworked, and challenged for time, that working on the accounts was very low on their priority list.

Near the end of the meeting, Dr. Ciro de Quadros, the SEP's chief epidemiologist, burst into Kurt's office, introduced himself and began asking whether I had been told about the accounts and whether I knew about *Ato* Teferi Seyoum, the office manager for the program. Ciro was in his 30s, with a bushy mustache, sideburns, and long, curly, thick black hair. He was about 5'9", thin and appeared to be quite fit. At my first glance, I thought Ciro's piercing brown eyes conveyed high intelligence and suggested a demanding individual who seemed to be good hearted, so I thought I might be able to get along with him. I answered his questions briefly and promised to keep Teferi in the loop as soon as he returned from the field.

Ciro took a seat on the only bare spot on the corner of Kurt's mammoth grey metal desk, and then the two proceeded to inform me that they wanted me as their operations officer. As such, I would work in Addis in order to establish a new accounting system, and conduct economic studies concerning the use of funds in the provinces. They would probably want me to take on additional responsibilities later, which I learned were sometimes referred to as "other duties as assigned." The vague description of these still unknown, but potential, duties left them too much for me even to imagine at the time. Nevertheless, I swallowed and agreed to give it a try.

SHARING AN OFFICE WITH CIRO

The next day, June 1, 1971, my first full day on the job, was spent getting accustomed to sharing an office with Ciro, which was located next to the suite of rooms occupied by Kurt, Teferi, Abonesh and Yolanda. I felt a bit awkward at first, sitting at a long table directly across from Ciro's wide desk. There was no other desk for me to use, which only served to remind me of the Ministry of Agriculture fiasco in Mekele. Yet, this situation was totally different because it was obvious that Ciro and Kurt thought they really needed me, and it definitely seemed like there was a lot of work to be done — a lot of work.

Ciro addressed me in a business-like manner at first, making sure he understood exactly what I planned to do about the accounting system, and when I could get it done. Initially, he wanted me to prepare economic studies and set up a system for accounting and forecasting. I told him I hoped to be able to pull all of it together in a month, even though I had no idea how long it would take to set up the new system or how bad the current system might be. All of this was so new to me that I didn't even consider whether my interventions could improve the current reporting system.

We managed to get through that first day with a few laughs and a lot of conversations about the workings of the SEP and Ciro's opinions about some of it. He repeatedly lit his wooden pipe and blew smoke across the room, but it didn't bother me, a former pipe smoker.

The thing that impressed me most was Ciro's dazzling smile. Even during our serious conversations, he seemed to be armed and ready to flash that smile at a moment's notice. He could radiate joy without trying, and his smile was almost always followed by a humorous remark and a matching, high-pitched and contagious laugh.

Teferi returned to Addis the next day in the late afternoon and called a meeting in his office, saying he wanted to discuss my job description and our relationship. He was a tall, thin man, well-dressed, soft spoken, and well-educated . . . a sociologist by education. He questioned me at length about what I was going to do and how I planned to pull it all together. My answers were pretty much the same as I had given Kurt and Ciro, that is, I thought we needed to create a reasonable system and manage it well. He seemed to be concerned about my new role, even though he was my supervisor. He smiled and seemed to relax — a little — when I assured him I would do the best I could for the program and would get his approval before I did anything.

Teferi and I discussed his recent trip to Sidamo province, and then he paused as if he had suddenly remembered something. He focused on me, pointed his finger at me and suddenly announced that he had a plan to take a new Land Rover to Mekele at the end of the week and make a stop in Dessie, Welo province along the way. The new Land Rover was for the Mekele team, but he planned to deliver lots of camping equipment to the SEP's teams of sanitarians in both provinces. As he proposed that I should accompany him on the road trip, he stood up and hurried into Kurt's office so he could tell him about his idea before I was able to express my amazement at the prospect of returning to Mekele so soon. Moments later, Kurt popped out of his office and enthusiastically confirmed his agreement. He saw this as a great chance for me to work on the accounts with the Ethiopian sanitarians in Dessie and Mekele. I didn't know what to think of the idea, but the ironic prospect of returning to Mekele so soon was both exciting and overwhelming.

Teferi also told me that they wanted me to use my findings from the trip to recommend how the accounting and reporting systems should be improved. We would leave on Friday, June 4, 1971 and would share driving responsibilities.

The trip went as well as could be expected, despite some minor disagreements about who would drive the Land Rover at various stages of the journey, as well as his complaints about my less than expert ability to negotiate hairpin turns while driving down the very steep and narrow mountain roads.

Teferi and I spoke about many things during the trip, such as the thesis he wrote for his doctorate degree in sociology. The topic of the thesis was the incidence of prostitution in Addis Ababa, which he believed had reached epidemic proportions there due to the migration of provincial families and the lack of viable employment opportunities. He was ashamed of this, but accepted it as a way of life in Ethiopia. I was impressed by the fact he showed deep feelings of sympathy and frustration about the plight of the female population. Despite Teferi's concerns about my driving abilities, we managed to form a bond that served us well in the following 14 months.

We intended to meet and work with the local sanitarians, Abebe and Tessera, on Saturday, June 5th at the Dessie Provincial Medical Office. There were no PCVs working there because at that stage of the SEP, PCVs had not been assigned to either Welo or Tigre. Unfortunately, Tessera, the team leader, was out in the field, so we were very disappointed when Abebe told us that the team leader kept the records at home and that he, Abebe, didn't know anything about the accounts.

Teferi threw up his hands in frustration over the lack of coordinated effort between the sanitarians, shook his head and motioned for me to join him outside to help unload the camping equipment for the Dessie team. Then, we shook hands with Abebe, climbed in the Land Rover and drove until we reached Mekele late that Saturday night.

On Monday, June 7th, we were able to meet with both of the sanitarians, Gebre and Yahaleshet at the Mekele Provincial Medical Office, but they were clueless about record-keeping. We were appalled to find that Gebre, the team leader, had not written anything on the check stubs in the program's check book for the five checks they had written. In addition, Gebre admitted that he had thrown out the five cancelled checks and account statements when they were returned to him by the bank. Consequently, the majority of my time with them was spent trying to instruct them in the concept of reconciling their bank balance using the check stubs. They seemed to be interested in learning more about their accounts, but their lack of experience made it very difficult. It became obvious that there would be much educational work to be done in the coming months.

I enjoyed seeing the shocked looks on the faces of my American and Ethiopian friends and acquaintances in Mekele when we arrived there. All of them were very surprised that I had returned in just one week in my new-found job. My old PCV roommate, Larry Workman, was totally stunned to see me, and, in obvious disbelief, asked, "What in the hell are you doing here?" The PCV nurses could not get over it and kept telling each other how amazing it was. The irony and amusement was much appreciated, but short-lived, and I returned to Addis by plane on Thursday, June 10th. Teferi stayed there an extra day before officially delivering the Land Rover to the Mekele team.

When I arrived at the office in Addis the next day, I discovered that Ciro had gone into the field while I was in Mekele. I felt alone at first, but that didn't last long because Kurt burst into the office, flopped down in Ciro's desk chair and announced that I should prepare a full trip report, including what I had observed, plus my proposals and recommendations for improving the accounting system. In addition, he said that I needed to prepare a budget for the remainder of the year for the SEP Ethiopia project, which caught me off guard. Kurt then explained that WHO Geneva had warned him not to exceed the 300,000 Ethiopian dollar budget, which meant he needed to forecast the expenses for the balance of the year and spend accordingly.

I watched with utter incredulity as Kurt flashed a smile, jumped out of the chair, blasted through the door and returned to his office. I sat there for a while resting my chin on my hands and wondering how it could be that they really didn't know how much they were spending.

Eventually, I began writing a report recommending that the expense items in the accounts needed to be broken down into separate categories rather than lumped together. I also suggested that we should establish a headquarters control file for all expense records submitted by all of the teams.

Although I was a novice to the SEP, I realized that the teams in the field were so pressed for time and overworked that they simply didn't have enough time to prepare expense reports. Thus, it was impossible to prepare a summary report without paging through the reports that had been submitted, and attempting to figure out what had been done and what had not been done.

There was also the issue of the economic analysis I was supposed to prepare. I wasn't sure where to start, but I thought I remembered enough from my economics, accounting and business courses to make an educated guess regarding what it would take to prepare such an analytical report. I simply didn't have enough information, and needed to gain a better understanding of the status of the expense reports to date, i.e., what the teams were supposed to do and what they had done.

Working at Ciro's desk. Left to right, Ciro, Jim Lepkowski and Dr. Petrus Koswara. *Photo by Jim Siemon.*

I quickly discovered that there were a few PCVs and sanitarians who frequently visited the SEP office, and they also needed to work on the table opposite Ciro's desk.

Jim Siemon and Jim Lepkowski, who were assessment officers and members of the Central Assessment Team, were the main occupants of that space. I considered both of them to be friends from the few times our paths had crossed during training. They enjoyed sharing that space with me, and told me a few amusing stories about the way in which Kurt, whom they had nicknamed "the big Rocket," and Ciro, whom they had nicknamed "the little Rocket," had interacted since the inception of the program. The stories were based on a recurrent theme about one or the other of "the Rockets" who would get an idea and take off in the direction of the other one's office while screaming the other man's name all the way, and then they would engage in a wild conversation about whatever new proposal had come to mind.

I was fortunate to witness a few such amusing events in the coming months.

There were times when other PCVs, such as Gary Urquhart, an assessment officer, and Jay Anderson and Dan Kraushaar, surveillance officers, and *Ato* Mamo Faye, an Ethiopian health officer and assessment officer, also needed to find a place to sit so they could prepare their reports. At such times, there was barely enough room for me and I felt like the odd man out, which I was.

At times, Ciro or Teferi observed that there was virtually no space for me when the office was so crowded, and they managed to find something for me to do that required my presence in Teferi's office, using the side chair to Teferi's desk or his desk chair when he was out of the office. It was fun being in that suite of offices because the occupants were friendly and always ready to assist me and share a laugh while doing so.

Near the end of June 1971, Kurt and Ciro met with me and announced that I should take over the responsibility of reviewing and compiling the number of smallpox cases based on "Form No. 1 Smallpox Surveillance Reports" and monthly assessment reports prepared by the Surveillance Officers and sanitarians in the field. They wanted me to keep my accounting and budgeting duties, of course. I welcomed the additional work because it would keep me busier and it would give the other Jims — Siemon and Lepkowski — more time to work in the field.

The routine of occasionally using Teferi's desk served me well until late July when a new desk arrived for me at the office and was placed on the other side of Ciro's desk, next to the window. All of a sudden, I had my own work space and could actually depend on using it whenever I was in the office, which was most of the time. Kurt and Ciro seemed to be even happier about the arrival of my desk than I was because — to their credit — they realized that I hadn't felt like a full-fledged member of the SEP project team.

```
┌─────────────────────────────────────────────────────────────────────────┐
│ Imperial Ethiopian Ministry of Public Health      Province _____     │
│        Smallpox Eradication Programme             Awraja _____     │
│                                                   Woreda _____     │
│        HOUSEHOLD SURVEILLANCE RECORD              Village _____    │
│                                                                           │
│                                           Date of visit _____        │
│  I - Method of case-finding  [  ]  NOTIFICATION, by _____ (date)____  │
│                              [  ]  INVESTIGATION                          │
│                              [  ]  OTHER                                  │
│  II - First case in the household:                                        │
│     No. 1 NAME_____ AGE_____ SEX_____               │
│     Vaccination scar: [ ] YES _____ (date)  Variolation: [ ] YES____(date)│
│                       [ ] NO                              [ ] NO          │
│                       [ ] UNKNOWN                         [ ] UNKNOWN     │
│     Date of onset of rash _____  Did this patient die? [ ] NO        │
│                                                            [ ] YES____(date)│
│     Source of infection on this patient:                                  │
│                    [ ] Other house in same village_____   │
│                    [ ] Other village or area_____(specify)  │
│                    [ ] Hospital_____(specify)  │
│                    [ ] Other (e.g. School, etc.)_____(specify)  │
│  III - Other household members:                                           │
└─────────────────────────────────────────────────────────────────────────┘
```

No.	NAME	AGE	SEX	Vaccination scar				Variolation				Smallpox			Died			*
				NO	?	YES	DATE	NO	?	YES	DATE	NO	YES	DATE	NO	YES	DATE	
2																		
3																		
4																		
5																		
6																		
7																		
8																		
9																		
10																		
11																		

* Check this box if you vaccinated the household member during your visit.
REMARKS:

Surveillance Officer_____   Signature _____

Form No. 1 Surveillance Report. *Provided by the author.*

It didn't take long for me to understand that Ciro wanted to spend more time out in the field than he did in the office in order to assist and supervise the surveillance officers and sanitarians.

Ciro had a vision of how smallpox would be eradicated in Ethiopia, and he pursued it tirelessly. It was crystal clear that he lived for the opportunity to eradicate smallpox and was so dedicated and enthusiastic that he

SEP seminar in Addis Ababa, photo from *The Ethiopian Herald*, August 17, 1971.
Photo provided by the author.

was able to instill a sense of urgency and purpose in all of the PCVs and
sanitarians who came into contact with him. To this day, I believe Ciro's
devotion and determination were the catalysts that made SEP Ethiopia
such a success. When I think about those early days with the SEP so many
years ago, I can actually visualize Ciro's kinetic energy and enthusiasm.
He always seemed to be ready to jump into action, even though he was
focused on the work he was doing at the moment. Ciro was so persuasive
that all of us wanted to follow his direction and do whatever we could to
help make the program succeed.

In just two months, it had become clear to me that we had the privilege and the honor of working with an absolute genius; a great man who
would remain an important figure in the lives of many of the PCVs long
after we left the Peace Corps.

On August 16, 1971, at the height of the Ethiopian rainy season, the
SEP's Seminar was held in Addis Ababa at the Ras Hotel. Dr. D.A.

Henderson, the WHO's global head of SEP, was in attendance, as were many other important figures, including Drs. Weithaler and de Quadros, and WHO HQ Medical Officer Dr. Isao Arita, as well as all of the surveillance teams from the provinces in attack phase. The Amharic edition of The Ethiopian Herald ran a photo of the meeting room on August 17, 1971, showing the doctors and Ethiopian ministry representatives in the front rows.

The surveillance teams were seated in the chairs behind them and I was barely visible in the last row. Not many of the SEP workers knew me, except the Shoa province PCVs, the assessment officers who worked with me and counted on me for assistance, and a few others, so I was roundly ignored by everyone else.

There was one exception, however. D.A. Henderson was very interested in the budget figures and the forecasts for the coming months. D.A.'s congenial curiosity made me realize that I was fulfilling an important function, making me feel even more fortunate to be participating in the program. That realization made my commitment to the program seem even more worthwhile. I eventually realized that one of D.A.'s most significant qualities was his wonderful way of making each of us feel important by taking us and our respective roles very seriously.

Such minor, personal victories were few and far between during the SEP's Seminar, but I didn't care because I thought my role was much less important than the surveillance officers' and sanitarians' roles. My job was to support the epidemiologists and the administrative personnel on the staff in order to document the SEP in Ethiopia, and I was lucky to have the opportunity to do so. By that time, I fully understood that the SEP's mission to eradicate smallpox was truly heroic in nature and that the surveillance officers and sanitarians working in the field were full-fledged heroes.

On August 30th, I arrived at the office a few minutes before Ciro appeared. When he walked in, he stared at me for a moment, scratched the thick beard he had recently grown and then asked if I had forgotten to shave. Without delay, I admitted it was the first day of growing my new beard, to which he responded by laughing, clapping his hands and wishing me luck with it; he also advised that I should be patient because it would look bad for at least a month. I told him I could be patient because I had all the time in the world, and he laughed again and slapped me on the back before taking a seat behind his desk.

That was one of many times when I truly appreciated the personal touch that Ciro could give.

Being responsible for working on the Form No. 1 Smallpox Surveillance Reports entailed countless phone calls to and from the provincial offices and what seemed like endless disconnections from the very unreliable telephone system. Regardless of whether I initiated the call, I would say "hello" over and over again until I got a weak response from the other end, and, almost on cue, the call would fail and I would eventually slam the phone down in its cradle.

At that stage, whenever Ciro was in the office, he would begin teasing me and making humorous remarks. This served as entertainment, even though he knew I was really frustrated. There were times when the "hellos" and the phone slams became so repetitive that Ciro could not control his laughter. I would glance over at his desk and he would have his head buried in his arms in an attempt to muffle his guffaws. It irritated me at first, but then I would start giggling, until the chuckles built to a belly laugh that was out of control. Eventually, the two of us would calm down until another call came in and Ciro would start howling all over again before I could pick up the phone. Needless to say, these hilarious moments made me feel closer to Ciro.

In mid-September, Kurt called a meeting with Ciro, Teferi and the Jims, now including me along with Siemon and Lepkowski, to discuss strategy for the program now that the rainy season was coming to an end. The figures for reported smallpox cases and vaccinations performed in August were low due to the interference of the heavy rains. Kurt was convinced that other provinces, namely Gojam and Bale, should be put in attack phase in order to have the entire country under surveillance operations. Ciro disagreed, arguing there were problems elsewhere, such as in Gemu

Kurt Weithaler standing in front of the chart for 1971 cases and vaccinations. *Photo provided by the author.*

Gofa, which were more important and should be addressed prior to expanding the program. Then, Kurt asked Siemon, Lepkowski and Teferi what they thought about it. Lepkowski seemed to differ with Ciro for technical reasons, but Teferi sounded a bit ambiguous, believing there might be enough money to cover the expenses through the end of the year. Although I was the low man on the totem pole, I had prepared the budget and was monitoring it, so I felt obligated to tell them my opinion. With some hesitation, I took a deep breath and declared we would not have enough money to make it through the end of the year if we expanded the program. Ciro literally jumped out of his chair and leaned on Kurt's desk, insisting we should wait until the New Year to put the other provinces in attack phase. Kurt grudgingly agreed, but appeared rather upset with his upstart operations officer.

There were times when Ciro would give me a ride up the hill to the Piazza area where I lived. On the way, there would invariably be one or more instances in which a woman would stop her car next to Ciro's Land Cruiser and wave to him. Ciro would return the wave with that broad smile of his and sometimes they would roll down the windows in order to exchange a few words. His personality was so magnetic that it seemed everyone was drawn to him almost immediately. I would just watch and marvel at the spectacle, sensing that such captivating charisma was God-given and could not be learned. Or imitated!

Early on Monday, January 10, 1972, I reviewed the monthly account reports that had arrived over the weekend and compiled the numbers for the month of December, 1971. When I calculated the totals for the year, I was absolutely relieved to find that the program had come in under our 300,000 Ethiopian dollar budget by a mere 343 Ethiopian dollars. After completing the budget/accounts chart in Kurt's office I stared in disbelief at the numbers before he arrived to join me in studying the bottom line. Kurt was very complimentary, as were Ciro and Teferi, but I knew it was just the result of good fortune.

Later that morning, Lepkowski and Siemon were working feverishly in Ciro's office, preparing the December monthly report and the year-end numbers for smallpox cases discovered and vaccinations performed. Seated across from them, Ciro concentrated on his year-end report to D.A. Henderson, but seemed to be oblivious to what was happening. Lepkowski eventually got Ciro's attention by making a very loud comment to the effect that he couldn't believe the final numbers. Ciro finally looked up and surveyed the chart on the wall behind them, paused a moment and then jumped up and declared that he had been correct about his predictions, namely over three million vaccinations and 26,329 cases reported. He congratulated us for being part of history and then called on Kurt to join us to view the final numbers. Kurt thought it was a dream come true, and Ciro was so excited that he offered new predictions: the eradication of smallpox in Ethiopia would be achieved by the end of 1973 and five million vaccinations would be performed in 1972. Kurt thought those prognostications might be wildly optimistic, especially the short-term eradication of the disease.

I joined the other Jims for lunch at the Ras Hotel that day, where we enjoyed club sandwiches while we analyzed the year-end results. There had been a record 3,333 cases reported in December, 1971, which was the reason the annual total had reached over 26,000. Lepkowski expected as many as 30,000 cases to be reported in 1972, while Siemon believed a total of 20,000 was a more achievable target. I agreed with Siemon because his projection seemed more reasonable.

A total of 7,573 cases of smallpox were reported in the first quarter of 1972, which was only slightly less than the fourth quarter of 1971. As for vaccinations, a total of 1,038,755 had been performed, which was a record for a three-month period in Ethiopia. At this point, I began to believe that Ciro's prediction of five million vaccinations for the year just might be correct.

During the first half of 1972, I had several chances to work with Ciro on various reports and projects. I was continuously struck by his uncanny ability to be a task master and a mentor at the same time, which I believe was one of the primary reasons he was able to inspire the Americans and Ethiopians to work harder and do more than anyone ever believed possible.

He knew he could depend on me for whatever needed to be done, but I could also tell that he made an effort to avoid asking me to do things that required technical scientific knowledge that I did not possess. Whenever he was in the office, we worked seamlessly and without any tension whatsoever, regardless of the assignment at hand. There was mutual trust between us and a true sense of brotherhood in terms of our devotion to the project. He made me feel like I belonged, and I will forever be grateful to him for that. Ciro even occasionally called me the "Iron Man" in recognition of my ability to work on reports and forms without a break for hours at a time.

In early June, one of the new Peace Corps trainees from Group XVII was designated as my replacement in the SEP/Ethiopia program, which meant that I could terminate early from the Peace Corps if I decided to do so, and I did. I was almost as happy about that as I was about the figures we compiled in early July for the second quarter, which were 5,031 cases reported and 925,036 vaccinations.

As things evolved, however, a total of 16,935 cases were reported in 1972 (close to Siemon's prediction of 20,000), and 3,237,449 vaccinations were performed, making a 2-year total of 6,446,938 vaccinations. That was quite an incredible accomplishment since that figure represented nearly 20% of Ethiopia's population.

REMINISCING ABOUT CIRO

I left Ethiopia on July 16, 1972 with mixed feelings because I identified with the SEP so strongly, but at the same time I felt like I should be in a hurry to go to law school and become a lawyer.

I didn't know whether I would ever see Ciro again.

As luck would have it, Ciro eventually moved to Washington, DC, in 1977 to work on the Expanded Programme on Immunization for the Pan American Health Organization, the regional office for the Americas of the WHO. I was fortunate to have a law practice that occasionally took me to Washington, DC, on business, which gave me opportunities to visit Ciro. I recall one instance in the 1980s when Jim Siemon, Phil Kneller and I were in DC simultaneously, and we visited Ciro and his lovely wife, Susana, at their beautiful home. Many years later, I met Ciro and his delightful daughters, Julia and Christina, for dinner in DC, and he talked openly about his reaction to cancer treatments he was undergoing and the state of his health. He had lost weight and looked a bit frail, but he was still in good humor, working hard, traveling and giving presentations around the world, despite the fact that he was not well.

In 2010, I attempted to organize the 40th reunion of the Group XIV PCVs. It turned out to be bad timing for many of the guys, including myself for health reasons, so we waited until the next year and set the event for Friday, September 23, 2011, and to be held in Washington.

Ciro was in the center of the planning, and he volunteered to use his home in DC as the meeting place for the group. As the host for the get-together, Ciro welcomed Jim Siemon, Jim Lepkowski, Vince Radke (and his wife Marilyn), Phil Kneller, Russ Handzus, Scott Porterfield, Peter Carrasco and me.

The group who attended the reunion at Ciro's house, Washington, DC, September 2011. Seated left to right: Vince Radke, Russ Handzus, Jim Lepkowski, and Ciro; standing left to right: Jim Skelton, Peter Carrasco, Jim Siemon, Scott Porterfield, and Phil Kneller. *Photo by Marilyn Radke.*

It was raining so hard that evening that Ciro could only take us out on the back porch to show us the picturesque back yard and his beloved barbecue pit, which was where he had hoped we would gather. Due to the heavy rain and the fact that Susana was out of town, Ciro had arranged for a local caterer to serve a delicious Peruvian chicken dinner. A fine Argentinian Malbec wine was also served and the group thought it was a perfect match for the meal.

There were, of course, lots of hugs and back slaps among the group, especially those who had not seen each other for over thirty-five years. We were truly happy to see each other again and had a great time talking about everything and everyone we could think of, and, as always, we took a few photos.

Vince had purchased copies of the book entitled *Smallpox Zero: An Illustrated History of Smallpox and Its Eradication* by Jonathan Roy for all

The SEP attendees at Ciro's memorial service, Washington DC, November 2014,
left to right, Peter Carrasco, Jim Siemon, Steve Jones, Alan Schnur, Jim Lepkowski,
D.A. Henderson, Jim Skelton, Vince Radke, Stuart Gold, Robert Steinglass and
Gene Bartley. *Photo provided by the author.*

of us, and we proceeded to autograph the first page of each one for each
other. On the first page of my copy of the book, in reference to the reunion,
Ciro wrote, "You made this happen, Jim," which really made me happy.

Russ won the prize for traveling the farthest to attend the reunion —
all the way from California, and Vince and Russ won my unofficial prize
for telling the best stories about the good old days working in the SEP
project in Ethiopia. Ciro and the rest of us laughed a lot and enjoyed a
renewed sense of camaraderie for those few precious hours. Unfortunately,
that was the last time I ever saw Ciro, but I did keep in touch with him
by email and snail mail over the next two and a half years.

In early May 2014, my wife, Merrilyn, and I had dinner with Vince and
Marilyn Radke while they were visiting Houston. As Vince regaled us with

tales of some of his challenging and memorable experiences in Ethiopia, I was suddenly struck with an idea that I told them about as soon as he finished one of his amazing stories. Out of nowhere, it had occurred to me that we should encourage the Peace Corps guys to write about their experiences in the SEP in Ethiopia for a book dedicated to Ciro. Vince thought it was a good idea, but our wives seemed to think it just might not be a realistic plan. Nevertheless, within six months the editors and contributors to this book had agreed to participate in the project, and as they say, the rest is history.

Ciro had become quite ill by that time and was not seeing visitors when I called to share the book idea with him. He was very positive about it and I believe he was amused when I promised that I would tell the story about the way we used to laugh so immoderately when I was trying to take the smallpox vaccination and case reports over the phone. I've included that story above and, somehow, it makes me feel a little bit closer to him.

Sadly, on May 28, 2014, Ciro lost his courageous battle against pancreatic cancer. A private memorial service was held shortly thereafter, with his public memorial service held on November 18, 2014 in Washington DC. A large contingent of smallpox PCVs from Ethiopia was in attendance, as was D.A. Henderson and his wife, Nana, and their daughter, Leigh, and dozens of Ciro's other friends and colleagues. Every one of us felt like we needed to be there for Ciro just like he had always been there for us.

The memorial service was sponsored by the Sabin Vaccine Institute, for whom Ciro had served as Executive Vice President and head of the Vaccine Advocacy and Education Program since 2003. Many wonderful things were said about Ciro by the speakers, the most important of which were contained in the speech made by D.A., who reminded us of Ciro's fabulous work ethic, brilliant intellect and amazing personality. Of his decision to hire Ciro as the Chief Epidemiologist for the SEP in Ethiopia, D.A. told us it was the greatest decision he ever made. We missed Ciro more than ever after that inspirational speech, and it made those of us involved in the book project feel even more determined to honor his life, career and memory.

Ciro was truly a hero, and the content and spirit of the speeches made during the memorial service showed that he was regarded by his peers as a veritable giant in the world of public health. He worked diligently throughout his career to save lives and did everything he could to ensure that children would not die from preventable diseases. The obituary that appeared in *The Washington Post* on May 30, 2014 credited D.A. with the observation that Ciro "helped prevent the deaths of hundreds of thousands of people through his immunization efforts." The Sabin Vaccine Institute's memorial service pamphlet also mentioned the amount of time Ciro dedicated to mentoring other public health professionals, and described such efforts as "perhaps one of his greatest gifts to the global health community." Many of us were witness to the fact that Ciro's proficiency in mentoring came to him naturally, making him an effective leader and a teacher at the same time. His friendship was a wonderful gift to those of us who were privileged to have known and worked with him.

•

9

My Adventures in Welo
and
on the Sudan Border

by John Scott Porterfield

I had registered for the U.S. Army draft in June of 1970, knowing full well there was still a war going on. Three months later, Mrs. Myrtle Culver, head of the local draft board, informed me that I was classified as "4-F" or "unacceptable except in times of war." I pondered her rationale and wondered what criterion defined the Vietnam War considering it had cost us so much blood and treasure. Consequently I went back to college in the fall of 1970 to begin my senior year majoring in Liberal Arts.

That October I was having coffee at the student union and noticed a fellow running a Peace Corps information booth. I talked with him for a bit, and then filled out an application. He told me that only one out of seven applicants were chosen for the Peace Corps. I did not have high hopes.

In November my roommate told me that he had just taken a call for me from someone from Peace Corps, Washington. I called the number back and spoke with the Peace Corps home office person. They told me of two openings for which I would be qualified — one was in India, repairing wheat combines, and the other was in Ecuador, helping peasants grow corn. I chose Ecuador as it did not seem to be on the far side of the world like India. The Peace Corps person said that enrollment papers would be mailed to me to fill out and sign.

The papers did indeed arrive about ten days later. However, to my surprise, the site assignment was listed as Ethiopia rather than Ecuador. I took a deep breath, filled out the paperwork, signed my name, and mailed it back.

I have no idea if the change in program and country was a clerical error, or divine intervention, but Ethiopia, the people I worked with, and the job I was given to do, changed my life forever.

Early in 1971 I had about three months of "immersion" language and culture training with Peace Corps/Ethiopia Group XV in a small town named Nazaret, which was south of Addis Ababa.

My first assignment as a Peace Corps Volunteer (PCV) was in Adwa, Tigre province, famed for the battle between the Italians and the armies of Menelik II, who, in 1896, were the first Africans to defeat a European army on the field of battle. My job was to teach Ethiopian school children to grow vegetables. Unfortunately, the land on which the school garden was to be located became the site of a land feud between a powerful local farmer and the school. The school lost, and I was reassigned to Agaro in Kaffa province to build a dam for a village named Dalechew.

THE TRANSFER

Not long after arriving in Dalechew, I grew quite bored with the stop-and-go and delays of the dam building project I had been working on there. As a consequence, I started helping Jim Siemon and Russ Handzus, fellow PCVs who were working in the Smallpox Eradication Program (SEP), giving smallpox vaccinations in the Jimma/Agaro area of Kaffa province. It was a massive project that took about a week of steady vaccinations and following up on reported outbreaks. Jim Siemon and I found a case in a nearby village that was extremely virulent. I remember Jim looking at me and saying, "Does your smallpox vaccination itch? You better hope so."

I had become quite fluent in Amharic . . . to the point that I could command a donkey and get it to follow my directions in Amharic. I found that development to be shocking because I had finished dead last in testing at the end of Peace Corps language training.

I liked the smallpox work, and I heard that there were some SEP openings elsewhere in Ethiopia, so I asked Jes Portugill, the Peace Corps /Ethiopia Country Director if I could transfer into the SEP.

Jes gave me a fairly difficult time with this request because my host-country national representative, Asefa Bogale, who worked in the Ministry of Agriculture, had reported that I was "rude, abrasive, and immature" in my dealings with the local populace. At the time I was staying with Jim Skelton in Addis, and his friendly advice was to go talk to Jes and quit before they could fire me. I took Jim's advice, and set up an appointment with Jes to tender my resignation.

When I went to his office and started to tell Jes that I was going to resign from the Peace Corps, he cut me off. He said, "I am going to let you take that smallpox position because I think they will be getting a very good Volunteer." I was stunned but relieved, and told Jes I was very grateful. Unbeknownst to me, my former PCV roommate in Adwa, Rick Baes, had gone to Addis Ababa and talked to Jes about a personal incident that I had been involved in with him earlier, and Rick's information had apparently been an important factor in Jes's decision to let me transfer to the SEP.

The incident Rick had discussed with Jes was related to the time when we had been stationed together. He was an architect by training and was working on a town plan for the city, and he was one of the few PCVs who had a motorcycle to get him around to conduct his surveys of the town and surrounding areas.

From time to time we had to shop for supplies in Asmara, Eritrea, and Rick and I would go up to the city for a weekend of good Italian food and to enjoy the sights. Asmara seemed like a slice out of a city in Italy and was extraordinarily peaceful at that time.

This time, Rick headed out on his motorcycle and I was to take the bus a few hours later. About two hours later, a boy ran up to me and said that the *mohandies* (engineer) was injured and had been taken to the

Adwa hospital. I asked a local American minister to give me a ride to the hospital, and found that Rick was there, completely incoherent and injured very badly.

The bus driver who had rescued him said they found Rick unconscious in the desert next to his mangled motorcycle. With help, the driver grabbed him and his bike, turned the bus around and brought him back to the hospital in Adwa. The hospital was run by a Russian physician, who, from my standpoint, did nothing at all to care for Rick, and the hospital had no facilities for feeding patients, so I had to bring food in and feed him myself.

The missionary's wife scrambled a dozen eggs with onions, and brought them up to the hospital for Rick. He ate a couple of bites and said he was full. Then, as I would move away, he would say, "Hey, where are you going with my food? I am starving!" This went on until Rick had eaten the complete dozen eggs.

It was clear to me that Rick was in trouble with probably a concussion or worse, so I called the Peace Corps office and told them of our dire situation. The Peace Corps office called the base commander at Kagnew Station (a U.S. military communications base in Asmara), which dispatched a Huey rescue hospital helicopter.

My orders were to signal the chopper and tell it where to land. *Signal with what*, I asked myself? I had a bright blue sleeping bag that I thought would do the trick.

Later that day, the sound of a helicopter could be heard in the distance, so I started waving my blue sleeping bag and it circled back and landed about 50 yards from me. Quite a large crowd of Ethiopians had gathered to watch the show by then. When the helicopter landed, two armed U.S. soldiers jumped out. They told me they had seen all these Ethiopians and did not know what to expect. I started laughing and said, "Well I live here." They gathered Rick up on a stretcher and loaded him into the chopper. I remember vividly Rick yelling, "For God's sake Scott, take some pictures for *The Volunteer Magazine*."

Leo's Land Rover pick-up truck in Welega on the way to Asosa, 1972. *Photo by the author.*

ON THE SUDAN BORDER

In March 1972, I was in Addis Ababa for my yearly physical and staying with some fellow PCVs. They had a nice house with plenty of room to crash. I helped pay my way by teaching their cook some different ways to serve up food for the guys.

Shortly after the Peace Corps had approved my transfer into the SEP, Jim Skelton, one of the guys who lived in the house, who worked with the SEP, told me that Dr. Ciro de Quadros had called to report that his Land Rover had become disabled right on the Sudanese border. Ciro and PCV Alan Schnur were working there when their vehicle broke down on March 15, 1972. The only mechanic that the SEP could find in Addis on such short notice could not speak Amharic, only Tigrinya, which I was somewhat conversant in having spent four months in Adwa, Tigre province. I was to accompany the mechanic as a translator, and an older PCV gentleman named Leo Landkamer, who was responsible for vehicle operations at SEP HQ, was to go along with us.

Land Rover traveling down a sharp rock hill, in Welega on the way to Gizen, 1972. *Photo by the author.*

Our mission was to take a new axle and drive about 600 kilometers (373 miles) due west from Addis Ababa to Gizen, Ethiopia, on the border with Sudan, as rapidly as we could to rescue the team that was stranded there. We were driving a Land Rover flat-bed truck the back of which was covered with a tarp. The road was long, and not of great quality. After the first 125 kilometers of paved road out of Addis, the road became part rocky and part gravel, with some pavement here and there. At one point on the first day, we lost the driver side windshield to a stone that had been whipped up by a fast-moving passing car. We drove the rest of the way to Gizen with a busted windshield. The road got progressively worse as we got farther from Addis, with the last 30 kilometers of the road hardly qualifying as being called a road.

After two days of driving, we arrived in the small, dusty village of Gizen. It was a primitive, semi-desert area, only about 200 yards from the Sudanese border. There were Ethiopian combat soldiers patrolling the area due to sporadic fighting between various Sudanese tribal factions.

At midday on the third day of the trip, we found no sign of either Ciro or Alan, but we did find the disabled Land Rover parked at the health station and the mechanic immediately set to work on it. It turned out that we had brought a long axle instead of a short axle like the one that had broken. So, we had to radio back to Addis to have the correct axle urgently shipped out on a flight to Asosa . . . about 79 kilometers (49 miles) from Gizen.

I found refuge in one of the schools that had been built with Swedish assistance, and bedded down for the night.

At about two o'clock in the morning, I was awakened by a man shouting orders in English with a heavy Portuguese accent. It was Ciro and Alan returning from looking for smallpox cases. Ciro ordered up some *doro wot* and we all sat around a fire and debriefed about what had happened and what to do next.

Ciro told us that he had used a police radio to make the call about the broken axle, so the size of the axle was probably misunderstood by the police in Addis, who had forwarded the message to the SEP office.

I recall that Ciro made us a fantastic Brazilian chicken dish for dinner one night, and he did a lot of cooking, in particular for dinner, but there was neither food nor water that was easy to come by. We had brought along some U.S. military C-rations and that sustained us when we tired of Ethiopian and Sudanese food.

We had a severe lack of water, even for sterilizing the bifurcated needles, so we hired a guy to dig down into the dry river bed to reach water. He did find water, but it percolated up slowly and it was muddy so it took a while to yield about a half-gallon or so of water that we filtered. Alan boiled the needles for 20 minutes and then he made a big pot of coffee with the same water with which we boiled the needles. I think that must have increased our protein intake for that day.

I am happy to report that they did have an Ethiopian *buna* bet in the town where you could get warm Meta beer for about three Ethiopian *birr* (dollars). It was expensive, but I was happy to pay the price.

We remained on the Sudanese border for almost a week waiting for the correct car part to arrive by air to Asosa from Addis, but we all felt safe . . . there was an Ethiopian army battalion stationed there that placed a soldier out on point every night with a rifle and a night vision scope.

I remember that one of the Ethiopian health officers stationed permanently in Gizen roughed up his wife a bit while we were there. Ciro was upset about it, so he visited the man and set him straight.

While we were there, Ciro heard of an outbreak of smallpox across the border in Sudan, and he suggested that we needed to "proceed immediately" to check it out. I pointed out to Ciro that none of us had passports and there was the small matter of a shooting war going on between the Sudanese Arab North and Christian South that we might get caught up in. I don't remember my exact wording, but I believe I made it clear that while I was happy doing my job, dying for it was not part of my contract. But Ciro was totally focused on eradicating smallpox, and I think he would have been ready to take the risk if we could have gotten clearances from the Sudan government.

The correct axle finally arrived and the Tigre mechanic, who had been a good sport about having to stay in that hell hole for twice as long as he was supposed to, repaired the Rover in short order on March 28, 1972. On March 29th, we left and drove the damaged Land Rover back to Addis for full repairs.

It had been an interesting trip, seeing the border with Sudan, and getting to spend some time with Ciro in the field, but I was not sorry to leave the hot and dry semi-desert area of Gizen.

OFF TO WELO PROVINCE

After the trip to the Sudan border, I packed my bags and caught the morning flight out to Dessie in Welo province on April 4, 1972. PCV Gene Bartley met me at the airport in Kombolcha; all my gear had arrived earlier. I was assigned by the Welo team to the Land Rover with license plate UN 627, while Gene had UN 626.

My first assignment to look for smallpox cases began on April 13, 1972. The distance from Dessie to Wegeltena in Wadla Delanta *awraja* was about 90 kilometers as the crow flies, but the drive was really difficult. Despite my thoughts about the Asosa roads, those to Wegeltena made

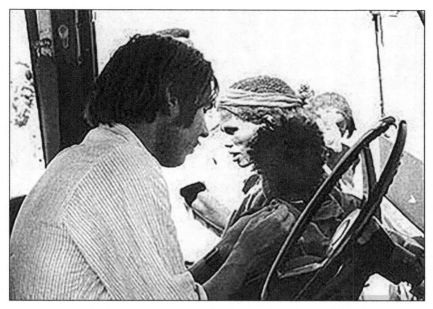

The author vaccinating a girl from his Land Rover. *Photo provided by the author.*

the trip to Asosa seem like a picnic outing. About 10 kilometers out of Dessie, the road went through dry river beds and mountain paths, where I needed to drive in 4-wheel drive low reduction for most of the way. We crossed the Beshilo River, which drained into the Blue Nile, was fast and deep in places. We even hired some folks to throw rocks into the river to see where we could cross. The last 10 kilometers or so were straight up the side of an *amba*, or mesa, rising up from the lowlands, with Wegeltena located at the very top of it.

There was no electricity and no potable water in the town, other than what we carried. I spent the night in one of the schools built with Swedish assistance. Those schools were great because they had cinder block walls and a cement floor, which meant they didn't have any bedbugs, fleas, or lice, and were not smoky, like a *tukul* would have been.

I found that Wadla Delanta *awraja* had plenty of smallpox cases, and they weren't hard to find. We vaccinated about 300 people the first day.

That week I ran into resistance to vaccination in a village that had active cases of smallpox. Despite extended discussions, and attempts to

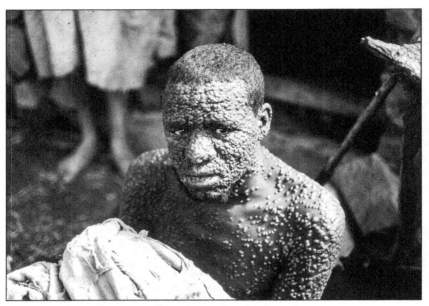

Man with smallpox in Wadla Delanta. *Photo by the author.*

convince them, the people would not budge and refused to be vaccinated. I had been told that in cases like this, you could call in the authorities and they would help convince the village to comply. So, I went back into Wegeltena and brought two of the territorial policemen with me, who were happy to have a chance to ride in the Land Rover. I made sure that their rifles did not have rounds in the chambers. When we got back to the village, once again, the village elder refused to comply. So, one policeman went over and slammed his rifle butt down on the gentleman's foot. I was shocked! But that was the end of all resistance and dissent in the village regarding taking smallpox vaccinations. I was unhappy with the policeman's violent behavior, and vowed never again to call the police to help me with such problems.

Despite the basic conditions and lack of supplies in towns and villages, I learned over time that I really did not have to take any food with me, such as C-rations. The Ethiopian people were so hospitable that they always insisted on having us eat with them. They were poor, but all shared what

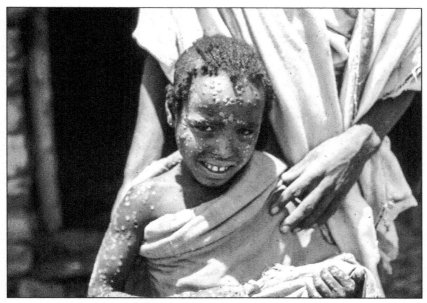

Girl with smallpox in Wadla Delanta. *Photo by the author.*

they had with us, which was always *injera* and *wot*. Hospitality was em-
bedded in the culture. It was a universal custom that if someone visited
your house while you were eating, you would invite them to join you.
The invitee could be polite and say that they had just eaten, but even so
one usually had to take at least some food to show respect for the host.
One of the examples of hospitality I observed was related to the long,
winding footpaths through bean fields that looked completely random.
I was told that travelers were allowed to gather and eat the beans along
the footpaths as long as they kept moving through the field.

The WHO Epidemiologist assigned to Welo while I was there was Dr.
Petrus Koswara, who was from Indonesia. I was fortunate enough to have
him accompany me on a trip to Wadla Delanta. He was a very nice man
and was extremely knowledgeable about smallpox. The one night we were
there we stayed, once again, in one of the schools built with Swedish aid.
Dr. Koswara snored so loudly that we had to ask him to sleep in another
building. Unfortunately, Dr. Koswara died of a heart attack about a year

later. I have often wondered whether what had sounded like sleep apnea had contributed to his untimely death.

On another occasion, I loaded the Land Rover with extra gas and vaccine in preparation for a 10-day trip into western Welo. My dresser, Abebe Baiyou, had been replaced by a university-trained health officer, whose name I've forgotten, but whose English language skills and attitude were outstanding.

On this trip *Fitawari* (local administrator) Mogus Ali, asked if he and his wife could ride with us in the Land Rover, and I said yes; but not only did his wife accompany him, but also a heavily-armed retainer. The *fitawari's* retainer had the responsibility for being the "taster" of anything that the *fitawari* ate or drank while out in the field. At night in his small hut in Wadla Delanta, the *fitawari* would sit at his desk with a loaded 38 Smith and Wesson revolver next to him. Whenever he was brought some food, he would take a handful in his right hand and hand it to his retainer, who would bow, thank him and perform his taste test.

The trip was uneventful until we arrived in Wegeltena, where one of the town's dressers ran up to me and told me that a six-year-old son of a farmer had been bitten by a rabid dog; and said that the only vaccine available was in Dessie. So, after being in the village for less than 10 minutes, I had to ask the *fitawari*, his wife and the retainer to get out of the Land Rover, and I loaded in the farmer and his son. I drove the rough 90 kilometers straight back to Dessie, stopped at the hospital, and watched incredulously as the staff began the series of 21 rabies vaccinations over a 14-day span. The father thanked me profusely before going to be with his son. I was exhausted, so I decided to go back to my own house to get some rest. The next morning, I got up and headed back to Wolge Tena. I never found out what happened to that young boy, but I hope he had a normal life after that day.

Unexpectedly, I became good friends with *Fitawari* Mogus Ali. He was respected and feared in the territory, but I found him to be a fair man who dispensed justice swiftly.

I recall being quite impressed with his retainer/taster, too, when the *fitawari* asked him to escort me back to the Swedish mission where I was sleeping. The retainer always wore a bandolier of ammunition draped across his chest, usually carried a Belgian assault rifle, and had a Thompson submachine gun slung over his shoulder. He was a very tough character and a very imposing figure.

I told the *fitawari* that I was quite capable of negotiating the 200 yards back to the school. I was surprised when the retainer intervened and reminded me that it was after sundown on market day, and insisted on walking me back there. Sure enough, about halfway to the school a couple of drunks started yelling insults and threats at me. The retainer stepped in and basically told the intoxicated pair to "bring it." The pair quickly realized he was the *fitawari's* armed guard, which turned those two loud men into apologetic and fearful subjects.

On May 2, 1972, Gene Bartley sent word to Dessie that his Land Rover had broken down in the town of Tenta. I was in Dessie at the time Gene's message arrived, so I drove off to his rescue, taking a mechanic from Dessie with me named Teshombe, whose father was Italian and owned the best repair shop in town. Actually, it was the only repair shop for 500 kilometers.

The road to Tenta was tougher and even more dangerous to travel than the one to Wegeltena . . . which I found hard to believe. The last two miles of the road had hair-pin turns at a very steep incline, with steep drop offs on either side.

Gene's Land Rover was not repairable, so we towed it all the way back to Dessie, which was no small feat. We accomplished that the same day I received the message.

The entire time I served in Welo Province, my guide and dear friend was a peasant farmer named Dejini Duba. He was probably in his 40s and lived in Wegeltena with his wife in a very dilapidated *tukul*. The health officer in Wegeltena introduced me to him on one of my first visits. When we were out on patrol, Dejini and I were inseparable. His *dula* (walking stick) was ever present and at the ready at the first sign of trouble. Dejini was very helpful in translating, though his English was non-existent, but he and I understood each other. I traveled with him throughout the highlands of Welo for almost 20 months.

One night, we came upon a village after a long day of searching for smallpox. The villagers had a working still and had just brewed up a batch of whiskey called *katikala*, which was Ethiopia's version of "white lightning" and was quite powerful stuff. Unfortunately, Dejini somehow managed to spill his onto our pup tent and it was close enough to the fire that it burned a hole in the tent doorway cover. That night, while we slept, a hyena came into camp. We woke up to see that hole in the tent flap filled with the entire fierce-looking head of the hyena. Dejini, yelled "relax!" and smacked it across the snout with his *dula* and it ran off. We did not sleep much the rest of the night.

Another time, our Land Rover broke down in Wegeltena and the only parts available in the area were in Dessie. So, Dejini, the health officer, and I decided to walk the 80 kilometers (50 miles) or so to Dessie.

A caravan was leaving the town at 4:00 in the afternoon and they were happy to have us walk along with them. We all carried *dulas*. The caravan consisted of a pack train of about 20 mules, and there were probably 15 people. At 3:00 in the morning, we were attacked by a pack of hyenas that ran through the mule train trying to hobble the mules by biting at their hocks. We screamed and yelled and whacked at them as they ran through. We didn't lose any mules, but some of us felt a bit thinner, and we had a lot more adrenalin rushing through our veins after that event. Thoroughly exhausted, we reached Dessie about 7:00 a.m. the next day. Dejini turned right around with some of the mules and headed back to Wegeltena without any rest.

Dessie was located just above the escarpment of the Rift Valley.

During the rainy season, we would head down into the desert to search for smallpox cases. It was much easier to convince tribesmen living in that zone to get vaccinated because the desert heat made smallpox much more severe and dangerous.

During one visit, I heard of an outbreak due east from Dessie by Lake Abbe, which was located on the border between Ethiopia and French Somaliland, and I was told that it would be very wise to obtain permission from the local ruler, whose name was *Haji* Alimirah Hanfare.

I found Alimirah in a tent sitting on a chair/throne with throngs of Afar tribesmen surrounding him. I asked him if we could have permission to go farther inland to the town of Abbe Haik to search for smallpox. He said yes, wrote a letter, put his personal seal on it and gave it to me to guarantee our safe passage.

Our destination was the Danakil Depression, the hottest inhabited place on earth, or so I have been told. By 9:00 a.m. the temperature was always over 100 degrees Fahrenheit and by midday easily 115–120.

The first night we came upon an Afar encampment. They had homemade "cots" to sleep on that were elevated about five feet off the ground. They claimed that the bugs would not bother you if you slept on the tall cots, and they were correct. They were singing songs about going into battle with the Issa, their sworn enemies. There was a shaman there who warned that a battle was imminent and that a chief's son would be killed.

We arose at first light and headed east. We made it to the edge of Lake Abbe by probably the third day into our journey. We found another camp of friendly Afar who invited us to get out of the stifling heat. It was much cooler under their portable huts that were lined with straw mats. They had built a fire in the ground in a hole that was lined with clay. They let the fire burn down to charcoal, removed the coals and dropped in a small goat that they had slaughtered. The tribesman then put a clay lid on it and covered it up with dirt for a few hours. When they uncovered it, the goat meat just fell off the bones and was wonderful to eat.

I recall that the west side of Lake Abbe was covered with wine bottles and debris. Our guide told us that the French would fly out in helicopters from Djibouti, have a picnic and then fly away, leaving their garbage.

We were told that there was an Ethiopian military unit stationed on top of two mountain peaks about another day's journey from there. During our trip there, I took a student with me named Usrot and Gene's old dresser, Tessera, who was a wonderful man whom you could trust with your life. We reached the military encampment by mid-afternoon the next day when the sun was at its hottest.

I was in very good shape having been in country for almost two years, but it turned out to be a very vicious climb for me and about two thirds of the way up the mountain I was felled by heat exhaustion. The Ethiopian soldiers came down and two of them carried me up to the relative shade of their tents. I came out of my stupor slowly, but they gave me scads of hot, sugary tea and that helped a lot.

I estimated the size of the unit to be about a company, which was led by a major. The encampment was located between the two mountain peaks. Oddly enough, there was a lake up there as well. After I had recuperated, the Ethiopian soldiers asked if I wanted to go swimming. It must have been quite a sight as we all stripped down to nothing but our boots, and ran to this lake about 100 yards away. An Ethiopian soldier stood guard with a rifle on top of a large boulder just offshore. Evidently, there were hippos in the area that could be dangerous.

We were kept under a loose guard while there until we got up the next day and headed back to our base camp in Asosa, which was about a 3-day journey.

About three months later, Gene and I were in Addis headed for the bar at the Hilton Hotel. As we were entering, Alimirah Hanfare was coming out with a body guard. They were both dressed in western suits. He recognized us and said in English, "Hi, how are you?"

Such were the ironies in the land of Ethiopia.

On May 21, 1972, a new smallpox eradication PCV named Dexter Fairbank, III arrived in Dessie.

The next day, we started searching for smallpox cases in the town of Kombolcha, which was down the mountain from Dessie on the main road to Addis.

On June 2nd, I received word that Gene had busted another axle in Tenta, which was across the valley from Wegeltena. I drove back to Dessie and grabbed the parts I thought he needed. One of the mechanics came with me and we made it from Dessie to Tenta in 3 hours and 45 minutes. All of us were back in Dessie by 8:00 p.m. that same day, which may have been a record.

After rescuing Gene for a second time, later in June, I headed to Addis Ababa for a medical exam, for repairs to the Land Rover, and to say goodbye to some old friends who were leaving Ethiopia. Three PCVs that I had become close to during my stay in Ethiopia were all leaving at the end of their two-year tours: Rick Baes, Jim Skelton, and Jack Quillman. Though I had not been stationed with them in Addis, I had always made their house my hotel when I was there, and enjoyed my stays with them as they were all great guys. I was sad to see them go. To celebrate, one evening after a beer or two, or maybe more, and maybe some other beverages as well, we shot small rockets out of bottles from their patio and then we all signed our names on their house with magic markers. I am ever hopeful that the statute of limitations has run out on that piece of vandalism.

My final trip into the Ethiopian highlands turned out to be my hardest one. I didn't know it at the time, but I had been stricken with hepatitis A, which was slowly wearing me down. My plan had been to repeat a one way run to Gondar through the river beds. I got as far as the town of Nefas Mewcha, and had become completely exhausted. I was unable to go any farther. One of the *balabats* came to the camp to analyze my situation. Dejini started to update him on my condition, but the *balabat* basically told Dejini that he did not have the status to deal with him and to back off. Dejini stood up to his full height of 5 feet 4 inches and said, "You do not have the right to say what you did. This is my brother. I will take him back to Dessie, and if you touch him, I will strike you," or in so many words. The *balabat* left immediately and that was that.

When we got to Wegeltena, I said my good-byes to Dejini and his wife because I felt like I would not be returning. That turned out to be accurate. I gave Dejini about 200 Ethiopian *birr* in one-*birr* increments as he did not have a sense of larger sums when it came to money. He immediately put it in a leather bag and buried it in the floor of his *tukul*. He then bought his wife a dress.

I arrived back in Dessie and was shipped out to Kagnew Station two days later, where I remained for the rest of my time in Ethiopia.

I will never forget Dejini Duba, who was my friend, and salt of the earth.

While seeing off these three friends, I thought back to the why and how I ended up in this strange and wonderful country. I had been a mere farm boy from a small farm in Michigan on the Ohio border. I had never even flown on an airplane when I boarded the flight from Toledo on the first leg of my trip to Ethiopia. My idea of an adventure before Ethiopia was driving through the small town of Morenci on a Saturday and circling the two blocks of downtown looking for girls to pick up. Not to mention that my language skills at the time were the equivalent of a "D" in high school Spanish.

This team of PCVs that I was part of had helped bring about the end to one of the scourges of mankind, and I was part of it. That adventure has remained part of my moral and personal framework ever since.

MEDICAL CHALLENGES
Many PCVs faced potentially very serious medical issues related to their work and living in Ethiopia. These are some examples of medical challenges that I faced during my stay.

In April 1972, I had just returned to Dessie from a ten-day trip to Wadla Delanta in the Ethiopian Highlands.

My normal routine on getting back was to take an overdue hot bath, work on reports, and do maintenance work on the Land Rover. After my bath early that evening, there was knock on my front door. I opened it to find a teenage boy with a baboon that had a rope tied around its neck. I had just opened the door when the baboon leaped up, bit my hand and ran out the gate toward the mountains from which he had been captured. The boy ran away close behind him. I rushed into the kitchen and washed the wound with hot soapy water, recalling with much trepidation that several months earlier a PCV I knew had died and was diagnosed at autopsy with rabies. I immediately called Dr. Jon Ey, our Peace Corps physician in Addis Ababa, and asked for advice and counsel. He told me to "Get to Addis Ababa by the quickest means possible." So, I caught the next flight out of the Bati airfield a day later.

At that time, the treatment required the patient to take 21 shots of rabies vaccine in 14 days, which was just the opposite of fun. I abhor needles of any kind, which in the business we were in at the time was sort of ironic. It was a tough two weeks for me because there were times from both a mental and emotional standpoint that I felt like I was on death's door. I was due for my gamma globulin shot at the same time, but Dr. Ey cautioned that if I took gamma globulin while I was taking the rabies series, it would make the rabies series ineffective. The rabies vaccine series apparently worked and shortly thereafter I returned to work in Welo.

The decision to delay the gamma globulin shot probably contributed to my coming down with hepatitis A the following spring. When I began to get sick, I traveled to Kagnew Station in Asmara, Eritrea province, and literally walked past the MPs at the guard station, entered the 10-bed hospital there and said, "Here I am." None of the doctors or nurses had any idea why I was there, so I said, "Look at my eyes," which were bright yellow from the jaundice. They admitted me right away.

That day I was given a room about suppertime, and an orderly came through the door with a tray filled with southern fried chicken, mashed potatoes, biscuits, and gravy. I'm not sure why, but I just lost it in front of the orderly, and sobbed uncontrollably.

Shortly after I had checked into the hospital, I wrote my parents a cryptic note stating that "I was a little under the weather," but didn't communicate with them for the next two months since I was mostly sleeping 20 hours a day. One day, the base commander showed up at my bedside and said my mother had written the Army demanding to know my condition. He had pen and paper in hand and strongly suggested that he was not leaving until I penned a note to my family telling them that I was okay. I complied, and he said the message would be telegraphed to them immediately.

I became pretty much ambulatory and bored in the weeks that followed. One day, I decided to go into the PX to see if I could buy a copy of the *New York Times* I knew they carried. The clerk tossed me out, declaring, "You have no right to be in here!" So, I paid a visit to my new "pal" — the base commander — to see if he would give me permission to buy a newspaper at the PX. Well, he had a fit! He gave me an Officer Privileges card that allowed me full access to anything that Kagnew Station had to offer. So, I marched back into the PX and bought a copy of the Sunday *New York Times* and a Snickers bar, much to the clerk's chagrin. This card also enabled me to get into both the enlisted men's club and the officer's club, and I took advantage of those privileges as well.

In July 1973, I was discharged from the Kagnew Station Hospital after spending three months in that hospital battling and eventually recovering from my bout with hepatitis.

I made my way back to Dessie and, wanting to continue working for the SEP, I applied to be a smallpox Operations Officer in the province of Bali in southern Ethiopia. Dr. Ey would not hear of it due to my health issues, so I began planning to travel home through the Far East, hitting Australia, Singapore, Japan, and hoped to end up in San Francisco by Thanksgiving of 1973. Dr. Ey advised me to take a shorter route home. I still remember him admonishing me about the "high cost" of my 3-month stay at Kagnew Station, which was $2300, — a bargain in comparison to today's prices.

In August 1973, I mustered out of the Peace Corps. Most of my friends were long gone by then, but I was still sad to leave a place that had been my home for over 28 months. Unfortunately, I had to use my Kagnew Station card one more time. That occurred when I attempted to check my baggage through customs at the airport in Addis Ababa and the agent told me I had to pay another $900, which I thought was definitely an attempt to solicit a bribe. I was quite fluent in the Amharic curse words by then, and this customs man got a blast out of every Amharic derogatory word I threw at him. Then, I yanked my baggage out of customs, bought a bus ticket from Addis Ababa to Asmara, and marched through the front gate of Kagnew Station again. I found one of my military buddies, who helped me ship all my stuff back to the States via military transport. The total bill at the airport in Addis Ababa was going to be over 1800 *birr* to ship all of my stuff back home, but Kagnew Station only charged me $50 U.S. What a deal!

At that time, the Peace Corps made the PCVs' service payments in *birr*, and the exchange rate was terrible. At the Kagnew Base bank, however, the exchange rate was great, so I changed all my Ethiopian dollars into greenbacks at their rate. Suddenly, I felt like a rich 23-year-old. I immediately flew back to Addis and asked my travel agent to prepare my airline ticket for Cairo, Nicosia, Tel Aviv, Frankfurt, Newark, New Jersey and then Toledo, Ohio, my last stop. The agent informed me that because the Arab states and Israel were still at war, that I would be arrested in Cairo if they saw that destination on the ticket. So, he wrote two tickets, with one showing I was traveling from Cairo to Frankfurt. The second ticket had the original route and this I hid in the false bottom of my camera bag. Everything worked out well as I flew into the Newark airport towards the end of August 1973.

Whilst in Tel Aviv, I had purchased a box of Cuban cigars knowing full well that they would be confiscated upon my arrival in the States. I bought a second box of "legal" cigars and switched the wrappers and box with the Cuban cigars. Upon arrival at customs in Newark, there was a big sign on the wall that read, "All passengers arriving from Yemen, Egypt, and Ethiopia may be subject to full search." The agent looked at my passport and said, "You have been gone a while. Do you have anything to declare?" I said, "Yes, I am glad to be home." He said, "Pass on through, son."

And my adventure was over.

EPILOGUE

Almost daily, I think about the inherent danger of some of the situations in which we found ourselves in Ethiopia, and how exceptional it was that we all survived without permanent damage.

I also continue to be reminded of the great and lasting friendships we made there.

In 2013, my wife became seriously ill with breast cancer. It was like all the air in the room had been taken out. I took her to the University of Michigan medical school for a second opinion.

Jim Lepkowski, one of the smallpox PCVs I worked with in Ethiopia, was a professor there. I had hours on my hands since my wife was being examined by all sorts of medical staff. I had not talked to Jim in a long time, but I found his campus number and dialed him up. I briefly told him what was going on, and Jim stated, "Let me cancel my classes and I'll be right over." I think this illustrates the "Band of Brothers" that the Ethiopia smallpox PCVs became.

In the fall of 2011, Ciro De Quadros and some of the PCVs organized a reunion of several former smallpox PCVs, which was held at his house in Georgetown, Washington, DC. I drove from Ohio and found, to my chagrin, that my GPS was worthless in Washington, DC, because they are forever blocking off exits and entries to the freeway for presidents, dignitaries, etc. I called Ciro to let him know I would be late. He laughed and said, "Scott, we have all been on this journey together for over 40 years! Don't worry about being late." I observed that it did not matter if you were suffering from heat exhaustion with Ciro in the desert, or sitting in his living room in Georgetown, Ciro was a man's man.

Lastly, through my experience working with Ciro on the Ethiopia-Sudan border, I became aware that Ciro had a great sense of moral justice. He told me that in Brazil, whole smallpox expeditions would get wiped out by indigenous Indians. He said that despite these threats, the smallpox teams' motto remained, "Die but never kill." Ciro was a leader to be admired, respected, and followed. I am proud to have known him and called him my friend.

•

10

The Road That Led to Smallpox Eradication in Welo Province

by Gene L. Bartley

It is my intention to honor and dedicate this essay to the people of Ethiopia who touched me so long ago. From July 1971 to October 1972, I was vaccinating them with bifurcated needles during the introduction and implementation of the Smallpox Eradication Program (SEP) in Welo province, in northern Ethiopia. These are true and, hopefully, interesting highlights of my experience, which I have attempted to document from my memory that has started to fade since my arrival in the ancient land of Ethiopia (formally Abyssinia) more than 45 years ago.

•

I had completed six months of successful work with the SEP in southwestern Ethiopia in Welega province under actual field conditions, and felt like a smallpox "warrior" who could face any obstacle put in my path. In retrospect, I realize that Welo was in many ways different from Welega, and it presented more challenges than those at my previous assignment. Even though I thought I was well prepared, Welo always presented new obstacles to overcome and challenges to face, which meant that I had to find the types of solutions that would work best in this new location.

The 1972 census information[1] reported the Welo population as 2,355,600, and the total Ethiopian population as 24,319,000.

According to the 1994 census report,[2] the largest ethnic group reported in the Northern Zone of Ethiopia was the Amhara with 99%, with the remaining 1% Oromo and Afar. Amharic was spoken as a first language by the majority of the population of Welo, while the remainder spoke the Oromo and Afar languages.

In northern Welo, 82.7% of the people practiced Ethiopian Orthodox Christianity, and 17.1% of the population said they were Muslim, while in southern Welo 70.9% were Muslim, and 28.8% of the population said they practiced Ethiopian Orthodox Christianity.

To this day, the northern highlands are dominated by the Amhara and Tigray ethnic groups. The highlanders grow grain crops such as *teff* (a grain indigenous to Ethiopia), barley and wheat, along with chickpeas and beans. They also raised livestock, including cattle, sheep and goats. The lowlands of Eastern Ethiopia in Welo and Tigray provinces are inhabited by the Afar tribe. They are semi-nomadic pastoralists who own large herds of camels, cows and goats, and subsist mainly on the blood, meat and milk of their animals. They speak a Cushitic language.

Welo province is geographically comprised of central highlands with mountains, deep gorges and valleys, where the Amhara eke out a living off the thinly covered top soil of mountains and hilly slopes. They mainly plant *teff*, beans, chickpeas, barley and wheat, while the areas below the highlands, known as *wayna-dega*, are planted mainly in corn, millet, sorghum, cotton, *teff*, and hot pepper. In the semi-desert and desert areas, the plantings are mostly millet and sorghum, sunflowers, chickpeas, flax, *teff* and cotton, with the pastoralists herding their cattle, camels, and goats.

---

1 SEP Newsletter, "Smallpox Surveillance in Ethiopia No. 24," Monthly report for January 1973 and summary 1972.
2 1994 Population and Housing Census of Ethiopia: Results for Amhara Region, Vol. 1, part 1.

In Welo, I worked with two main ethnic groups, the first of which was the Amhara, who are a very proud and independent group living mostly in the highlands. The Amharas fought in the front lines against the Italian invasion during the early days of World War II in Ethiopia, and eventually threw the Italians out of the country later in the war.

The second ethnic group was the Afar, which is comprised of fierce warriors who inhabit the semi-desert and desert areas of the Rift Valley in eastern Welo.

From my brief observations of the second group, I can say that unless you live with the Afar people it is not possible to know them well, but they are a gentle people. Before my arrival in the Danakil Desert in eastern Welo, I feared the nomadic people living there, but, as I found out during my several trips there, the Afar were genuine and kind people who were open to vaccination. They are a nomadic group who freely move between Djibouti, and the provinces of Welo and Eritrea (Eritrea was a province in Ethiopia during our SEP work, but later became independent). They live mostly in small huts covered by woven grass mats and the skins of their animals.

Each of the cultural groups had its own unique behaviors, beliefs and practices in divergent geographic regions, which made it a challenge to reach and work with them and, more importantly, to get them to agree to vaccination. Furthermore, the frequent movement of the nomadic Afar created a special problem for surveillance that required coordination with the neighboring country of Djibouti. It was in this environment that I worked and struggled for one year and four months with the goal of eradicating smallpox.

A NEW ASSIGNMENT, ADVENTURE AND THE INTRODUCTION OF THE AEROGRAM

In preparation for my next assignment and the trip to Dessie, the capital of Welo province where I would be based, I packed all my worldly goods and household furnishings, which included a bed, a small refrigerator, a two-burner gas stove and some clothing, into my new blue Land Rover, for which I had signed over my life. Later, I came to view my vehicle as my "best friend." I took good care of it and, in return, it served me well in many difficult situations, only rarely letting me down.

The distance from Addis Ababa to Dessie is a total of 387 kilometers (240 miles), which required seven hours to drive in 1971. The road was partially paved to the outskirts of Addis, but the remaining roadway was made up of all-weather roads.

This drive from Addis to Dessie was the first time I had been on my own since arriving in Ethiopia. The road took me through town of Debre Berhan that was located on a mountain top (2,840 meters) about 130 kilometers (81 miles) from Addis Ababa in Shoa province, then descending from the steep mountain slopes to the low land through hairpin turns, very similar to roads I traveled in my birthplace in Colorado.

This trip was made during the big rains in July 1971, and on either side of the road, I passed agricultural fields glistening green with crops of maize, millet/sorghum, wheat, barley, and *teff*, while the cattle grazed on grass covering the hills.

An Indian friend of mine, D. N. Sharma, once eloquently described this season of the year in the following way, "the green velvet carpet of *kerumpt* (big rainy season from June to August) has been rolled out on the hills of Ethiopia."

I continued driving through the lowlands until I reached the city of Kombolcha, where the airport for Welo province was located, some 21 kilometers (13 miles) from Desssie. Then, I started to climb, zigzagging back up into the highlands and my destination, which has an elevation of approximately 2,500 meters above sea level.

Late that afternoon I drove into the city where I would spend the next 16 months of my life in the pursuit of the eradication of smallpox along with my Ethiopian counterparts and other PCVs to be assigned there including Scott Porterfield who arrived in April 4, 1972 and Tom Duffy, in October 1971.

I had no time to waste in my new assignment, in fact, orientation started the next day after my arrival. After locating the Provincial Health Office (PHO), I was introduced to the two sanitarians assigned by Ministry of

Health (MOH) to the SEP in Welo province named *Ato* Abeba Baiyou and *Ato* Tessera Kassa.

High on the agenda that day was establishing a reporting system that utilized postal aerograms for informing the SEP office in Addis Ababa about suspected cases of smallpox. This innovative system had been introduced for the first time in Ethiopia by the SEP.

An aerogram was a single, thin piece of blue writing paper that could be folded in half and sealed on the three open edges, and addressed on the outside so that there was no need for an envelope. For easy and instant mailing, all aerograms that were distributed to us were pre-addressed to the PHO in Dessie. These pre-addressed and pre-stamped aerograms made it easier and more effective for government health facilities and other health providing organizations and individuals anywhere in the province to report smallpox cases. They had only to complete a simple form inside the aerogram, seal it, and send it through the postal system, or, in the case of government health facilities, use the existing mailing system/pouch.

While health facilities were required to report cases of smallpox immediately by telephone or telegram, this innovative reporting system was introduced to establish routine reporting, and improve the reliability of reporting suspected cases of smallpox from health facilities, organizations and other ministry offices in the province.

The reporting forms were not only used for reporting the number of suspected cases of smallpox cases monthly, but also for zero case reports. Once the system was in place, it became part of our job to follow-up on delinquent reporting even with those facilities that did not have cases to report. The concept behind the use of this reporting system was basically twofold: to improve reporting, and, more importantly, to attempt to reduce the amount of time it took for the information to reach the SEP office in Dessie as well as SEP/HQ in Addis Ababa, which in turn allowed the team to take the required action to verify and investigate any reported cases. What we did not realize, however, was that the development of this system would result many years later in the improvement of the process of reporting of other vaccine preventable diseases in the newly established Expanded Program on Immunization (EPI).

DANAKIL DESERT, COTTON PLANTATION, SURVEILLANCE AND VACCINATION

The thought of going into a desert was intriguing, scary and exciting all at the same time. It would be my first time being in such an environment. The stories I had been told about Afar customs and behavior made me a bit apprehensive about going there. Apparently, they had a custom of proving one's manhood, which entailed displaying an enemy's genitals as a trophy after he was killed!

I had learned that this custom had been practiced in previous generations, but, even though it was discouraged by the government at the time we arrived, I was still a little apprehensive.

The Afar people, who speak the Cushitic language, live in small huts supported by flexible wooden branches covered by grass mats that can be easily disassembled and transported. Their diet is supplemented with bread made of corn or millet, which is usually not grown by the Afar, but purchased from the open market. The bread is baked inside small pits in the ground that are lined with flat rocks and heated by wood coals at the bottom of the pit. The dough is prepared and placed onto the hot, flat rocks lining the pit, then the pit is covered with rocks and soil and the dough is allowed to bake.

They occasionally barter wool and skins, mainly with highland people, to obtain cotton for their clothing. The customary dress of the Afar male is a cotton, woven, cloth shawl on the shoulders and a wrap-around bottom similar to a cotton sarong with an ever-present curved-dagger at the waist called the *gile*. Women typically wear a wrap-around skirt with no top garment.

We planned to set up a base camp in the city of Asayita, 292 kilometers (180 miles) east of Dessie. The road to Asayita was a combination of asphalt and all-weather gravel so we were able to use it in all seasons. We did not have to worry about traveling on smaller, dry-weather dirt roads since there was little or no rain in the desert, although when it did rain it caused temporary flooding that could be a problem. Our journey took us through Kombolcha and then Bati, which is 66 kilometers (41 miles) from Dessie. Bati is a town located on the plateau, at the edge of the Rift Valley, after which the road slowly winds down into the lowlands and semi-desert area.

Bati was a very unique town, which had a most diverse open market because of the three ethnic groups of the area. Afar, Oromo and Amhara, gathered together to sell, buy and barter in one location. In this market one could find various items that were distinctive to each culture. One of the attractions in the Bati area was the natural hot water springs that were used for bathing and therapeutic practices.

Upon our descent into the Rift Valley, we saw camel caravans coming up into the highlands to sell or barter mostly salt blocks and hides in exchange for commodities, such as corn, millet, sugar, tea, coffee and other products they could not find in the desert.

On our way to Asayita, we passed through the towns of Millie, Tendaho and Dubti. A very large, irrigated cotton plantation called Tendaho Cotton Plantation was located at Dubti. The workers hired by the plantation were mostly from the highland Amhara and Oromo groups rather than local Afar, who traditionally preferred a nomadic style of life.

The primary objective of the first trip to the Danakil Desert was the surveillance and vaccination of the Tendaho Plantation area, including the staff and families of workers on the cotton farm.

This was the oldest mechanized cotton-growing farm in the country, and was located about 580 kilometers (360 miles) from Addis Ababa on the main road to the Eritrean port of Assab (part of Ethiopia at the time of our work). Tendaho was originally established as a share company in 1960 between the Ethiopian government and the British Mitchell Cotts group. A ginnery was built on-site in 1964. Just before its nationalization in 1975, the plantation had grown in land size to 10,000 hectares (100 square kilometers). After the *Derge* government came to power in 1975, the plantation was split into two cotton farms, totaling 8,000 hectares.[3]

As I had learned from my experience in Welega province, when approaching an area of suspected unreported cases of smallpox, the first priority was to introduce oneself to the officials in power. In this case, we

3 Commercial Reports. Kind Cotton Feeds Royal Textile Hopes, U.S. Embassy – Addis Ababa, Commercial Section, Dec.1999.

sought out the Director General and administrative officials of the Tenda-ho Cotton Plantation in an attempt to find out the best way to proceed. During our introductory meeting, we received their blessing to proceed, and were told they had a medical office on the Plantation that was staffed with Ministry of Health workers who could help us develop a strategy to reach this unique population, which would require us to mobilize both staff and family members for vaccination.

After talking to the medical staff, we understood that, due to the sheer size of the plantation area and the large number of workers, we would be required to hire more manpower to vaccinate and more guides for passage through the plantation roads. The families of the workers, living in housing provided by the company, would prove to be more accessible than the workers themselves since they were usually in the cotton fields, except for Sundays and holidays.

The medical staff agreed to send out information in advance to the various plantation sub-offices to inform them of the date and time that our team would arrive at the designated points for surveillance and vaccination.

We understood that the male workers needed to be informed in advance of our visit to their families in order to get the cooperation of their family members, so we asked the plantation company to inform the male workers in meetings, as well as posting a letter for information about the team visits to the family quarters for the purpose of vaccinating the women and children.

Subsequently, we observed that the Amharas and the Oromos on the plantation, who were more accessible and educated, were more highly resistant to, and stubborn about, being vaccinated than the local Afar population.

We did find some old cases of smallpox among the plantation staff and their families, which led us to believe that there were probably cases among the Afar population at large.

After completing our work on the plantation, we moved to Asayita, where we planned to establish our base camp, and was approximately 50 kilometers (31 miles) from Tendaho. This was the area in which the leader

MOH/SEP Surveillance Officer Abebe (seated center, wearing hat) recording outbreak information with Afar tribal members. Asayita, Welo province, August 1971. *Photo by the author.*

of the Afar people was located, and we hoped to obtain his assistance in gaining the cooperation of the local nomadic population.

We were introduced to *Bitweded* (recognized leader) Sultan Alimirah Hanfare, who was the leader of the Afar in the Danakil Desert. He commanded genuine respect and honor for his position, and was recognized by the Afar people for his leadership and his ability to modernize their lives. He was both a political and tribal leader, and whatever he said was law. We developed a very good relationship with Alimirah and he was, without question, completely convinced of the importance of our plan to vaccinate all his people against smallpox. In this light, he provided us with two of his most respected and trusted leaders as guides, whose presence would instantly allow us to carry out surveillance of the people and vaccinate them without resistance. The cooperation we received was a major boost for our operation in the desert and allowed us to move freely without security problems. I will always remember Bitweded Alimirah's

Ciro de Quadros second from right, leader of the outbreak team, PCV Tom
Duffy fifth from right, with MOH/SEP sanitarians Abeba Baiyou, second from
left, and Tessera Kassa, fourth from left plus Afar guides and guards. Asayita,
Welo province, November 1971. *Photo by the author.*

leadership, which was crucial in gaining the cooperation of his nomadic
people, and was essential for our being able to vaccinate them.

We did find a few active cases of smallpox in the sparse population
of the Afars and quickly notified authorities in Djibouti.

Since this was my first opportunity to work on a smallpox outbreak
in Welo with the Afar ethnic group, Dr. Ciro de Quadros decided to visit
us. During my first experience in Welega, Ciro had shown me the fun-
damentals of proper surveillance work, and now it was my turn to show
Ciro what I had learned. He and I were friends by then and we made a
good team, so I introduced him to *Bitweded* Alimirah, and that turned out
to be an instant success story since Ciro was able to identify and obtain
cooperation with people from the very first meeting.

As always, Ciro pushed us to the limit in the heat and dust of the
desert, but our work was effective and we discovered several fresh cases,
which were traced back to the highland workers who came to work in
the cotton plantation, or had set up small restaurants and shops in the
Danakil areas.

Each evening, we would return to Asayita to take a shower, and to
dine on roasted kid goat, known as *bekel*, and beer, not necessarily in that

PCV Tom Duffy blocks the sunlight with his hat while MOH/SEP Surveillance Officer Abebe vaccinates a child. Assisting is SEP Surveillance Officer Tessera Kassa. Asayita, Welo province, February 1972. *Photo by the author.*

order. Incidentally, the kid goat had a taste similar to chicken, and since it was so tender we ate meat and bones alike. After dinner, we would go up to the roof of the guest house where we were staying to discuss the achievements of that day and plan for our travel when the morning light peeked over the desert landscape. Sleep always came, even though the oppressive heat persisted throughout the night.

We were happy with our successes, especially since the population did not perceive the eradication of smallpox or vaccination as a health priority; their priority was to see malaria disappear from their homes.

We were not only there to achieve an increase in vaccination rates, but also to question patients being treated in the local health facilities about smallpox cases that they were aware of, and to emphasize with the local health-care givers the importance of rapid reporting whether or not cases were found!

When we weren't chasing after smallpox cases, we were known to chase ostriches in the desert with our vehicles. What I learned from Ciro's visit, which only lasted one week, was that we could never keep up with the ostriches, but we could conquer smallpox with our persistent surveillance, active questioning, probing and tracking until all active and suspected cases were identified.

ACTIVITIES BETWEEN OUTBREAK INVESTIGATIONS

Although it is said that all roads lead to Rome, I preferred the road that led to Dessie for rest and relaxation, especially after being in the desert for a month.

Dessie is a beautiful town, located in a narrow mountainous valley that can only be reached after climbing almost 1,000 meters (3,281 feet) in 25 kilometers (15.5 miles) from Kombolcha. It is flanked on both sides with mountains, and, during my stay, minor earthquakes would send boulders racing down the sides of the mountains that, luckily, did not reach our house. The valley has rivers and beautiful grass-filled meadows. It was a place where you could own a horse, which we did for relaxing in between outbreaks.

Dessie was a sleepy town with little entertainment, but on special occasions an old movie might be shown in the local theater or maybe there would be a card game with Ethiopians and other PCVs living in the area. Our rented house was in walking distance of the SEP office, from which we could see a beautiful meadow called Hota through our window.

During our stay we provided financial assistance to help educate two students, Joseph and Yousef. Many years later, I was fortunate to have the opportunity to meet Joseph again, in Addis Ababa, where he was studying engineering at the government-supported University.

After recuperating from our desert trips, Tessera Kassa, the SEP sanitarian, and I would prepare and send a report to the SEP/HQ about the most recent outbreak investigation, budget expenditures for that period, and, more importantly, we would follow-up on aerogram reports of suspected cases, or zero cases reported.

The follow-up to suspected cases that we reported was urgently carried out by a SEP team that was not in the field, or by a government health facility near the area of the suspected cases, at our request.

Regarding the reporting of zero cases, there were always a few institutions that did not like to report zero cases, so they would simply not send in a report. Maybe they thought that since there were no cases there was no need to report, or that reporting zero cases meant they were not doing their work properly. This made our work more difficult because we had to either make a telephone call or send a message as a follow-up to each facility that did not report during a period of one month. The SEP/HQ required our reports because they were used to update the overall country figures. We included the smallpox figures collected by the PHO, but we had to make sure there was no duplication of reported numbers of smallpox cases and vaccinations.

When the administrative issues were taken care of, the SEP team members would start to plan the next outbreak trips and decide on the composition of the teams. When we traveled, all teams made it a habit to stop at all hospitals, private and mission clinics, health centers and health stations along the route to replenish the aerogram supplies and to ask the staff members about the latest news or rumors about suspected smallpox cases.

Since arriving in Welo, I had not visited the Amhara highlands, so during a meeting of all team members one day, we agreed that my team would go to the Amhara highlands, while the second team would go to the Afar or Oromo areas, which included the Danakil Desert, to follow-up on our work as well as investigate new suspected sites.

ROADS, MOUNTAINS, VALLEYS, CLIFFS, HISTORIC SITES AND VARIOLA MINOR

The road that leads out of Dessie to the east went to the Danakil Desert, to the south, Addis Ababa, and to the north, the main all-weather road that continued on to Mekele and Asmara. It was the road west that lead to the highlands.

Early one morning, my team took the westerly road out of Dessie toward Tenta, which would be a completely new experience for me.

It is not easy to describe the mountainous highlands and their roads in Welo, especially for someone who has never been on the road between Dessie and Tenta, a distance of approximately 98 kilometers (61 miles). The first portion of the dirt road was flat and wound through a forest of 100-year-old eucalyptus trees, reaching the hamlet of Kutaber, 22 kilometers (13.6 miles) outside of Dessie. This small village was known for serving a local golden brew of fermented honey called *tej* (similar to mead).

After Kutaber, the road started to wind sharply down into the valley where it followed the river bed at the bottom. I was feeling good that morning because there were no loosely built bridges to cross or fall through, which I had experienced in Welega during the outbreak in the Begi area. The road continued and snaked back and forth for another few kilometers until we reached the turn off to Gishen Mariam Monastery (St. Mary Church). Gishen Mariam is a well-known Christian pilgrimage site for Ethiopian Orthodox Christians because it is believed that the monastery holds a religious relic — a piece of the true cross — which was brought into Ethiopia in the 15th century.

We continued on the road without any difficulties, meeting the usual local villagers and their donkeys and other livestock. Then, we passed near another bridge that was built by the Italians during their occupation of Ethiopia. We then turned onto the road that would take us to Tenta, which is located on a mesa above the valley floor. We were about 80 kilometers (50 miles) from Dessie, which meant we were only 18 kilometers (11 miles) from our destination and our campsite for the night.

At the time I did not realize it that this road would be a challenge for me as well as my Land Rover. The final part of the road near the top of the mesa was my own personal challenge that day and was almost impassable by vehicle due to the extremely steep incline. It is very difficult to describe accurately the final ascent to the top of the mesa and Tenta. The nearest I have come to describing the location is the term, *amora gadale*, the Amharic phrase used by my Ethiopian counterparts, which literally means "cliff of the eagle!"

Steep, narrow, rugged road leading to highlands district.
Tenta, Welo province, January 1972. *Photo by the author.*

Basically, this road was the only way to get up onto the mesa and reach our destination of Tenta . . . we couldn't avoid it. The steepest part of the road was only about 200 meters long, but it was sheer hell to climb it. Before I started the ascent, I got out of my vehicle to try to figure out what would be the best way to approach this extreme incline. One thing I remember seeing that scared me was all the black tire marks on the rocky slope that had been left by previous vehicles.

In retrospect, I regret that I never took a photo of this part of the road because I was always either too busy driving to take a picture or so happy to reach the top that I never looked back. I am reminded of the famous saying, "a picture is worth a thousand words." In this case, it would definitely have been appropriate to have taken a picture.

When we finally reached the top, it felt like we ascended into the clouds and reached "heaven" on earth.

After arriving on the top of the mesa, we set up camp in the compound of the Tenta *awraja* police station.

The author using the most appropriate transportation to a remote area to check for suspected cases. Wadla Delanta, Welo. April 1972. *Photo by Tessera Kassa.*

However . . . even before we could erect our tent, we were informed of suspected cases of smallpox across the valley in Wadla Delanta *awraja*, which could only be reached by a one-day mule ride. So, we completed seting up camp, had dinner at the only restaurant in town and made plans to leave the next day with a guide.

The smallpox work always presented new challenges, and this time the challenge was to learn how to ride a mule. I had ridden horses in the States and liked them, but the mule is a totally different breed of animal. The mule will stop when you least expect it and go when you want to stop. But a mule is the best form of transport when you want to travel the Welo mountains because they are sure-footed beasts, especially on those small paths that twist and turn as you go up and down the steep mountainsides.

The "Grand Canyon" of Welo required crossing to investigate suspected smallpox cases, Wadla Delanta, Welo, April 1972. *Photo by the author.*

Another problem was the style of the Ethiopian saddles, which were not your conventional saddles by any means. Indeed, they were made of wood with a thin cloth cover. If the rider was not used to this type of saddle, it would cause sores on the buttocks in a matter of hours. As a consequence, I would only ride for an hour at a time and then get off and walk for the next hour.

In order to reach the area of the suspected cases, we had to traverse what I called the "Grand Canyon" of Wadla Delanta. I have visited the Grand Canyon in Arizona, but never had to cross from one side of a canyon to the other by mule. That day was hazy and the valley was so wide, I could barely see the other side, and could not even see the river at the bottom.

We started to cross the valley at 8:00 a.m. in order to reach our destination before sundown. Going down the side of the escarpment was not so difficult, and it only took four hours to reach the small river at the bottom, but it took another six hours to climb up the other side to reach the top, and by that time it was starting to get dark. We traveled by the light of a half moon and stars for another two hours to the area of the suspected cases, arriving at our destination at 8:00 p.m. I remember the nights in the highlands as beautiful . . . clear and bright with no interference from the city lights.

We were completely worn out by the time we reached our destination, which was the house of the leader of that area, where we would sleep for the night. I did not want to eat or drink or talk upon arrival, I just needed to lie down on the nearest bed. With a funny smile on his face, my counterpart, Tessera Kassa, asked me what bed I was talking about. Only then did I realize that we were going to share the dirt floor of the house for sleeping that night. I replied that I didn't mind sleeping on the ground because I was so tired.

I was not aware of all of the traditions and customs of Ethiopian hospitality in the countryside, and as I was getting ready to go to sleep, the members of the host family would have none of that.

First, I was told to sit down, and one of the family members washed my feet. I felt embarrassed and honored at the same time having my feet washed by someone else, but that was the tradition, especially in the rural areas. This tradition apparently dates back to Biblical times when Christ washed the feet of his disciples to show his humility, thereby teaching them to show love for each other.

Second, for dinner we were fed the traditional food of *injera* and *wot*. If the family thought you were not eating enough and were not filled, they would give you a *gorsha*, which meant the host would start to feed you with his hand until you could eat no more.

Third, we were then treated to the traditional local Ethiopian beer made from barley and hops, called *tella*. The *tella* can be intoxicating, especially if you have travelled all day on a mule. The other advantage of drinking *tella* is that it helps a person sleep and forget about the fleas and mosquitoes as well as the bumps of the dirt floor.

The next morning, we discovered that the suspected cases of smallpox were actually chickenpox, so we did not have an outbreak after all, which was fortunate and allowed us to vaccinate everyone in the area with the help of the leader. We continued to vaccinate that day and spent one more night there, leaving early the following morning for the return trip back to the base camp in Tenta.

While working in this remote area we learned of an interesting point of view held by the people that was a complete surprise to us. Because the type of smallpox contracted in Tenta *awraja* was the milder "variola minor" strain, the people were not so afraid of being infected with the disease, but were more concerned about typhus and typhoid, which were health problems in that area that caused more serious hardships and complications. In fact, we observed resistance to vaccination in many areas in the highlands of Welo province for this reason.

Continuing our surveillance, we also observed several old cases of smallpox that had been transmitted by local healers vaccinating using the variolation technique — people were inoculated with live smallpox virus taken from smallpox patients. This was referred to as the *habisha ketebat* (local vaccination given by a traditional healer). In the absence of smallpox vaccine, the practice of variolation by the traditional healers had become common in the community. The recipient usually developed only a mild case of smallpox, and was protected from future infection, but could spread smallpox to unvacinated people. Although we advised that this type of local vaccination could result in a severe case of smallpox in some instances, the traditional healers did not appear to be willing to change, no doubt because of the profit they made from this practice. Variolation was very dangerous since it introduced active smallpox virus and could spread infection in villages among those not vaccinated. After resuming our work in the Tenta area, we did not discover any fresh cases of smallpox, but we were able to perform many vaccinations in the area.

While in Tenta, I discovered plenty of cool *tella*, which was stored in large, earthenware pots, called *ensera*. I was invited by members of the household where we were staying to drink the *tella* and I accepted. The *tella* would actually be cool because of evaporation through the sides of the earthenware pot. The alcohol content was supposed to kill some of the bacteria and other organisms, so I definitely preferred the local beer over untreated water.

Drs. D.A. Henderson, A. Haijan, Kurt Weithaler, and Ciro de Quadros facilitating a SEP review meeting following the completion of 18 months of surveillance and vaccinations in the field, Addis Ababa, September 1972. *Photo provided by the author.*

On another trip up to Tenta, we broke our crank shaft on the section of the escarpment road that had been trouble before, due in part to the rugged terrain. As you can imagine, there were no garages or stores for parts, and unfortunately I had not carried an extra crank shaft.

So one of our team members walked up to Tenta, and made a call back to our SEP team in Dessie. As luck would have it, my PCV colleague, Scott Porterfield, was in the office and made immediate preparations to pull us off the mountain.

This might sound easy, but towing us off the mountain on those narrow roads was no easy task. We had to get the vehicle turned around so that we would be facing in the right direction to be pulled down the mountain. Scott was fearless that day, whereas I would not have attempted the task. We went slowly and prayed that we would not meet another vehicle or large herds of livestock.

That was my longest day, and I will always remember what it means to have a friend like Scott on whom I could depend.

During my one-and-a-third-year's stay in Welo province, the SEP team managed to identify 982 smallpox cases, and provided 90,851 vaccinations in 1971, and in 1972 a total of 1,150 cases were discovered and 78,893 vaccinations given.

According to the SEP Report,[4] 10 out of 12 *awrajas* in Welo province were affected in 1971, and 9 out of 12 in 1972. Nine out of 32 *woredas* were affected from January to June 1971, and 11 of 32 from July to December 1971. In 1972, from January to June 14 *woredas* were affected, and 13 out of 32 from July to December 1972.

REFLECTIONS

I will never forget the experiences I had during the early 1970s in the provinces of Welo and Welega chasing smallpox cases. This was the greatest gift I could be given, and I thank God for providing me with the skills, abilities, time and energy to help improve the quality of the lives of the people of Ethiopia. I completed my Peace Corps experience after five years, working the last three years as a high school teacher in remote areas of Ethiopia, and finally departed in November 1976. I left with a heart full of good memories, but, most importantly, I was leaving with my wonderful Ethiopian wife, Teji, at my side.

The benefits and richness I gained as a PCV are numerous, and to this very day are still affecting my life. Since my arrival in Ethiopia over 45 years ago, I have never regretted the consequences of my decision to join the Peace Corps. As a result of my smallpox work in Ethiopia, I was fortunate to be recruited as a Technical Officer for the WHO Regional Office for Africa in Brazzaville, Republic of Congo, where I worked for 18 years, and at the end of my career as a Polio Immunization Consultant with the Bill Gates Foundation in Kenya and Uganda. I am most fortunate

---

4 SEP Newsletter, "Smallpox Surveillance in Ethiopia No. 35, Monthly report for December 1973 and summary 1973," Table VI: Number of Affected Awrajas and Woredas in Ethiopia 1971, 1972, 1973, 10.

article quoted people called public health experts, and that was the first time I ever heard of public health. So, I decided I would educate myself by talking to as many people with a background in public health as I could locate in Milwaukee and Madison. Those people guided me, sharing valuable information and exciting stories that influenced my decision to apply to the Peace Corps.

On my application, I brashly informed the Peace Corps that I would only volunteer to work in public health, and, furthermore, would only consider serving in Ethiopia. I discovered later that these demands must have been a surprise to them because the agency doesn't usually receive — or consider — such bold requests.

I had imagined that public health might be an area that would combine my interest in an overseas cross-cultural adventure, and my wish to contribute to something good. The reason I chose Ethiopia from among the Peace Corps list of countries was that I wanted the most remote country, one that owed as little as possible to my western culture, heritage and upbringing. I wanted to escape from my cocoon, my comfort zone, and test myself with something totally alien.

Strangely enough, I applied to the Peace Corps while hitchhiking, something which is also alien, at least in today's world. A friend and I were wending our way down to Mexico and were stranded by the side of the road in a remote part of Arizona. Waiting almost all day for any car to pass, I filled out the application in my backpack.

Many months later I received a mailed invitation from the Peace Corps to serve as a Volunteer in Sierra Leone; the project was to revise the school social studies curriculum. Irritated, I picked up the phone and said something to the effect of "Didn't you people read my application?" I was 23 years old and really didn't understand the process, so I went on, "You've got me in the wrong file, just move me over to the Ethiopia file in public health." The amazing thing was that not every country even had a public health program under the Peace Corps. I could have been asking, in other words, for the impossible. Yet, after a month or two, I received a phone call asking if I would be willing to go to Ethiopia in six weeks. I discovered later that this short advance notice was unusual because the

Peace Corps normally would give you about six months to prepare to live abroad for two years.

As I was to learn later, Peace Corps had just oriented a batch of public health Volunteers for Ethiopia in Denver, and a World Health Organization (WHO) epidemiologist, Dr. Ciro de Quadros, who had been working in Ethiopia, had conducted that orientation session. Apparently he had so scared one or two of the prospective Volunteers that they had quit. At that point, the Peace Corps had to quickly find a replacement and looked through their files to see if they had anybody who requested maybe Africa or East Africa. Lo and behold, they found me, someone who had specifically requested to work in Ethiopia . . . and in public health. Talk about luck!

During that six weeks I quickly tried to read whatever I could find about smallpox in the local library. The Peace Corps didn't provide a briefing on smallpox, but they did send me some general information on the country, culture and climate. This wasn't much to go on to feed a curious mind about what to expect over the coming two years.

We were only allowed to bring one backpack, so I packed it to the brim, hanging things from various loops. Assembling in Philadelphia, the others all knew each other already because of the orientation several months earlier. As a last-minute addition, I knew less than anyone else about what to expect. But I had gotten exactly what I had wanted and was fully vested in the upcoming experience.

TRAINING

I arrived in Addis Ababa with Peace Corps Group XIX in July 1973, just as John Dean began testifying at the Watergate hearings. We had a sense of adventure and curiosity, and a willingness to immerse ourselves deeply into the local culture and the Amharic language.

Addis is at nearly eight thousand feet above sea level, and we had been warned that at such a high altitude we might initially experience headaches and have difficulty sleeping. It might have been true because I didn't sleep for about two days, although that might have been because I was so excited to be in Ethiopia. Our group stayed at the Itegue Taitu Hotel, named after Empress Taitu, and where Haile Selassie had been crowned Emperor in 1930. The hotel was the setting for Evelyn Waugh's 1938 satirical novel *Scoop*. It had been *the* hotel fifty years earlier, but by 1973 it was more than ragged around the edges . . . it was a dump.

A Peace Corps Volunteer (PCV) who lived in Addis had met our group upon arrival, and within five minutes I was eating spicy Ethiopian food for the first time with him, learning how to handle the floppy *injera* bread with my right hand, and being careful not to irritate my eyes with my red-stained fingers.

We stayed in Addis Ababa for a few days, and every time I walked up a flight of stairs I was winded because of the altitude. After two or three days, we were bussed to a tiny town named Awasa, which was five hours south of Addis, and was just in the early planning stages of development. At that time, it had just two short, unpaved perpendicular streets. It was unnerving to discover that this tiny, dusty and alien cow town was where we were going to spend our next six weeks in language training. (Awasa is now a large city with about 200,000 people and has become a great place to live in Ethiopia.)

We endured intense Amharic language instruction for six hours every day, six days per week for six weeks. After a couple of weeks, we were sent in all directions to our prospective volunteer sites. That turned into an extremely disturbing and life-changing visit for me.

I was bussed with two other trainees (Jim Brown and Doug Arbuckle) north to Addis and from Addis further north to Welo province. I had no frame of reference to understand what I was about to see along the road from northern Shoa province through southern Welo province. The bus driver had to maneuver slowly around emaciated children begging for food and in some cases lying on the road. The smell of dead livestock was pervasive. People on the bus were shocked and threw rolls and other food out the windows as we continued on our way north.

There was about a two-hour stretch of the road that was really bad before we finally arrived at our new home in the city of Dessie. Since nobody had warned me, "Brace yourself, you're about to go through an area that's really having a rough time," I just told myself, "My goodness, I always knew that things were bad in Africa, but I had no idea they were this bad." Soon afterwards, I learned that I was seeing the end stages of a major famine, but I was unaware of this as I stared wide-eyed out of a bus window.

The world hadn't yet learned about this famine. Emperor Haile Selassie had tried for political reasons to keep it quiet. About three months after my bus trip, a BBC correspondent named Jonathan Dimbleby smuggled out film alerting the world to the famine, which would take the lives of about 200,000 people.

The three of us were going to meet our new housemates (Dave Bourne and John DeVleming), who were members of the previous year's Peace Corps group working on smallpox. We were supposed to go into the field with them to learn first-hand what it meant to be a surveillance officer. Instead, these hardened PCV veterans saw our visit as an opportunity for us all to take a vacation. The last thing they wanted to do was to return to the grueling field work with a bunch of rookies. So we hopped into a Land Rover and drove for about five hours to Assab, where we dined on lobster and bathed in the Red Sea. (The port of Assab is now part of Eritrea, but it used to be part of Ethiopia.) We got to know them for a few days, learned about the job vicariously, drove back to Dessie, and retraced our bus route back to Addis and Awasa. In the space of one week, I had passed through famine to feast to famine.

After language training, we briefly visited a leprosarium just outside Addis, which I think was just simply used as the venue for the training and not because leprosy had much to do with smallpox. A young man, Dr. Tore Godal, briefed us. (Dr. Godal recently retired as head of the Global Alliance for Vaccines and Immunization (GAVI) Secretariat and is now a Special Advisor to the Norwegian Prime Minister.)

We were given some technical orientation on smallpox and what the work would entail. We learned from a PCV veteran, Peter Carrasco, how to do a cursory inspection of a Land Rover in case we were issued a vehicle. We were trained on a piece of equipment called a jet injector, which had been used in flatter terrain in West Africa to vaccinate as many as five hundred people in an hour. We were trained how to take the jet injector apart for cleaning each day, prepare it for the morning, and what to do when it broke down. When it malfunctioned, which was frequent, it took a half-hour to fix, and was usually because of a little five cent plastic rubber O-ring that had snapped. The jet injector turned out to be inappropriate for us to use in the roadless mountains where we were headed because one didn't want to be lugging this heavy piece of equipment on foot.

We were also taught how to vaccinate using a bifurcated needle. The needle was first dipped into a vial of reconstituted smallpox vaccine, and by surface tension, the needle would hold a thin film of the vaccine between its two prongs. We were then to lay the loaded needle flat against the upper arm of a recipient, so that the liquid transferred to the skin. Finally we were to give about ten quick shallow percutaneous jabs into the skin through the film of vaccine, just enough to draw a drop of blood so that the vaccine would be absorbed into the arm.

INTO THE FIELD

After training, we were sent to different corners of the country. It was early September 1973 when I started my smallpox field work. On my very first trip, Doug Arbuckle and I were accompanied by John DeVleming to a mountainous area in Wadla Delanta.

That trip was a rude awakening because I suddenly realized that I wasn't nearly in the great shape I had imagined. When we reached the end of the motor road and started our trek, we were at about 5,500 feet elevation, and it was a steady, all-day climb to about nine thousand feet, all the time carrying a backpack which, as a novice, I had over-filled. I was extremely winded.

At one point, I was so exhausted that I didn't have the energy to swat the flies attracted to my sweaty face. I recall taking note of that moment because in the West we're not accustomed to tolerating flies on the face; we only see that sort of thing in photographs or videos of poor people in remote places. I didn't have the energy to even lift up my arms to swat them away.

John found a mule skinner, who was basically someone with a mule willing to let us ride it in turns or carry our backpacks for part of the jour-

The author on the road in Wadla Delanta, Welo province, 1973. *Photo by John
DeVleming.*

ney. It was then that I started to learn how to communicate commands
to different kinds of domesticated animals in Amharic.

Being in the field for this first trip with a veteran PCV was a great
help to Doug and me because we learned how to interact with villagers
and ask technical questions in Amharic. We had a small, two-sided picture postcard of a child covered in smallpox lesions that we would show
people and ask if they had seen anyone recently with a similar disease.

Then, we would try to find affected villages, and if we found active
cases, we went into a different mode of trying to contain the cases. We
would determine where any infected people had been in the previous two
or three weeks and who may have visited their houses while they were
incubating or had the disease. We would do "ring vaccinations" around
the infected cases and in neighboring villages, all the while looking for
new cases. I quickly learned that it was good to have a trusted local person
with me to help with the surveillance and vaccination.

Since there were no restaurants or shops of any kind in the remote rural areas, I depended on eating in the homes of local people. I would also pay villagers to fill up my traditional lunch box, or *agilgel*, a leather-covered circular reed basket with a carrying strap. Every few days I would get layers of the distinctive bread called *injera* interspersed with layers of a spicy stew made from lentils, chick peas or split peas. I ate an Ethiopian vegetarian diet for all my meals while in the field, since it would have been risky to eat meat or chicken for multiple days in the absence of refrigeration.

We slept each night in local people's *tukuls*, their simple mud and wattle homes, moving from village to village for up to three weeks at a time, eating local food for each meal, climbing up and down mountains looking for smallpox, getting totally immersed in the culture and the language.

I must have been quite a sight. In one small village on a recently extended dirt road, hours from any sizeable town, I was surprised to see a bottle of soda for sale and purchased it. Having already shocked the shop-keepers by my very presence, let alone my ability to speak Amharic, they were thoroughly amazed and exclaimed, "And he knows Coca Cola!"

Once back in our shared house in the provincial capital of Dessie, I would take my rest and recuperate for 10 days before starting over again.

In the rural areas where I spent most of my time, my Volunteer wages went a long way. One *birr*, which at the time was equivalent to about 50 U.S. cents, would buy about 40 eggs — just to give an idea of how inexpensive it was to live.

One nuisance was that local people in these remote areas didn't accept some types of Ethiopian currency, for example paper notes and some coins. Given the high purchasing power of money in a largely cashless society, they would only accept the Ethiopian 10 cent coin, which at the time was worth U.S. five cents. So I had to carry several kilos of coins on my excursions with no chance of replenishment, but those coins went a long way. At one point, to avoid the long journey back to Dessie on foot, we rented a simple house made of local materials with spaces between the vertical wooden poles — no mud in between — that cost about 10 Ethiopian dollars for the entire month.

I got to know well the two WHO smallpox epidemiologists who supervised us. One of them was Ciro de Quadros, the very man who had reportedly frightened some prospective Volunteers in Denver in 1973, thus paving the way for my own recruitment. Already accomplished, Ciro would become one of the most highly respected public health officials in the field of immunization. The other, an Indonesian named Petrus Koswara, was my direct supervisor. He was a pleasant guy with a nice family who invited me to his home in Addis a couple of times. In 1974 at the age of 43, he died way too young of a heart attack "upon returning from Welo one afternoon after weeks of exhausting strenuous field work."[1]

Usually, at the start of a field trip, I didn't know precisely where I was heading. I knew the general area that needed to be visited, because no surveillance officer had been there for a long time or maybe there was speculation that smallpox virus was circulating. During the famine, tens of thousands of people had come down from the mountains to the main roads, and every ten or twenty kilometers there were settlements, where, by late 1973, foreign humanitarian organizations had set up relief camps to distribute food. It was in those camps that we could do good surveillance work because the people, especially the new arrivals, had come on foot from far away. By showing the picture of a smallpox-affected child, I could understand whether the virus was circulating over a wide area.

While there was a general area assigned to me, I had a lot of autonomy regarding exactly where I was going to go on any particular trip. Upon reaching the general area, I would talk to villagers, show the photo, and ask if there was any rash-like disease in the area. Based on the information I obtained, I walked to the villages that might be affected. As evening approached, I began to look for someone willing to let me sleep inside their house, often alongside domesticated farm animals, or outside with a small fire to keep warm in the cold mountains.

Depending on where PCVs worked in Ethiopia, the reception was very different. I understand that in the southern part of Ethiopia, people

1 F. Fenner, D. A. Henderson, I. Arita, Z. Ježek, I. D. Ladnyi, *Smallpox and Its Eradication* (Geneva: World Health Organization, 1988), 1022.

Camel caravan in the Danakil Desert near Assaita, Welo province, 2013. *Photo by Barry Steinglass.*

welcomed them with open arms. In the mountainous north of Ethiopia, it was a different story. The reason I had wanted to go to Ethiopia in the first place was that I was looking for a place that had retained its traditional culture and had not been exposed to western influences. People in the remote mountain heartland of Ethiopia had held on to their culture for millennia; part of the way they had preserved that homogeneous culture was by being suspicious of outsiders with different religions and ideas and defending themselves against periodic invasions.

I mostly worked in areas where the Ethiopian Coptic Christian religion was practiced, and where the local priests were greatly respected. The local leaders and population perceived outsiders as alien and potentially dangerous. I sometimes worked in areas that had never seen foreigners because there were no roads, no commerce, and no travel to the world beyond. These were areas up to one week's walk from the nearest dirt road, and even farther from the nearest telephone.

The reactions of local people upon seeing me varied. In one village on a high plateau, the headman acknowledged my arrival by ordering his serf to wash my feet in a biblical gesture of respect. Yet in a nearby village, a priest told the people to chase me away. In almost all villages, mothers would grab their children and flee to higher ground upon my approach. My reception was not helped by showing around a picture of a child with smallpox, and discussing such an unfamiliar idea as vaccination to prevent disease. It was all highly suspect.

Not only did I get to see smallpox cases and prevent outbreaks, I also saw the consequences of people trying to protect themselves by an ancient tradition called variolation. Variolation was the way people without access to smallpox vaccine would sometimes protect themselves. In Ethiopia, the way I understood it, variolators would remove scabs from a person with active smallpox, grind it up into powder, and insert the powder under the skin of the person being variolated. Variolation would protect the individual (if it didn't kill or blind them), but it was a dangerous practice for the community at large because the variolated individual was infectious and could spread smallpox. Sometimes variolation didn't work at all and the person would get a full-blown case of smallpox through that procedure, and sometimes they even died in the process of trying to protect themselves.

Within one family in Lasta, a few days' walk from Lalibela with its ancient monolithic rock-hewn churches, I found three children who had been variolated, all of whom had come down with smallpox. I had a cheap little throwaway camera in those days, but I respected the local culture too much to be a sort of medical tourist, gawking and taking photographs, so, consequently, I don't have any photographs of what must have been some of the last cases of smallpox in the world caused by variolation.

The work was exhausting. In fact, there was a point in late 1974 when the SEP officials decided that walking through the mountainous core of Ethiopia, the part of Ethiopia that was known throughout history as Abyssinia, took too long. You could start walking in early morning and by evening look back and see exactly where you had started because all you had done was walk down a deep escarpment and back up the other side. You could see the village from which you started that morning. Later in the program helicopters were introduced to speed up the work.

But before the helicopters, the smallpox program relied on foot soldiers like me. It was tedious and challenging because I could spend a lot of time just to reach a distant village that, because of nearby smallpox, I determined should be vaccinated. I could then spend all day going door-to-door, sometimes with the help of the local leader, but, frankly, in many cases the local leaders weren't all that receptive either. I would try to convince people, in their own language, about the importance of accepting smallpox vaccination. But the reality was that it was too foreign a concept to a traditional, closed and devout society that attributed disease to divine intervention. In such cases, there's very little that one man could do to alter what was perceived to be the will of God; behaviors, in any event, were based on faith and not on medical interventions. In some villages, local leaders suspected that I was trying to change their people's religion. Sometimes the people absolutely resisted my efforts; I could spend an entire day and vaccinate just fifteen or twenty people, so I felt ineffective.

I did the SEP work for about eight months, but then I increasingly connected my efforts with the famine relief effort. It was easier for me to associate myself with the food relief program because I could strategically position myself at the relief camps in between the local authorities with the grain and the mass of starving people coming, family by family, for their rations. By so doing, with the help of the local people I had hired, we could vaccinate a thousand people in a single day compared to just ten or fifteen, but the children were so emaciated and their skin so leathery that it was difficult to pinch enough skin to give the shallow, percutaneous vaccination.

At one of these famine relief camps, I met Dolores Crudge — my future wife — who was running a camp in the area where I was looking for smallpox. Dolores was the first Irish Concern volunteer in the country, and my contact-tracing had led me to her camp . . . and to her. We are still married, and just celebrated our 43rd wedding anniversary. Back then, we were the only two eligible, non-Ethiopian, non-clergy in a 30 kilometers radius. In retrospect, it seems to have been ordained!

While working more directly on famine relief, I was closer to the main roads, and as a consequence, there was an expectation for me to report to the SEP Addis office once or twice a week by radio. I had a long antenna that I would attach to the Land Rover to submit my report to the Japanese volunteers working on the program at SEP headquarters in Addis. I would report where I had been, what I was seeing in terms of cases, what villages had been visited, and how many smallpox vaccinations had been given, among other things.

Nowadays, even people in remote areas have cell phones and are in instant contact with the world. In contrast, the PCV experience in those days was more isolated. If I wanted to phone home, I would have to be in one of a handful of towns that had phone service, and it would literally take me all day to do it. I'd have to book the call in advance and wait all day for the call to go through. I only did that once in two years, so, like other PCVs, I communicated with my family by letter.

Over time, I became more involved in famine relief work than smallpox eradication, because that was the higher priority as compared to protecting people against a disease that might or might not be in the vicinity. These people were dying of starvation and needed to be fed; yet for various reasons the food distributions weren't taking place as planned. For a long time, they weren't taking place for the simple reason that there was no food to distribute. However, even with the arrival of more donated food, it would be warehoused and not distributed. Apparently it wasn't good economically for feudal landholders, who were also the local politicians, to suddenly flood the market with free grain. So I became much more involved in making sure that the relief distributions were happening, at first because I needed to do my smallpox work on those days. After a while, and in light of the need, my smallpox work started to fade into the background, and I became much more involved in immediate famine relief. I traveled south to Addis Ababa and asked Peace Corps to transfer me from the smallpox program into the emergency relief program, which was approved, and I was then assigned to a different province called Tigray, just to the north of Welo.

My work in Ethiopia coincided with a major historical transition. Working in the famine relief program in Tigray province, I was invited to dine with the local king of Tigray, *Ras* Seyoum Mengesha, who was married to Haile Selassie's granddaughter, and who many considered to be next in the line to succeed Haile Selassie on the throne. Soon after I had arrived in Ethiopia, the celebration of Haile Selassie's 82nd birthday had been a national holiday. Within a year, he was unceremoniously taken away from his palace in a Volkswagen Beetle and imprisoned. While I was in Ethiopia, this diminutive yet all-powerful emperor, known officially as the "Conquering Lion of the Tribe of Judah, His Imperial Majesty Haile Selassie I, King of Kings of Ethiopia, Elect of God," who had been in power for 45 years, was being overthrown in slow motion throughout late 1973 and into 1974, and a revolution had begun.

I had been assigned to work in Tigray by Shimelis Adugna, the head of the Relief and Rehabilitation Commission in Addis Ababa. My job entailed moving throughout the province to track relief shipments and distributions, and the use of donated trucks — and asking lots of questions . . . too many questions. Although I found a very well-run operation, the job was more political than customary for a PCV.

I ended up being fired by the Tigray authorities during the same momentous week in August 1974 in which Richard Nixon resigned, and the king of Tigray fled to Sudan by helicopter into self-imposed exile.

Back in Addis, looking for my next adventure in the Peace Corps, I tried to figure out the domino effect.

REFLECTIONS

The smallpox work in Ethiopia was difficult and tedious. Imagine every day for three weeks strapping on a backpack and walking in the mountains searching for something that was becoming increasingly rare. Doing that day after day was mind-deadening, but culturally rich. You have to hand it to public health people who were so committed to this work. I owe a lot to the SEP in Ethiopia, as it opened my eyes to see what smart and committed people with vision, energy, and passion could achieve.

What I also experienced as a young man in Ethiopia is a good example of how, as outsiders, we sometimes bring our own pre-formed ideas to the problems facing local people. The public health community has been known on occasion to impose its own rigid prescriptions and be tone deaf to the local culture. They believe that they know what needs to be done and are dead set on getting it done. But it may not meet the needs of the people. At that particular time and place in northern Ethiopia, I was privileged to be able to make a real difference for people since donated food was finally just starting to arrive. I saw that the need for me, first and foremost, was to feed the people to prevent death rather than to focus only on smallpox eradication.

Ethiopia and the Peace Corps certainly fulfilled my desire for adventure but also my aspiration to do something good and contribute to society. My smallpox eradication and famine relief work convinced me to pursue a career in public health. I had had only a vague idea of public health before I went to Ethiopia. Upon returning home, I studied for a Master's degree in public health at The Johns Hopkins University School of Hygiene and Public Health.

Before joining the Peace Corps, I had written to a number of public health schools to inquire whether I had the right sort of undergraduate profile and experience to gain admission. Each school had discouraged me because I had not majored in science or pre-med. After I returned from the Peace Corps with two years of international public health experience, I applied to the very same schools of public health and was accepted by all of them. I decided to attend Hopkins, where I believe I became the first non-doctor and non-nurse ever admitted to the Department of International Health. Many of the PCVs who worked in the SEP in Ethiopia similarly became interested in public health careers and eventually joined the WHO Expanded Program on Immunization, which was just starting up in the late-1970s.

After completing my Master's degree, I worked again on smallpox eradication in the Yemen Arab Republic for WHO, as part of the final global certification of the eradication of smallpox. My assignment was to design, manage, implement, monitor, and document a program to prove that smallpox no longer existed -- methodologically a challenge because it is extremely difficult to prove the complete absence of something, or at least to provide convincing evidence of the complete absence of smallpox.

The SEP in Ethiopia was an amazing success. I totally lucked out to have been a part of it. I was 23 years old, and I just fell into the greatest public health success of all time in a country that I longed to visit. My smallpox eradication and famine relief experience set me on my career path and I still am grateful that I had that opportunity through the Peace Corps. I had not wanted to become a PCV, but it helped define my life's work and it gave me great confidence in my ability to meet and overcome all sorts of cultural, programmatic and interpersonal challenges. In some ways, it made me who I became and who I am. I was fairly young at the time and, as the years go by, the memory of smallpox has faded in people's minds. When I lecture at Hopkins or Harvard and mention that I was in the SEP in Ethiopia, professors and students alike have a hard time believing it because it seems like ancient history.

Since earning my Master's degree from Johns Hopkins in the mid-1970s, I have been involved in building the capacity of Ministries of Health to design, manage, implement, and monitor nationwide immunization programs throughout the world, first for WHO and then for John Snow, Inc. My job has taken me to some 50 countries over the past 40 years, and at global level I advise WHO, UNICEF, GAVI the Vaccine Alliance and others. I find great satisfaction in technically supporting the development of routine programs capable of immunizing all children, not against one disease at a time but regularly against all the diseases for which there are vaccines.

The SEP first shaped my understanding of the difference between time-limited disease eradication initiatives, which often depend on lots of external funding and staff, versus the long-term task to develop a country's capacity to routinely, equitably and timely immunize all its children — regardless of how remote or marginalized they might be, day in and day out and year after year — irrespective of the epidemiology of any single disease at any given point in time or in any given location.

One anecdote reminds me of the difference between what I learned from the smallpox eradication work in Ethiopia and what I now do to strengthen immunization programs as an integral part of the broader health system. When I showed a man in remote Ethiopia the post card of a child with smallpox and asked if he had seen any similar cases, he answered, "Yes, there was such and such a person in such and such a village . . . ." a full day's walk away. I dutifully walked there to locate that man. It turned out that he had a broken leg and I discovered that this man was the cousin of my informer in the distant village. Clearly, the informer knew that his cousin did not have smallpox, but he likely thought I was a doctor who could provide medical care.

We PCVs in the SEP had a specific, narrow and externally identified task; we knew what we had to do, but we weren't permitted to even do the simplest additional thing, not even to give out an aspirin. We were arriving in communities that had never had health workers, let alone a foreign health worker, visit their villages. It all seemed very one way to me — it seemed like we were taking their time, learning from them the information we needed to get our job done, but we weren't giving anything back to meet their local needs in the community. That is still a lesson I think about from time to time because I think it's tempting — and certainly often rewarded with career advancement — to become fixated on a single disease of global public health importance, while still not meeting the needs of individuals and the community. That's something I've kept in mind all these years.

REMINISCENCES

When memories were still most intense, shortly after returning to the States in 1975, I eagerly shared my experiences, such as the momentous events in Ethiopia's long history that I had passed through, what working in smallpox eradication and famine relief had been like, how alien was Ethiopia's remote culture, and how unprepared I had been to face it. It was all so fascinating, or so it seemed to me. But watching friends' and family's eyes glaze over was a rude awakening. Plus, in the re-telling, despite impromptu embellishments, these unique experiences risked getting old and losing their meaning to the person who mattered most. That would be me.

Naturally, I learned quickly to keep the memories to myself, with one or two occasionally reclaimed from the vault to entertain my peers on global vaccination programs these past four decades. The multi-cultural world of global development and disease control is in some ways an insular world, where outrageous but true experiences are traded as currency. But how accurate are some of these experiences really? By what measure can we know whether the sheer weight of the embellishments — not what you wished you had said but the more pedestrian actuality of what you really did say — has transformed these memories into fairy tales, some personal mythology? I would catch myself mid-rant about the slow-motion overthrow of Haile Selassie or the spotted hyenas — you know, the ones that are also scavengers — coming into famine relief camps to exhume newly-dug, shallow graves of infants.

Years later, I would realize that the combination of an intensely lived experience and the excited acceleration in my already speedy New York delivery, must have made me sound like Rick Moranis as the possessed Keymaster in the movie "Ghostbusters" explaining that the Traveler came as a large and moving Torb before the Third Reconciliation. I suspect any returned PCV can relate to this.

In his travel memoir "Arabian Sands," published in 1959, the Oxford-educated explorer Wilfred Thesiger describes his upbringing in Addis Ababa in the early 1900s, and his attempt in the early 1930s to determine what happens to the long Awash River on its way from the Ethiopian highlands into the world's hottest inhabitable desert, the Danakil. How does one lose track of a 750-mile-long river? Why didn't it seem to have an outlet to the sea? Why didn't anyone from the West know the answer? Of course, this was pre-Google Map, before we no longer needed to wonder. He explains that "the Danakil journey had unsuited me for life in our civilization . . .." Searching for smallpox, I had the opportunity to drive into and fly over the Danakil.

On one of my journeys, I hitched a ride on a Luftwaffe helicopter doing famine surveillance where the foothills of the settled Oromiya

The author (wearing a straw hat) is just to the right of fellow PCV Doug Arbuckle in the Danakil Desert near Mille, Welo province, 1973. *Photo provided by the author.*

people meet the desert of the nomads. We flew over villages with no sign of people or plowed fields. We even flew below ground level, twisting and turning along the towering riverine cliffs along the Awash and Mille Rivers.

We landed among Afar nomads who were breaking camp with urgency, attaching to their camels their collapsed "igloos" made of supple reeds and mats, in anticipation of an imminent attack by Issa nomad enemies. We landed alongside the animal pens of a nearby Afar settlement, the helicopter agitating sand and tumbleweed. Nobody emerged from the igloos. Finally, a tiny and frail old woman emerged, or was pushed out, to confront the beefy Germans, each one well over six feet tall, with all manner of tools dangling from their orange flight suits. She informed them this was where her goats and camels grazed so, if the large bird was hungry, it should find grazing elsewhere.

To cope with the intensity, to process these experiences, I kept a journal, actually several journals. My parents kept all my letters home . . . and these were no ordinary letters. They were single-sheet aerogrammes on feather-light paper with pre-defined dash marks to guide their precise folding into self-envelopes. I filled every space with orderly paragraphs that required, asterisk by asterisk, dendritic scribblings along the entire narrow length of the aerogramme. Art historians and psychologists have noted that filling the entire canvas with minute details — as in the art of Bruegel, Bosch and Ensor — is a hallmark of some of the most tormented minds.

Once I retire, I hope to sort through the memorabilia and detritus of those tumultuous years in Ethiopia, although I doubt I will ever be able to do it justice.

•

12

SEP Work and Life in Northern Ethiopia

by Dave Bourne

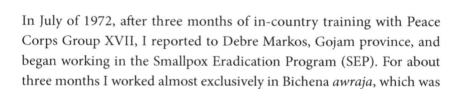

In July of 1972, after three months of in-country training with Peace Corps Group XVII, I reported to Debre Markos, Gojam province, and began working in the Smallpox Eradication Program (SEP). For about three months I worked almost exclusively in Bichena *awraja*, which was bounded on the east by the Blue Nile River.

Then responsibility for the SEP in Gojam province was given to the newly arrived Japanese Overseas Cooperation Volunteers, and I was to be transferred. I was given a choice between working in either Gemu Gofa or Welo provinces.

I chose Welo, and worked there through the end of my 27-month tour in July of 1974. While in Welo, I worked primarily in Borena *awraja*, which was bounded by the Blue Nile on the west. Thus, I spent most of my smallpox career on either side of the Blue Nile. In addition to Borena, I worked in the Danakil Desert in eastern Welo, primarily during the rainy seasons, when travel to and within Borena *awraja* was not possible.

After Welo, I extended my term of service for about two months to help train a new group of Peace Corps Volunteers (PCVs), which included nine new smallpox eradication Volunteers. I left Ethiopia to return home to the U.S. in late September, 1974.

I hope the following series of stories provides insight into the people I worked with and encountered during my PCV service, as well as the places where I conducted smallpox surveillance and containment operations.

MY BRIEF TIME IN GOJAM

On my first assignment in Gojam, I drove from Debre Markos to the town of Bichena, the *awraja* capital. From there, since there were no roads, I walked about eight hours to the top of the west side of the Blue Nile Gorge where there was reported to be an outbreak of smallpox. I found no active cases, so I vaccinated about 500 or so people in or near the gorge. I understand that this proved to provide protection years later when smallpox was present near this area late in the SEP campaign.

During my few months in Bichena I worked alone, with a translator, generally in areas near the gorge, walking to the areas, and sleeping and eating with the people for about two weeks at a time. I also worked in other areas closer to Debre Markos under the same conditions.

GOJAM EXPERIENCES

In general, the people in both Gojam and Welo were hospitable, but not always friendly, and not generally receptive to smallpox vaccination, although the elders usually allowed me to vaccinate their children, claiming that they themselves had already had smallpox. On occasion, villagers were overtly hostile to being vaccinated.

At one point, in an area north of Debre Markos, I encountered a smallpox outbreak. The residents of the infected village refused to be vaccinated or to let their children be vaccinated. Therefore, I vaccinated the people in all of the surrounding villages, thus containing the outbreak to a small area.

During one of my trips to Bichena, upon arriving in town in the early evening, I was met by the Bichena health officer, who was in charge of the Health Center, and who told me that there was a person with tetanus who needed to be transported to the hospital in Debre Markos.

Bichena, Gojam province — capital of Bichena *awraja*, 1972. *Photo by the author.*

The family had been told by a private party that they could transport the patient for $100 Ethiopian, but the family could not afford it. I immediately agreed to transport the patient to Debre Markos. The people who wanted to transport the patient for a fee tried to block my Land Rover with their Land Rover, but I was able to swerve around them and they did not pursue us. I returned to Bichena the next day and resumed my smallpox duties. Later I learned from the health officer that the patient survived and was fine.

I don't remember encountering any smallpox in Bichena, but I do recall finding about 25 cases north of Debre Markos.

I probably vaccinated about 1,500 people in Gojam during my brief time there.

MY TIME IN WELO

In Welo, I worked almost exclusively in Borena *awraja*, on the east side of the Blue Nile Gorge. There was a lot of smallpox in this *awraja*, especially in Saynt, the northernmost of three *woredas*.

View of the hills and valleys of Saynt *woreda* where a lot of smallpox cases were found, 1973. *Photo by the author.*

My general routine while in Welo was to take an Ethiopian airlines flight on a DC-3 from Dessie (where all the smallpox PCVs lived) to Makane Salam, the *awraja* capital, in one day; then, at dawn the next morning I would walk for 12 hours to Ajibar, the capital of the Saynt *woreda*.

I would typically work for about four weeks in Saynt, make the one-day trip by foot back to Makane Salam, and then take the DC-3 back to Dessie where I would spend the next two weeks or so working in the smallpox office and relaxing. Then, I would start the whole routine over again.

I had found about 25 cases of smallpox in Gojam, and found about that many a month in Borena, the vast majority of which were in Saynt. All told, I believe I found about 250 cases or so, and vaccinated around 5,000 people during my time in Borena.

I became very familiar with all parts of Saynt, from the mountains and deep gorges to the searing heat of the lowlands. To a large extent, Saynt consisted of gorge after gorge. I would often descend to the bottom of a gorge, go up the other side, and shortly afterward have to go down another gorge. At one point, a small group of us took a helicopter from Ajibar to the northernmost village in Saynt. Upon our return, the helicopter pilot told us that due to weather conditions, we would have to leave one passenger behind. One of our Ethiopian colleagues drew the short straw and had to walk back to Ajibar. It took us less than 15 minutes by air, but, because of the gorges, it took him nearly a day.

I also worked in the other two *woredas* in Borena. Makane Salam was the capital of the central *woreda*, and I believe the *woreda* itself was also called Makane Salam. The other *woreda* was in the southernmost part of the province and was called Kalala. There was not much smallpox in the Makane Salam *woreda* and virtually none in Kalala. As a result, I spent the vast majority of my time in Saynt.

I recall one grueling road trip when fellow PCV, John DeVleming, and I drove from Dessie to Makane Salam. The distance was only about 128 kilometers (80 miles), but it took two or three days for us to drive there on a shell of a road built by the Italians some 30 years before.

For the first year, I generally worked with a guide and a translator, then just with a guide for the second year. At times, I went with or met up with John and, towards the end of my tour, I took a newly arrived PCV named James Brown to Saynt for a 30-day orientation trip. I kept James out about a week longer than my routine trips to Saynt on the theory that his first trip would be his hardest and it could only get easier for him as his tour continued.

It was hard all right. The flight from Dessie to Makane Salam was quite a bit rougher than usual, and James wasn't feeling too well when we landed. Unfortunately, the town was about a mile from the airport, mostly uphill. After carrying our packs from the airport to the health officer's house, where I usually stayed, we were about ready to call it a day. Which we could and did.

The next morning at dawn, we left with our mules and a guide for the 12-hour trek to Saynt. James really enjoyed the first few hours of the trip, with both of us channeling the Marlboro Man. By hour 10 or 11, however, the thrill was gone and he asked me, "How long does this horror story last?" We eventually made it to Ajibar.

After well over 30 arduous days in Saynt, we returned to Makane Salam. Due to mechanical problems with the airplane, we had to tack on another two or three mind-numbing days waiting in Makane Salam for a working plane.

James was a great guy and a great PCV, but, in retrospect, I don't think extending an already brutal routine was such a great idea.

THE PEOPLE OF WELO

My experiences in Welo were very much like those in Gojam. As in Gojam, the areas where I worked, for the most part, had no roads or electricity. The people were from the same Amhara tribe. And, as in Gojam the people in Welo were almost always hospitable, but not always friendly, and they generally allowed at least their children to be vaccinated. The people almost always wanted medicine for other problems, as most of the adults and decision makers had had smallpox in the past.

Unlike stories of crushing crowds and adulation for the SEP workers I had heard about in parts of southern Ethiopia, I had no such receptions in either Gojam or Welo. No one ever killed a goat for me as I had heard had happened with PCVs in the South. However, the people of Gojam and Welo would, on occasion, kill a chicken and make *doro wot* for me or they would give me hardboiled eggs.

As noted earlier, the people were very hospitable and, regardless how poor they were, they shared what food they had with me. I was very grateful for and humbled by their generosity.

A HEALTH SCARE

Although I was generally healthy in the early months of my Peace Corps service, for much of my time in Ethiopia I had various intestinal parasites and assorted other illnesses. I remember at one point being too sick to go with John on a short trip to the edge of the Danakil Desert, so I stayed behind in the house that we shared. When he came back to the house, I asked him if he had forgotten something, thinking he had been gone about 10 minutes. He told me had been gone for three days.

John told me that I weighed less than 100 pounds at that time, and that he took me to Addis Ababa, which was about 399 kilometers (250 miles) away, the next day in our Land Rover to see Dr. John Ey, the Peace Corps doctor.

I don't remember the trip, but I do remember that Dr. Ey discovered that I had both roundworm and giardia. With treatment I recovered fairly quickly, and resumed my smallpox duties. Fortunately, that was the worst it got.

GUAMEDA DEATH MARCH
& A MULE TRAIN FULL OF BEER

On one of my trips to Saynt with John, we went through Guameda, in the Saynt lowlands. It was very hot and the travel was arduous. After several hours of slogging through what we later termed the Guameda Death March, we reached Ajibar, a nice little town and the capital of the Saynt *woreda*.

It seemed that within minutes of settling into the house in which we stayed, we heard a string of mules with its cargo making clanking noises, which sounded like they were heading in our direction. This was such an unusual event that we dragged ourselves out of the house to investigate.

It turned out to be a mule train full of beer — actual bottled beer — brought by merchants from Dessie . . . a three-day trip on foot. We asked them how much they wanted for the beer. Unfortunately, the whole mule train was comprised of only about three mules, but we bought all of the beer.

So, one minute we were recovering from the Guameda Death March, and the next we were drinking from our newly acquired beer brought to us by mule train. A miracle if there ever was one! The merchants had to be thrilled, selling their entire cargo within three minutes of pulling into town. In retrospect, it's sad to think that we bought the whole town's beer, but I would guess it would have taken several months to sell that beer in Ajibar. In fact, I don't recall ever seeing any beer in Ajibar, and we would have surely found it if there had been any, so I don't think the people in that town ever missed it. At any rate, we drank our fill that first night and finished the entire mule train worth in the few days thereafter.

THE MAKANE SALAM MASSACRE

In the aftermath of the overthrow of Haile Selassie in 1974, there was a general sense of anarchy in Borena, and, I understand, elsewhere. One manifestation of this was in Makane Salam, where a judge was being transferred to Begemdir province. To safeguard his possessions, which were to be transported by land to Begemdir, the judge hired a group of 10 *shiftas* (essentially highway robbers or thieves) to protect his possessions,

Some students and others in Makane Salam did not like the *shiftas* and they believed the judge had no right to his possessions in any case since he had allegedly stolen them from the people. The students, some of whom were armed, surrounded the judge's house and eventually opened fire on the house, killing the judge, his wife, and four of the *shiftas*. The remaining six *shiftas* were seriously wounded.

On the day this happened, I was working in an area west of Makane Salam, and returned to the town in late afternoon, very shortly after the gunfire ended. As was my custom, I was staying at the house of the Makane Salam health officer, who at that moment was attending to the wounded *shiftas* in his clinic, and because he was attending to the *shiftas*, there were rumors that the students were going to burn his house down. We spent a somewhat restless night in the house; but, fortunately, there was no attack.

I was planning to go to Saynt the next day, but, due to the fact that most of the victims were from Saynt, there was widespread fear in Makane Salam that people from Saynt would attack Makane Salam in retaliation. As a result, I could not rent mules or get anyone to accompany me to Saynt.

Later that day, a special Ethiopian Airlines flight arrived in Makane Salam carrying many members of the judge's family who were heavily armed and were bent on revenge. Since there was no reason to stay, I got a ticket for the return flight to Addis Ababa on that plane. That was the last time I visited Makane Salam or Borena. Luckily I was very near the end of my tenure anyway.

DANAKIL DESERT

During the rainy season, essentially the summer months of July and August, the Welo smallpox crew generally worked in the Danakil Desert because the roads in the highlands, as well as the route to Borena, were rendered impassable by the rains.

It was quite a change from the highlands as we drove everywhere, either on the vehicle tracks through the desert or just straight across the desert. By that time, we were driving Toyota Land Cruisers, which had replaced the original SEP Land Rovers.

The population in the desert was comprised of nomads, Afars, I believe, and residents of the few towns in the desert. We spent a lot of time working at Tendaho, a British cotton farm near the town of Dufti, we stayed often at the air-conditioned home of the German doctor who worked there. We enjoyed staying there.

The workers at the farm had been vaccinated by the company and we vaccinated the nomads and others we encountered during our trips to the desert. We found few smallpox cases as I recall, and the desert trips generally provided a welcome respite to the months and months I spent walking through the highlands.

THE SULTAN

In order to vaccinate the nomads, or even find them, we had to deal with the Sultan, Alimirah Hanfare, who lived in a big ranch-style house near Asaita, one of the towns in the Danakil.

I always enjoyed meeting with the Sultan and his people. For one thing, they had the coldest soda in the country, if not the world. I spoke Amharic to an interpreter who relayed my message in Arabic to the Sultan. As much as I enjoyed going to the Sultan's house, my visits there were very brief because I never had to wait, and the Sultan was very helpful and would immediately send his son, Hanfare Alimirah, with us to wherever the nomads were located. Hanfare would tell the nomad leaders to let us vaccinate their people. Thanks to the Sultan, we vaccinated a few thousand people in the towns of Dufti and Asaita, the British cotton farm, and among the nomads. We vaccinated so many people, and had so few needles, we had to boil and re-use the needles several times. As they were designed for one time use, they became more and more blunt. Unfortunately, this made it tough on those we vaccinated.

THE DANAKIL CHOLERA OUTBREAK

During one summer in the Danakil, John and I encountered an outbreak of cholera. There were a few hundred cases, but, fortunately, relatively few deaths, about 10 as I recall.

The treatment for those with cholera is essentially hydration, which, if supplied early and often enough, is essentially 100 percent effective.

On one occasion, John and I were out among the nomads with some IV bags for intravenous infusion, and we encountered two cholera victims. We each started an IV drip on one of them and tied the IV to the top of the three-foot shelter they lived in. These shelters were essentially mats the nomads' camels carried for them. Neither John nor I had ever started an IV drip before, and we were both glad that we were successful on our first tries!

On another occasion, I was helping 20 or so cholera victims in a government clinic near Asaita. They were in need of rehydration, but the only water we had to give them to drink was muddy water from the Awash River, which was believed to be carrying the cholera. We had to put chlorine detergent in the muddy water to rehydrate the victims, even though it looked and smelled like dirty mop water. It was hard to do, but that was all we had.

After a day or two, we received clean water from the transportation department in Asaita that had come from a government well, and we were able to use that.

All of the victims at the clinic survived.

Overall, over 95 percent or so of the cholera victims survived. The outbreak ran its course and was over after a few weeks.

A LONG-DISTANCE RESCUE

After being relieved by a group of Japanese volunteers in Gojam, I rarely encountered them or their colleagues, but when I did I saw that the volunteer smallpox surveillance officers were very dedicated, congenial and good at their jobs.

Also in the Japanese group was a team of vehicle repair technicians who were always pleasant, and very efficient. One routine they followed was to travel to the provincial capitals and perform maintenance on the Toyota Land Cruisers and the incredible vehicle radios the Japanese supplied for the project.

One day I was sitting in our vehicle outside the SEP office in Dessie and I heard the voice of Jay Rowland, one of the Smallpox PCVs in my Group XVII coming from the radio. He was calling for Dr. Weithaler, saying "our situation is urgent!" He was in southern Sidamo, hundreds of miles away, but I could hear him in Dessie! He had four flat tires!

We immediately contacted SEP Addis headquarters and soon had a multi-party communication among Dessie, Addis, and Austrian volunteers, who were south of Addis, somewhere close to Jay.

The Austrians rescued him.

I couldn't believe the range of those radios.

ALI, THE TRANSLATOR

On one of my trips to Borena, I brought a translator with me named Ali. Previously Ali had translated for me in Gojam, and, when I happened upon him on the streets of Dessie, I offered him a job.

I paid him in advance for the month, and we flew to Makane Salam, leaving at dawn the next day for the trek to Saynt, as was my custom. It turned out that during the walk to Saynt, Ali walked so far ahead of me that he was able to circle back to Makane Salam. I had given him his round-trip ticket up front as well, so he apparently took the next plane back to Dessie. He may have been intimidated by the difficult walk to Saynt. I never saw him again, but I learned a valuable lesson.

When I got to Saynt that day at dusk there was, of course, no Ali, so I had to work without a translator. Although I regret being tricked out of some SEP money, it was one of the best things that ever happened to me. I discovered during the next month (and year) that I really didn't need a translator because I had to speak Amharic full time. As a result, I

Mecuria, an excellent guide for the SEP, on the outskirts of Ajibar, the capital of Saynt *woreda*, 1973. *Photo by the author.*

was forced to rely more on myself and to learn to speak and understand Amharic much better, which greatly enriched my Peace Corps and SEP experience.

MECURIA, THE GUIDE

Mecuria was a guide who lived in Ajibar, and John and I used him extensively as a guide. He didn't speak English, but he knew Saynt and Borena and was a great guy. John and I loved him, and employed him every time we went to Saynt. The rent for his *tukul* (residence) was a dollar a month. We paid him well over that on a daily basis, and he was worth every penny.

At one point in 1973, there was a comet named Kohoutek, which was supposed to be incredibly bright — they called it "the comet of the century." I told Mecuria to tell his friends that there was going to be a giant star in the heavens. I wanted him to be both rich and a prophet. Unfortunately, Kohoutek was an incredible disappointment worldwide and was essentially invisible. Shortly after the comet was supposed to appear, he asked me why he hadn't seen it and whether it was still coming. Sadly, I told him that it was expected to appear but didn't. He accepted this and we moved on, our relationship unchanged. What a great guy. I hope he hadn't told too many people about the comet.

ADDRESSING THE FAMINE

During the latter part of my time in Welo, famine conditions became so severe that a major international relief response was initiated. For Welo, the German Luftwaffe (Air Force) provided helicopters and crews and the Australian Red Cross, among other groups, sent relief workers. The four-person Australian Red Cross team was comprised of a doctor, an Emergency Medical Technician, a microbiologist and a driver. As my luck would have it, they were assigned to Borena to assess the medical impacts of the famine. By then, I knew Amharic and Borena well, so it was a perfect fit. I hooked up with them for their 90-day tour.

The Australians and I agreed that they would help me with my smallpox surveillance and vaccination efforts and I would help them by translating and working on their medical assessments. At each location, we set up clinics at various locations under trees and other places. The doctor examined people for various ailments while the technician and I asked patients about their health problems. Common complaints were coughs, intestinal worms and other chronic conditions. We tried as best as we could to alleviate the patients' conditions, but we discovered that most of the conditions were chronic and the people needed longer term treatment and assessment.

The great thing was that the Luftwaffe transported us via helicopter throughout Borena. Also, they were supposed to come twice a week, but usually came once a week or less. They brought food and, because these were Australians — and one very willing American — on each trip they brought a crate of beer (two cases). Nice! When they didn't come which was often, we paid the villagers to cook doro wot for us. This was also really good food, and we never tired of it. As a result of having the luxury of access to the helicopters, we were able to cover a lot of Borena during the 90 days. We found no smallpox cases, as I recall, but vaccinated a lot of people.

At one point, an American got off one of the two supply helicopters. He sought me out because he had mail for me from my colleagues in Dessie. I discovered that the man was John Palmer, a well-known announcer from NBC news. I had to leave shortly thereafter with the Australians on one of the helicopters for our next assignment, and wasn't able to spend much time with him, but I remember him as being a good guy.

About midway through our 90-day mission, I became quite sick with a high fever and chills. The doctor treated me with antibiotics, but insisted I go back to Dessie on the next helicopter, which, fortunately, arrived soon. As it turned out, I had strep throat and was able to return to the team a few days later.

IN RETROSPECT

I believe our Peace Corps experiences in the SEP were among the most satisfying of Peace Corps assignments. Actually living with the people for extended periods, though difficult, taught me a great deal about Ethiopia and even more about myself. Surviving the grind of week after week in the countryside, walking continuously over rough terrain, and not hearing or speaking English, prepared me for many of the challenges I have faced since then.

I will never forget the generosity of the people — sharing what they had with me even though they had so little. Nor will I forget the good times I had with my SEP colleagues and the many other good people I met along the way. Finally, I will never forget the feeling of walking out of a village once the containment efforts were completed, knowing in all likelihood that village would never have another case of smallpox.

•

13

Coming of Age in Gecha

by Russ Handzus

We left the town of Gore on our journey to Gecha in Illubabor province. There was no recognizable road. It took all day to navigate down the muddy, rocky path to Gecha.

We had two Land Rovers that were occupied by Dr. Ciro de Quadros (World Health Organization [WHO] smallpox epidemiologist), Jim Siemon (Peace Corps, fellow surveillance officer), Daweet (a dresser from Gore), and me. Ethiopian dressers worked in health centers diagnosing and treating patients under the supervision of a health officer. In some remote health stations, dressers worked solo and sometimes assisted the Smallpox Eradication Program (SEP) teams.

When we arrived in Gecha the local people told us that there were many cases of smallpox in all directions.

We stayed that night in the *tukul* of the local Ethiopian school teacher and his wife. This *tukul* had a frame of wood poles with walls made of woven sticks covered with hard-packed mud. The roof was made of straw arranged to secured shed rain. The floor was made of hard-packed mud, which was easy to sweep and keep clean.

That evening in the *tukul,* by the light of a kerosene lantern, we had a delicious dinner of *injera* and *doro wot* prepared by the teacher's wife. *Doro wot* is a spicy hot chicken stew. *Injera* is a thin spongy bread about the size & shape of a tortilla, or larger. Diners tear off a piece of *injera* and use it to scoop up a bite-sized amount of *wot.*

The teacher proudly said they had named their son *"werekut"* — which means paper — in hope that he would become a scholar. Their daughter was named *"tourist"* in hope that she would become a world traveler.

After dinner, the four of us became engaged in a discussion of smallpox surveillance and containment strategy. I had assumed that after a comprehensive assessment of the smallpox situation, Ciro would return to Gore in one of the Land Rovers, and that Jim, Daweet and I would stay in the Gecha area, do our smallpox work and then return to Gore in the other Land Rover. Therefore, it was quite a surprise to me when Ciro announced that he and Jim would return to Gore the next morning, and that Daweet and I would stay in Gecha for a week to find and document smallpox cases and vaccinate people. Daweet declared that I should be the leader.

At 22 years of age, this was the first time in my life that I was to be the leader of an important project. In my life back in the United States, it seemed like I always had a parent, teacher, friend or somebody else to take the lead with projects I was involved with. It was still early in my Peace Corps experience, so I felt overwhelmed and unprepared to take on this responsibility without the co-leadership of Jim. I tried to talk Ciro out of this plan, but he was not willing to modify it. So, I resigned myself to do what I could, although I didn't think it would work out well. The teacher volunteered to let me stay in his house during this time. Similar accommodations for Daweet were arranged with another family.

When the Land Rover carrying Ciro and Jim pulled away, I stood there dejected, watching it wind its way up the road until it almost disappeared. The teacher came up behind me, put his hand on my shoulder and said, "Stop watching."

There, standing in the road, he asked me, "Do you have enough vaccine and needles?"

I said "Yes."

"Do you have enough money to rent mules and buy whatever else you might need?"

Again, I said "Yes."

He continued, saying, "My wife will cook breakfast and dinner for you daily. Is this satisfactory?" I thought it was a very generous offer and said so.

Finally, he asked, "Do you want me to gather the local leaders this afternoon to meet with you?" I hesitated and reluctantly told him that was a good idea.

Then it hit me! I realized that I had almost all the ingredients I needed to take on this challenging week-long mission! The only thing missing was an attitude of self-reliance, although I couldn't articulate it at the time. I said to myself, "Well maybe I can give this a try, put my fears temporarily on hold, and just do what I can. I have come this far, I can't go back."

As promised, the local leaders gathered that afternoon. The teacher helped with the translations, which made things much easier. Each leader reported on the smallpox situation in his area and offered guides and mules to take us there. The Land Rover would be useless because of the thick forest and muddy paths and the fact that there were no roads in this area.

We worked out an itinerary based on which day of the week each affected area had a market day, which was the day when people brought their produce and other goods from the countryside to sell in the local open air market. Thus, we would be able to vaccinate the most people and learn the most information about smallpox cases in the shortest amount of time. Once I had this plan in place, I felt myself becoming more settled, less fretful, and started concentrating on just doing the job.

The next week had many challenges, but went surprisingly smoothly, except for one episode.

One morning toward the end of the week, Daweet and I and a guide took off riding mules for several hours toward the most distant village. After we completed our vaccination and case reporting mission early that afternoon, the chief asked me if we needed guides for our trip back to Gecha. The trail had been easy to follow in the morning with a guide, and since things were going so well and my confidence was at a ridiculous all-time high, I declined the guides.

Once under way, we encountered many people on the trail who asked to be vaccinated. We accommodated them all, but I started noticing that the sun was rapidly going down. As we rode through the forest, Daweet reminded me not to get off my mule because once off, this mule would not allow the rider back on. Also, he said that if my mule got loose, it would run all the way back to Gore!

The sun began to set as we were about half way to Gecha. We decided to press on. We knew we had to travel in an eastern direction to get to Gecha. As it got dark, I could see the stars when there were breaks in the forest canopy. I knew that if we kept the Big Dipper to our left, we would be going generally east toward Gecha.

Then I realized I hadn't seen Daweet for quite a while. The trail was hard to find in the dark and I came to several muddy dead-ends and had to negotiate my way back to the main trail. The saddle on my mule was painful to sit on. (I learned later that it had been made out of planks of wood covered with leather.) After about an hour of this, I couldn't take it anymore, so I tied a rope around the saddle horn, got off the mule, and let it pull me through the mud. After a while, I found that being pulled, slipping and stumbling over rocks and through deep pools of mud was equally unbearable. I was covered from head to toe with mud.

I didn't see Daweet for the rest of the night.

I tried several times to get back on the mule, but as Daweet had predicted, it would not cooperate. Finally, I made a flying leap to mount the mule but it kicked me in the chest with its rear hooves. It knocked the wind out of me, but I was otherwise okay. I finally resigned myself to continue being towed through the mud in the dark like a water skier.

Then I heard the weird laughing sounds of hyenas all around us, but not immediately next to us. The mule slowed down and walked closer to me. After about an hour of this, thankfully, I didn't hear hyenas anymore.

We continued our slog until around midnight when I found a fence and followed it to a gate. I called out, and two big dogs came running at us barking and snapping. I hopped up on top of the fence and yelled

"Help!" several times. Finally, the resident farmer came out to see what the commotion was about.

I explained the situation in my best Amharic, and, thankfully, he called off the dogs, took care of the mule and let me sleep in his hut. The farmer shared his tiny *tukul* with me for the rest of the night. He had eaten his evening meal many hours ago, and apologized that he had no food to share with me. I told him no problem and that I was just happy that he had taken care of me and my mule.

The next morning, the farmer kindly saddled the mule and pointed me in the direction of Gecha. When I finally arrived back in Gecha, I was happy to find Daweet, and we vaccinated more people, thanked our teacher friend and his wife and then drove back to Gore.

I felt relieved and also proud that I had been tested and had survived. I started looking forward to such projects with more of a sense of adventure than of dread. I have often thought about this episode over the years. Although I was upset with Ciro at the time for what seemed like abandoning me in Gecha, I eventually came to comprehend what a powerful coming-of-age experience he had set me up for.

When I saw Ciro at our 2011 Peace Corps/SEP reunion in Washington, DC, I recounted the above tale to him and thanked him. Ciro seemed pleased and said, "I knew you could do it."

Through this experience, I began maturing and became aware of the value of self-reliance, a precious gift that has enriched my life ever since!

•

At the edge of the Gishe plateau looking generally southward over the Kechene canyon to the Gera Midir plateau. Left to right: Ali Abduke, Lewis Kaplan, Girma, October 1973. *Photo by the author.*

at Rabel, the administrative town of Gishe, in late afternoon and went to the *woreda* governor's office to obtain assistance with hiring a local guide and a letter ordering the support of local village leaders and judges. The governor was absent so we met with the *woreda* secretary, *Ato* Shewakena Banjao.

Shewakena told us he would find a guide after arranging for us to stay with relatives nearby and for stabling our animals. The net effect, however, was being put under house arrest with our animals confiscated for several days until we realized that we could get our animals back if we decided to return to Mehal Meda. That is, we were essentially thrown out of Gishe without being able to survey for smallpox. So, we decided to leave SEP work in Gishe until we eradicated smallpox in Gera Midir.

PREPARATION FOR THE GISHE EXPEDITION
In April 1974, after six months of coordinated work by Lewis's and my

teams, no new smallpox cases were found in Gera Midir and we were ready to try Gishe again. Because of the significant time and effort required just to get to and from Gishe, and the general lack of cooperation to be expected for logistics and SEP activities while there, we knew that a self-sufficient, sustained effort was needed.

We developed the idea of a month-long, caravan-style expedition with multiple SEP teams working together to search all over Gishe for smallpox and vaccinate around cases. Lewis and I recruited Peter Carrasco to be a member of the expedition, if we could get it approved. Peter was a seasoned SEP PCV from Group XVIII who had been working with the Adal nomadic people in the Rift Valley to the east of Menz & Gishe. He was ready for a change from the lowland savannah and intense heat to the cool high plateau and canyon country.

Dr. de Quadros understood the issues (having received our reports and conducted several field checks with us over the previous six-seven months) and liked the approach. He also helped by assigning Assessment Officer Temesgen Gebru to work with us. Temesgen, an Ethiopian public health worker who had been with SEP for several years, had recently surveyed Mama Midir *woreda* of Menz & Gishe *awraja* and found it free of smallpox.

The target date to begin the expedition was Saturday, May 4, 1974. May is the last mostly dry month before the summer monsoon rains make travel precarious, especially in the canyons. If we could visit all quarters of Gishe to locate active cases and vaccinate around them, the heavy rains would then help the eradication effort. Smallpox transmission generally decreased during the monsoon because people traveled and visited less frequently, and because the smallpox virus was less transmissible through the air in high humidity.

In preparation, Peter and Temesgen stayed in Addis Ababa to assemble the necessary equipment, food, and smallpox supplies. On April 27th, Lewis and I drove from our home base in Debre Berhan (a large town 132 kilometers [82 miles] north of Addis) to Mehal Meda (another 148 kilometers [92 miles] driving distance) for the Saturday market. Overall our tasks for this trip were to buy animals, to contract with two local men to accompany us as animal tenders and camp guards, to have wooden panniers made for some of the donkeys, and to borrow western saddles from missionaries.

Lewis, Befekadu (my regular student vaccinator), and I spent Saturday and Sunday in Mehal Meda negotiating and renegotiating the purchase of three mules, two horses and seven donkeys. What we thought would be a relatively simple process spun out of control when the animals "disappeared." After they were found, we litigated their return (under the sage oversight of the Gera Midir *awraja* secretary, *Ato* Tsegaye Gebre Hiwot) by paying a "finder's fee," or small ransom, and generous stabling fees for the finder to watch our animals for the next week until we could return to buy several more animals and then actually start the expedition.

On Tuesday, April 30th, we drove back to Addis to coordinate with Temesgen and Peter on final arrangements and to get a letter that Dr. de Quadros had obtained from the governor of Shewa ordering assistance by Gishe officials for the expedition. Then Lewis and I drove back to Debre Berhan for our personal supplies and to pick up three additional student vaccinators who would meet us at our house.

On Saturday, May 4th, Lewis left Debre Berhan early in his Land Cruiser with his student, Tariku, to make the three-hour drive to Mehal Meda in time to look at the full selection of animals in the market, buy some more donkeys, and see if Tsegaye had the chance to find two muleteers/camp guards for us. Peter (with his student, Getahun) and I (with Kadir, my student for this trip) left after loading the remaining gear. We planned to meet Lewis by 2:00 p.m. at the latest.

The route to Mehal Meda first followed the paved trunk road north for 60 kilometers (37 miles) from Debre Berhan to Debre Sina and then took the gravel branch road the rest of the way, mostly along the edge of the escarpment between the Rift Valley and the Amhara Plateau. Peter took the lead in his Land Cruiser and I drove my larger, more heavily loaded Land Rover. Just beyond the small town of Bosh, the road curved at a bridge over a dry wash and climbed a steep buttress in the escarpment. I downshifted into 2nd gear but then felt no resistance from the gear-shift shaft — because it had separated about an inch above the floorboards and dangled freely in my hand. I kept the clutch pedal to the floor and coasted until there was enough shoulder for me to pull over and leave room for the road to stay open.

After hyperventilating and exchanging wide-eyed expressions with Kadir, I got out of the car to walk off the shock. Not long afterward, Peter came back to see why we stopped. It was getting late if we were going to coordinate with Lewis on new animals, prior animals, Tsegaye and muleteers/camp guards, and then get the animals to the Ashen school (our staging location on the way to the canyon crossing to Gishe). So, rather than driving while stuck in 2nd gear, we left Kadir and Getahun with the Land Rover (and camping gear and food), transferred as much as possible of the rest of the gear to Peter's Land Cruiser, and then raced for Mehal Meda.

As we were driving the straight-away approaching Mehal Meda, I could see Lewis riding toward us on the red horse we bought in the market the prior week. Lewis was grinning and pleased to report that everything was taken care of: five more donkeys bought, two muleteers/guards hired under contract, and arrangements concluded to have the muleteers/guards collect all our animals and herd them to the Ashen school that afternoon. And, fortunately, no new litigation had arisen.

Lewis noticed that Peter and I were both in one car only. When I told him about the gear shifter, Lewis got excited and said essentially the same thing happened to him in the market. He had been sizing up donkeys, and while scrutinizing yet another, he lifted the donkey's tail to determine its sex and most of the tail came free in his hand! Then Lewis suggested we switch places so I could ride over to Tsegaye's house and say hello to none other than *Ato* Shewakena, the secretary of Gishe *woreda* and our old nemesis from our reconnaissance trip to Gishe in October.

Tsegaye and Shewakena were sitting in front of Tsegaye's house on card chairs. After exchanging greetings, I thanked Tsegaye for all his help and then asked Shewakena if he had business that would keep him away from Gishe for very long. But he was ahead of the game and said he was pleased to hear of our plans to work in Gishe. Furthermore, he offered to accompany us on our canyon crossing to Gishe on Tuesday morning and he assured us of every assistance for our smallpox eradication work in his *woreda*.

Barely before dark, Lewis, Peter, and I drove to Ashen which was located between Mehal Meda and Gotera, where the main route to Gishe drops abruptly over the edge of the plateau into the Kechene canyon. The teachers at the Ashen school (a cinder block building built through the Swedish aid program) had graciously given our expedition access to two unused classrooms for staging and sleeping. And meanwhile, Tariku had accompanied our two muleteers (Haile and Makonen) and our animals from Mehal Meda to the school.

The next day, Sunday, May 5th, Lewis drove me back to my Land Rover, which I then drove very slowly to Mehal Meda with Getahun and Kadir. I stayed in Mehal Meda at the health clinic and arranged for storage of the Land Rover. By mid-afternoon, as was planned the previous week, Temesgen arrived from Addis with his student (Demessie) and with Befekadu, who guided them to the health clinic. Together we drove to the Ashen school before dark, where everyone and all the animals, gear, and provisions were finally in the same place for the first time.

We spent Monday, May 6th, making final preparations. First, we repackaged supplies by type: food, smallpox gear, clothes, sleeping bags, cooking supplies, tents and cots, tools and spare parts. Then we practiced loading a few donkeys and spent considerable time reinforcing panniers and adding rope loops to them to go over the donkeys' tails to keep the panniers from sliding forward on the steep canyon descent to the Kechene river crossing.

Befekadu helped with these tasks and then, with profuse good wishes all around, he left with the white horse and two donkeys to spend the month checking all over Gera Midir to see if smallpox really had been eradicated from this *woreda*. Dr. de Quadros insisted that Befekadu take this role rather than join the expedition because he was highly resourceful and thoroughly familiar with the territory and outbreak history from working with us since the fall.

We had a group meeting in the afternoon. The plan was simple: go everywhere in Gishe to search and vaccinate for smallpox, and vaccinate

Expedition members, animals, and gear at the Ashen school. Front row, left to right: Haile, Getahun, Tariku, Demessie; back row: the author, Temesgen, Lewis, Kadir, and Makonen, May 1974. *Photo by Peter Carrasco.*

as thoroughly as possible around active cases. Each evening, Temesgen, Lewis, Peter, and I would assess the day's progress and decide how to proceed. For the first day's journey, we planned to go only to the bottom of the Kechene canyon, a 4,000-5,000-foot descent, rather than also climb 4,000-5,000 feet to the Gishe plateau and risk pushing the animals past exhaustion while their loads were most full.

THE ROAD TO GISHE

On Tuesday, May 7th, we were all active before dawn. Despite practicing the day before, it took more than two hours to load everything because all the supplies and gear had to be made into balanced loads, and only Haile and Makonen could be trusted to do this. We were ready to move by 8:30 a.m. There was no sign of Shewakena, but considering past history, we were not disappointed. Our procession of 10 people, three mules, one horse, and 10 donkeys started moving north to the plateau edge, which

Haile and Peter reworking loads on the canyon trail,
May 1974. *Photo by the author.*

was usually a one-hour journey. Soon our caravan stretched over a quarter mile. Each of us watched a few donkeys to keep them from straying. We reached the plateau edge in about two hours and then started down into the Kechene canyon.

The canyon trail was steep and narrow, with numerous tight spots between large boulders that didn't allow the wide berth of the panniers to pass. Lewis and I had taken this trail before, but we hadn't appreciated how narrow it was when we designed the panniers. At tight spots, the donkeys carrying panniers tried to butt their way through, or turn around, or they just stopped. So, we had to unload and reload each of the seven donkeys that were carrying panniers at each narrow passage!

Also, we were frequently running up and down the trail when a given load would break its tail-piece mooring and slip down the neck of a donkey or roll off to the side. By the time we accepted that we couldn't continue down the canyon route, one of the panniers was split along a side and five of the remaining six were in need of servicing to varying degrees.

We gathered the animals on a gently sloping space that was maybe 30 feet in diameter. We unloaded everything and let some of the donkeys graze to keep them gainfully occupied and give us more room to work. The ground was strewn with panniers, saddles, foam pads, coils of rope, and assorted packs. We made emergency repairs on the worst-damaged panniers, and made rope chest supports to keep the panniers from sliding off the animals' backs on the steep return ascent. The four heaviest loads were put on the mules and horse, and the remaining gear and the saddles were distributed on the donkeys. After about two hours, we headed back up the trail toward the plateau edge 500 feet above us.

Within 50 uphill paces I dropped back to help Haile re-tie one of the donkeys. It was carrying a light load but the load (two field cots and Tariku's suitcase) was difficult to balance and lash tight, and the donkey wouldn't stand still. We were at a steep hillside traverse. I was uphill and leaning over with my shins at the donkey's hip and Haile was downhill with his knees at hoof level. Suddenly I was kicked in the shin and Haile was kicked once in the chest and once in the nose. After several attempts to get the load secure, we were able to proceed with the donkey carrying only two cots, and Haile carrying Tariku's suitcase in one hand while squeezing his bloody nose with the other.

Later up the trail, one of the mules lost control, started bucking, and spilled her load. We left this load where it landed and led the donkeys, horse, and mules to the plateau and unloaded and hobbled them. Makonen took two donkeys back to recover the spilled load. We pitched our tents near the edge of the plateau at Gotera, after eight hours on the move. But we were only five kilometers from where we started.

Wednesday, May 8th, was a day for repairing and rethinking. The panniers were inspected and strengthened with extra corner braces or

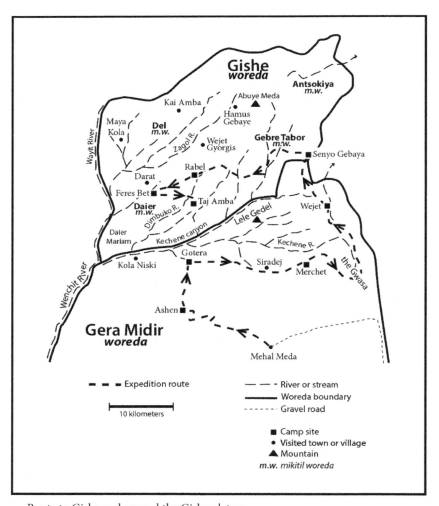

Route to Gishe and around the Gishe plateau.

leather straps fixed with wood screws. In the afternoon we sat on cots and saddles in the space surrounded by our tents to drink tea and consider how to proceed. From previous work in this area, I was familiar with the geography to the east at the head of the canyon where high elevation was continuous between the Gera Midir and Gishe plateaus. We could reach Gishe without narrow trails or major elevation change if we went east along the plateau-canyon edge, then crossed the Gwasa (uninhabited moors at the highest part of the plateau near the escarpment), then turned north

View northward over the Kechene canyon to Gishe from the edge of the Gera Midir plateau. Abuye Meda mountain is on the horizon in the middle of the photo, May 1974. *Photo by the author.*

at the source of the Kechene river, and finally passed over the escarpment wall to the Gishe plateau. This route would avoid a canyon crossing, but it would take at least three days.

On Thursday, May 9th, the route along the canyon edge was gently rising and falling, but we were walking directly into wind whipping over the escarpment from the Rift Valley. Farmers worked their fields, plowing the rich dark soil with oxen pulling metal-tipped wooden-shaft plows while shouting encouragement or insults to the oxen and cracking whips above them. Views of the landscapes were stunning, with the Kechene canyon in the mid-ground and the Gishe plateau beyond, including the round-topped Abuye Meda mountain (13,000-feet elevation) to the north.

After several hours, two men on horseback (Befekadu and Getachew, the local governor's *zebanya*) rode up to the front of the caravan and an animated conversation ensued. When I reached them, Befekadu was laughing and said at first he was surprised, but maybe not surprised, that

Villagers with donkey for sale at Merchet, May 1974.
Photo by the author.

we were still in Gera Midir and going in the wrong direction. Kadir gave him an update so he understood the situation. Befekadu was checking areas with old cases, but he was riding a brown horse. He explained that the white horse we bought in the market was sick (aha - why the price was only E$60) and he was renting another while the white one was recuperating. Befekadu was having a great time riding around the countryside, visiting and drinking with people where we previously found smallpox and struggled to vaccinate and glean information. And so far he found no new cases in this area. Too soon it was time to go our separate ways again.

It started drizzling by midday. The wind in our faces made it seem very cold. Then it started raining heavily when we were close to Merchet, our day's destination at the edge of the Gwasa. Merchet was a compact grouping of around 20 small compounds adjacent to each other with several paths winding through. Perhaps it was organized this way, rather than as more loosely distributed compounds elsewhere, for protection against predators from the wild Gwasa.

We rushed to unpack the animals, raise the tents, and throw everything inside. The heavy rain lasted an hour and then turned into dense, wet fog as afternoon became evening. Even so, our presence attracted a crowd of villagers who loudly and amusedly discussed everything about us and our camp. Lewis and I joined the crowd and let it be known we would buy a strong donkey or two for a reasonable price. We could tell that the loads were a bit too heavy and it would be good to spread them out more.

The next day, Friday, May 11th, we bought a donkey and then crossed the Gwasa - empty land with scattered low shrubs and 6-10-foot-tall giant lobelias. At times the fog was so thick we couldn't see beyond 50 feet so we moved slowly, in small groups of people and animals, and periodically gathered to count heads when the fog thinned enough. We reached Wejet, high on the escarpment wall, before dark. It rained hard Friday night and through the next day, so we stayed Saturday at Wejet and gave the donkeys a needed rest.

SMALLPOX ERADICATION IN THE GISHE HIGHLANDS

With a break in the weather on Sunday, May 12th, we left Wejet on the old jeep road (long washed-out and impassable for vehicles), initially climbing and then traversing below the top escarpment cliffs with expansive views of the Rift Valley 6,000-7,000 feet below. Then we left the jeep road and crested onto the Gishe plateau.

We made our camp near Senyo Gebaya (literally: Monday market) which was located by the junction of three well-traveled paths surrounded by fields of barley and wheat and evenly distributed, circular, rock-walled compounds. Just to the north of the crossroads was a school, which was a

Expedition caravan, and several curious children from Wejet, following the remains of the jeep road high on the escarpment wall between the Gishe plateau and the Rift Valley, May 1974. *Photo by the author.*

circular, rock-walled, one-room house with a conical thatch roof supported by a central eucalyptus pole. Nearby to the south was the old, circular, rock-walled and conical thatch-roofed Gebre Tabor Mariam church.

We finally did some smallpox work in Gishe on Monday, May 13th — seven days into the expedition! Several hundred people came to the market to trade in grain, beans, peas, lentils, chili peppers, chickens, eggs, butter, salt, cooking oil, onions, Wonji brand sugar packets, Nyala and Gureza brand cigarettes, candles, bangles, mirrors, buttons, cloth, notebooks, matches, and the like. Neither sheep (for a feast) nor beasts of burden (still looking for another donkey) were for sale that day. Most vendors were local, but there were several itinerant merchants who sold the manufactured or packaged goods.

We circulated through the market to check for rumors of active or recent smallpox cases, showing people the plastic-covered picture of an Ethiopian man with smallpox. People largely ignored us as they were absorbed in buying and selling and socializing. To help gain recognition

Market day at Senyo Gebaya in Gishe *woreda*, May 1974. *Photo by the author.*

for our efforts and perhaps overcome reluctance in the marketgoers, Lewis gave me a very public vaccination after Kadir, Tariku, and Getahun alerted people nearby that they should watch one *ferengi* give another *ferengi* a vaccination. We knew there was no harm in getting occasional repeat vaccinations.

The demonstration got some attention, which temporarily boosted success with our vaccinating efforts. Our post-market count of used bifurcated needles was 105, and we learned about several possible smallpox cases to the west in Daier *mikitil woreda*, but none were rumored to be nearby in Gebre Tabor *mikitil woreda*. In the middle of the day, Lewis and Tariku visited the school and adjacent compounds and vaccinated 56 people, mostly children, but they didn't hear any rumors of smallpox nearby.

As the market was thinning in the afternoon, Temesgen, Peter, and I came upon a well-dressed man to the side of the market. He stood with two bodyguards carrying vintage rifles and a youth holding the reins to a mule with a handsome Ethiopian saddle. The man wore leather shoes, a fedora, western-cut overcoat, and trousers rather than jodhpurs. When he saw us take notice of him, he crossed his arms at his chest in a stiff, almost-military pose.

We walked over to him, offered the usual greetings, and introduced ourselves. He returned the greetings, but his manner was cold. He introduced himself as the Daier *mikitil woreda* secretary. We said we were pleased to meet him and were looking forward to working with him on the SEP as we moved through Gishe. He said that he hadn't heard anything about a smallpox program and it didn't sound very interesting to him.

Temesgen showed him the letter from the governor of Shewa province, which ordered full and active support for the SEP from Gishe government and quasi-government officials. The Daier secretary read the letter with a detached expression, and then held it to his side by a corner as if it were a soiled handkerchief. After a moment, he asked why he should care about the letter because it was addressed to the Gishe *woreda* office and not to him. We smiled, asked for the letter back, and returned to the market to finish our work and purchase food for the expedition.

Back at camp after the market, we discussed our next steps over a *doro wot* feast prepared by Temesgen and Tariku from chickens, onions, chili, and eggs that we bought, plus tomato paste from our food stock, and supplemented with *injera* and *tella* purchased at nearby compounds. Although we gathered rumors in the market of smallpox in Daier *mikitil woreda* to the west, we decided to keep with the plan of staying together and proceeding through Gishe methodically to get thorough coverage by searching everywhere and concentrating on vaccinating around active cases as we discovered them. We would get to Daier *mikitil woreda* soon enough.

On Tuesday, May 14th, Peter's and Temesgen's teams crossed the stream by our camp and then split up to search and vaccinate on the ridges to the east. Lewis's team traveled to the northwestern part of Gebre Tabor to see if they could find the *mikitil woreda* governor who lived in that area and maybe make the rounds with him. Kadir and I followed the shallow valley to the north where it started rising up the flanks of Abuye Meda mountain. We vaccinated 35 people, but we talked with at least a hundred

Area north of Senyo Gebaya on the southern flanks of Abuye Meda mountain. Eucalyptus trees are generally associated with compounds, May 1974. *Photo by the author.*

others and visited many compounds without hearing any rumors of active or recent cases in this area. Altogether, our four teams vaccinated more than 280 people, and all teams had similar results from their surveys. So we decided to move to Rabel the next day, feeling relatively confident that there was no smallpox in Gebre Tabor *mikitil woreda.*

On Wednesday, May 15th, we reached Rabel in the early afternoon. Rabel straddled a low ridge in the southwest quarter of the *woreda.* Everyone knew we were coming at least an hour before we arrived — our procession of 10 people, three mules, a horse, and 11 donkeys was easily visible as we approached. Several rows of buildings (mostly mud-walled and tin-roofed houses with fences of eucalyptus poles or rocks or thorn bushes) thinned out to cropland, pasture, and rock-walled compounds further downhill on either side of the ridge. The main path through Rabel continued north and south out of town as principal travel routes.

We made camp in a grassy field at the north end of town, overlooking the Yesha canyon and broken-plateau mountains to the northwest. Afternoon sunlight flashed off clusters of tin-roofed buildings in the towns of Were Ilu and Kai Amba on two not-too-distant mountains. After setting up camp, Peter and Lewis visited the school while Temesgen and I went to the *woreda* office.

A few sheep were grazing in the *woreda* office compound. The *woreda* office had two rooms. The front room was for the secretary, *Ato* Shewakena Banjao, who had stymied the reconnaissance trip that Lewis and I attempted in October. The room brought back memories of sitting and waiting and slowly coming to understand how things were done in Gishe. Two long tables were almost completely covered with files. On one of the walls was a faded picture of Emperor Haile Selassie in white dress uniform that was barely visible under many rows of medals. Against another wall were shelves with more files.

Shewakena was not there, but a scribe was in the office upbraiding a child. The governor was not there either and Temesgen, after introducing us as visiting public health officials on government business, asked where he was. The scribe stood up and said, "Yes my lord, the governor is coming now," and then left to tell the governor what he already knew.

Soon the *woreda* governor, *Grazmach* Asfaw Dilneso, entered the office compound surrounded by talkative farmers and townsfolk. We came out to exchange greetings. Asfaw invited us to join him inside and then led us into his office, which was similar to the front room. He told us he was pleased we had come safely all the way to Gishe and then asked what he could do for us. Temesgen thanked him and said we had come to Gishe as part of the Emperor's program to eradicate smallpox. Asfaw smiled and asked, "What? Smallpox? Nothing else?"

We all had heard similar responses many times because smallpox was much less of a concern to people than typhus, typhoid, gonorrhea, dysentery, or (for those in lower elevations) malaria. The variola minor strain of smallpox that was endemic to Ethiopia caused much lower mortality than the variola major strain in places like south Asia, or Europe (previously). Temesgen presented the letter from the governor of Shewa province to Asfaw and said we hoped he would help us get local support because SEP work required door-to-door visits, and we were trying to cover the whole *woreda*. That is, we hoped he would send letters to the *mikitil woreda* governors instructing them to work with us and to direct *atbia danyas* in each area to work with us too. Temesgen also asked if the governor could address the Rabel market on our behalf on Saturday.

Asfaw said these were reasonable requests. He called for the scribe to take dictation, and while the scribe assembled the paper and carbon paper, Asfaw admonished us to be extra patient with people in Gishe, to never vaccinate women or children without the husband's or father's permission, and to never force people to take the vaccination against their will. All good advice. Eventually the letters were written, signed, given the official *woreda* stamp, and dispatched to people in town who would be going to the various *mikitil woredas*.

The next day, Thursday, May 16th, Lewis vaccinated at the school and other areas in town while the rest of us headed in different directions to trace rumors and search the countryside. Kadir and I covered a lot of ground, didn't find any smallpox cases, but gave 182 vaccinations. What really helped was the effective persuasion of *Ato* Mamo, the *atbia danya* from Setoch Washa, who spent the day with us. He escorted us about five miles up the ridge from Rabel to visit compounds and investigate a rumor near the Wejet Gyorgis church, and then we returned by a lower route so we could visit different villages on the way back.

We moved slowly, but this was because so many people liked Mamo and invited us into their houses even if husbands were in the fields, or somewhere else, as was common during the day. About midday, we reached the compound of the rumored smallpox cases. Mamo spoke with the homeowner while Kadir and I stood back. The homeowner looked at us for a moment and then smiled and invited all of us into the house and offered us *kolo* and *tella*.

We talked and drank for a while as the children took turns coming somewhat close to us for a better look before darting back behind large earthenware storage jugs. None of the children had pits or scars from smallpox. Eventually, I raised the subject of smallpox and asked the homeowner a few questions about the sickness his children had recently suffered. He said their rashes disappeared in a couple of weeks and the fever persisted much of that time. I said it sounded like chickenpox and then gave a quick pitch for the smallpox vaccination. The homeowner gathered his children around Kadir who gave them the vaccination. The children's expressions changed from dread to giddy amazement when they realized the vaccination really had been just a few not-very-painful skin pricks.

Then the father and children together went to nearby compounds and brought back 20 people in several shifts. When it was over, and we were finishing our *tella* and getting ready to leave, I asked the homeowner why some people in Gishe refused to be vaccinated. He said he could only speak for himself, but many people didn't trust *ferengis*. In turn, he asked me: "What was my age?" I told him to guess and he guessed I was 50, maybe 45. This surprised me because I was 25 and told him so. He laughed and asked, "Really?" several times, but finally he accepted it and said maybe the beard was misleading.

Neither Temesgen nor Peter found active smallpox either, but they were convinced it was out there nearby. Peter found five cases that had recovered several weeks previously, and Temesgen heard rumors of smallpox at the edge of the canyons near where he and Peter were investigating. Lewis heard similar rumors from students in Rabel. Altogether we vaccinated 522 people that day. At our planning meeting that evening, we decided to check the last few rumors for the plateau around Rabel the next day to be sure we weren't missing something before moving southwest to Daier *mikitil woreda*, the area of the new rumors and the rumors we gathered at Senyo Gebaya.

On Friday, May 17th, Lewis and Peter found active cases near the canyon edges: three cases in Set Amba and one case in Taj Amba. But the people were not receptive to the vaccination. Temesgen heard about additional cases in the canyons. Kadir and I traced a rumor in an area about three hours from Rabel, over two low ridges and up a shallow valley. We hired a schoolchild who lived near Kafo, the rumor location, to lead us there. As we were leaving Rabel, some men leaving town at the same time chided the schoolchild for guiding *ferengis*. They told him to go back to school because they could show us the way. We told the child to stay with us and we invited the men to join us if they wished. But they went in a different direction when they realized the child was staying with us.

We didn't vaccinate many people on the way to Kafo, but at least we didn't hear of any smallpox cases. Our guide led us as far as his own village and then pointed to a collection of compounds about half a mile upstream on the other side of the draw where the *atbia danya* lived. The *atbia danya* was not home, but his wife and mother were there and they invited us in for coffee and *kolo*. It felt good to sit in the cool, dark house. The women were crouching by the fire in the center of the house preparing coffee. Kadir explained the smallpox program and the particular rumor we were investigating. A couple of chickens weaved around behind the women and pecked at the dirt floor. I asked if the women knew when the *atbia danya* would return and his wife said he was away on business and probably wouldn't be back before dark. Neither woman knew, or acknowledged knowing, *Ato* Getachew Yigezu, whose house was rumored to have a case of smallpox, although the area of the rumor matched the name of the village where we were.

So we continued up the ridge which was becoming more barren and rocky as we gained elevation on Abuye Meda mountain. There was one more cluster of compounds about a mile farther up the mountain. Fortunately, we met a man at the first compound, *Ato* Wendeme Haile Mariam, who escorted us through the village and encouraged people to take the vaccination. He led us to a central location among the compounds and ordered all the children in sight to come for the vaccination. Most of them did, albeit hesitantly. Soon a few other villagers brought their wives and children from their houses. One old man came up to me as I was vaccinating a child and implored me to leave the children alone. I told him it was most important to vaccinate the children, and he gave me a horrified look which seemed to say that all the monster stories about *ferengi*s were true.

As we were leaving, and after warmly thanking Wendeme, a man came up and asked us to go with him to his house. He was very agitated and his tone was urgent. I asked what the matter was. He simply said someone was sick and needed the *ferengi* vaccination. As we entered his house, we could hear a woman moaning. Several young children began to cry and a couple of teenage boys ran out of the house. The sick woman, Werkenesh, was sitting on the edge of a bed of crisscrossed leather straps attached to a wooden frame. An older woman was sitting next to her, comforting her and wiping her perspiring forehead with a damp cloth.

We all exchanged greetings and I asked the man what the woman was suffering from. He said, "Yes my lord, you must vaccinate her leg." He pulled back her *gabi* from around her legs. Her right leg was very swollen and blood and pus oozed from two groups of puncture wounds. I felt light-headed and I could hear Kadir say, "Oh my God." The man said that Werkenesh, his sister, had injured her leg in a fall a couple of weeks ago and it didn't heal but rather became swollen and started festering. Then, only an hour earlier, she was bitten by a village dog as she sat outside for fresh air.

What to do? I said they should wash the wounds gently but thoroughly with clean soap and water that had been boiled. The man said they would do that. Then, after an uncomfortable silence, I explained that I wasn't a real doctor, and the only medicine I had was smallpox vaccine because I was a smallpox specialist. I suggested they try to get Werkenesh to the Mehal Meda health clinic by mule. Shocked and angry, Werkenesh's brother said, "You brought only the smallpox vaccination and nothing for sick people?" I told him I wished more than anything that I could help Werkenesh and I didn't blame him for being angry.

I doubted they would take Werkenesh to Mehal Meda. Normally the trip would take two days from there. But transporting a septic, feverish woman in serious pain by mule over the Kechene canyon trail was probably impossible. It was good that it took several hours to get back to Rabel because Kadir and I needed time to decompress.

The next day was the Saturday market in Rabel, the main event in Gishe each week. People came from all over the *woreda* to trade and socialize. So the market provided a good opportunity to survey for rumors as well as vaccinate and buy food. And Rabel was relatively close to new and recent cases, so it would be good to increase awareness about SEP.

Our first priority was to call once more on the *woreda* governor, *Grazmach* Asfaw. Lewis, Peter, Temesgen, and I went to his compound and were met at the gate by his *zebanya* who said the governor was "coming now." Soon Asfaw came out to meet us in the road and, after greetings, he asked if we were working hard and vaccinating many people. Temesgen said we were working very hard and having some success. He added that we had found active cases of smallpox in Daier *mikitil woreda* and we expected to find more shortly.

At that point *Ato* Shewakena joined us. I let out an involuntary groan which, unfortunately, was too loud to go unnoticed. We all went through the formal greetings and whenever Shewakena and I made eye contact, we held our plastic smiles - old adversaries meeting for another round, trading glares and empty good wishes. Peter reviewed plans for the market. Asfaw promised to address the market and take a demo vaccination in front of everyone. Shewakena added that he was already vaccinated, but he would certainly help us vaccinate people in the market.

We went back to camp to gather the students, vaccine, bifurcated needles, and plastic-covered pictures of Ethiopian people with smallpox. Lewis, in his capacity of expedition treasurer, gave the muleteers, Haile and Makonen, some cash. They only requested a small portion of their total earnings so they couldn't spend it all at once. Haile and Makonen knew to take turns going to the market so we always had a guard at camp.

There were two main approaches to the market. Peter, Lewis, Getahun, and Tariku took the northern approach, while Temesgen, Demessie, Kadir and I took the southern approach. Our plan was to vaccinate and ask people about rumors at the market entrances until about 11:00 a.m. when the market would reach its maximum. Then we would abandon those approaches and establish a couple of stations inside the market while sending the students around to check for rumors and encourage people to be vaccinated.

Shewakena was in the road waiting for us on the southern approach to the market. He showed us a place nearby where the road narrowed between fences on either side to funnel marketgoers to us. Temesgen and

Marketgoers passing our vaccination station near the Rabel market, May 1974. *Photo by the author.*

I started mixing vaccine while Shewakena, Demessie, and Kadir spaced themselves across the road and started telling the good news to the marketgoers. Traffic was heavy and we also attracted curious bystanders, so our station was crowded. A few of the bystanders encouraged people to take the vaccination, others advised against it, and others were entertained by the show. Quite a few people did take the vaccination, but many declined. Several people gave reasons for declining, including:

"My brother got a vaccination and it was good for both of us."

"I don't need the *ferengi* vaccination. God came down and vaccinated me when I was a child."

"I'm busy now. Meet me here tomorrow and I'll take the vaccination."

When we were occupied with vaccinating or trying to change some minds, Shewakena was shooing people on to the market. But whenever we turned to see if he had gathered more people to vaccinate he would nonchalantly switch roles and, half-heartedly, grab at passing *gabi*s, now and then collecting a few people for us to vaccinate. Occasionally he went to a plot of eucalyptus trees to conduct private or official business.

Eventually we thanked Shewakena for his help and left to set up several vaccination stations in the market. We also took breaks to purchase food for our camp (including a sheep for a feast) or to eat or drink in one of the restaurants or drinking houses at the edge of the market. I took a break in a drinking house in one of the rectangular, partially white-washed, mud-wattle buildings with a corrugated tin roof.

It was noisy and crowded inside. I found a seat on a bench at a table near the door and ordered a *berele* (round-based, narrow-necked glass flask) of *tej* — honey wine, or mead, with a flowery aroma and the taste of nectar. Several men at my table were eating raw meat, using curved knives to cut through the chunks of beef. Tariku came in and I called for the serving girl to bring him a *berele* also, but he said there was no time. The governor had arrived in the market and wanted us all to assemble by him when he addressed the market.

Everyone else was at the higher ground at the head of the marketplace. Peter was briefing Asfaw about the basics of smallpox eradication. The governor would speak to the people in the market about SEP, introduce us, and then take a vaccination himself. The students distributed themselves around the market to be ready to vaccinate after the demonstration vaccination.

The most difficult part of the operation was getting the attention of more than a thousand marketgoers absorbed in buying or selling or socializing. One of the governor's footmen raised a goatskin high in the air on his *dula* while another blew a horn, the traditional signals for attention. It took a few minutes but the message did circulate that something was happening up front. Heads turned and the governor stepped forward.

In a loud voice, Asfaw welcomed everyone to the Rabel market. Then he said, "The King, our father, Haile Selassie has sent some doctors to remove a pestilence from among His subjects. All of our people must work together and take the vaccination which is free, painless, and absolutely harmless. Even old people, women, and infants must be vaccinated for their own protection. And when you return home, spread this message. Now, let me introduce to you my dear friends, the smallpox doctors: three *ferengi*s and a *Habisha*. I have ordered them to vaccinate all of you. And to show you how simple and safe and painless the vaccination is, I will now be vaccinated myself. Watch!"

Asfaw removed his coat, lifted his *gabi*, and exposed his left upper arm. Lewis moved forward and poked him with a bead of vaccine on a bifurcated needle. It was done in a few moments, and the governor turned so his arm was showing to the crowd. There was a rush of per-haps 50 people right after the governor took his vaccination. But then the attention span of the market had been eclipsed and people resumed their market business.

We all left the market by 3:00 p.m., satisfied with the day's work. Our post-market needle count was 873 – by far the best market effort I had ever been associated with. And the smallpox rumors we gathered were only for the areas we already suspected by the canyons.

Sunday, May 19th, was moving day. Our caravan traveled southwest to Feres Bet on the plateau flats. Feres Bet was home to the Daier *mikitil woreda* governor, *Ato* Mulugeta Aweka. All the recently found smallpox cases were within a day's walk of Feres Bet.

Our initial encounter with Mulugeta was not very encouraging. When Temesgen and Peter approached him Sunday evening to explain our pur-poses, he demanded a letter to legitimize our presence. Temesgen asked if he hadn't received the letter sent by courier from the *woreda* governor. Mulugeta insisted he hadn't received the letter and suggested that we go back to Rabel until we could return with another letter. At that point, Temesgen produced the letter signed by the governor of Shewa province, but Mulugeta (as with the secretary of Daier *mikitil woreda,* that we met at Senyo Gebaya shortly after entering Gishe) was not moved. Mulugeta knew the matter would never reach the governor of Shewa or cause any repercussions back to him.

Regardless, our plan remained to fan out in four directions with four teams from this central location in Daier. The next morning we went back to the Daier *mikitil woreda* office to request letters from Mulugeta to local *atbia danyas* enlisting their assistance for us. As if nothing had happened the day before, Peter, Temesgen, and Lewis each received letters quickly and departed. But I was advised to wait for an actual *atbia danya* who lived near the office and would accompany me.

Waiting was enjoyable, for a while, as I watched Mulugeta attend to business. His rough-hewn desk was partially covered with worn-out pieces of carbon paper, stamp pads, the official seal of office, and many files. I waited for nearly an hour while he arbitrated among groups of insistent pleaders and then, at a lull in the shouting, I shouted that Mulugeta should give me a "to whom it may concern" letter so I could continue with the government's work. The crowd of pleaders was caught by surprise and it served Mulugeta to have a pause in the action. Soon Kadir and I returned to camp with a letter in hand, gathered our smallpox gear and my red horse, Orion, and headed off on our own to vaccinate and look for smallpox in Darat *atbia*, about an hour north of Feres Bet near the area where Lewis had found active cases.

At one of the first compounds in Darat we ran into the *atbia danya*, *Ato* Aseged Sebseb, who happened to be conducting personal business there. Aseged went with us from compound to compound and we actually vaccinated several people, including children, but we found no active or recent cases of smallpox. After moving through several clusters of compounds, Aseged complained that he was tired, so I dismounted and offered to let him ride Orion. The proud man refused, but then showed disgust when I told Kadir to take a turn on Orion because I wanted to walk for a while. Since when do bodyguards ride while their masters walk?

Aseged led us to a house in the next cluster of compounds near the edge of cliffs where he said his cousin lived and we could vaccinate many people, especially children. However, we only found an old woman caring for an infant. Out of courtesy, we waited for a while because Aseged said many people were "coming now." But no one came. Eventually I suggested we should move on, but Aseged declined, saying he would catch up with us shortly. We vaccinated a few people without his help and got a consistent story: no active or recent smallpox cases in Darat *atbia*.

Back at camp, Lewis reported similar experiences to ours for the day, but Peter and Temesgen found five active cases on the plateau finger that juts southwestward to the detached Daier Mariam table top. Temesgen suspected there were more cases off the edge there and volunteered to go that evening with Demessie, camping gear, and a couple of donkeys to be poised for an early start the next day to encircle the infected village. After our meeting, Lewis, Peter, and I attended to an argument in camp while Temesgen prepared to leave for Daier Mariam.

The argument was a continuation of the prior night's gamesmanship over our basic needs at Feres Bet. Apparently Mulugeta was a weak governor, partly due to his weakness for drink and partly due to his indecisiveness. We had noticed that the *atbia danyas* and most everyone else paid minimal homage to him. The issue at hand was the stabling and feeding of our animals. Usually when we made a new camp we were able to find people who willingly cared for some of the animals for a few *birr* per night. But it had been a recurring problem at Feres Bet. Mulugeta didn't want to take any of the animals himself and, when he ordered a couple of neighbors to take a few each, they refused saying he should mind his manners and stop pretending to be king. That was followed by yelling back and forth, but it was just sport because people took a few animals apiece when it got dark. Indeed, the maneuvering shifted progressively to who would take which animals, for how much, and who would have the last word.

On Tuesday, May 21st, I planned to head over the ridge to Taj Amba where Peter found active cases the prior week. I was surprised, however, to find Mulugeta waiting outside our tents with his mule, wearing a governor's horn around his neck and a formal wool-and-leather cloak. He demanded that I go with him to vaccinate the people, and of course I agreed. Kadir and I followed him to a hilltop compound of a prominent old man who was the father of several priests and a wealthy landowner. Actually, this was one of the places we had already visited with little success finding or vaccinating people.

Soon Mulugeta was huddled in conversation with the old man. It seemed like SEP was being ignored so Kadir and I got up to leave. But Mulugeta scolded us for poor manners and told us to eat some *kolo* while coffee was being made. Finally Mulugeta completed his business, we finished our coffee, and he led us to many compounds where he cajoled reluctant parents so we were able to vaccinate nearly 100 people, mostly children.

By Wednesday, May 22nd, we had visited and vaccinated nearly every place between the canyon edges on the west and south, Rabel ridge on the northeast, and Darat *atbia* on the north. We all had heard rumors of smallpox in the canyons to the south. On Wednesday, Temesgen finished working the areas on the upper canyon wall below the Daier Mariam table top while we three *ferengis* rode over to Taj Amba for a saturation vaccination effort around what appeared to be the last active cases of smallpox in the Daier highland outbreak. We gave the day off to Tariku, Getahun, and Kadir. Peter had worked this area before and led the way to the house of the *atbia danya, Ato* Eshete Danye. Eshete wasn't present, but his brother told us many people, including Eshete, were gathering at the Ligah Meskel church for an important funeral in the afternoon.

The Ligah Meskel church was at the plateau edge above the Wadyat canyon, a tributary to the Kechene canyon. Churches were commonly located in prominent and scenic locations, and were easy to recognize at a distance because they were the only features in the landscape with stands of mature tree species other than the fast-growing, non-native eucalyptus. We studied the layout of the deep tight canyons and realized we couldn't work the canyons with our whole group because the population was so diffuse and the terrain was such high relief. There wouldn't be any centrally located places for camps to serve four teams at once. And travel routes were as steep, narrow, and rocky as the canyon crossing we attempted that first day from the Gera Midir side.

The funeral was for a young boy from an important family. People started congregating around the church by noon. I think the body was buried early in the morning and the large gathering was the religious and social function that followed. People were converging on the church from several directions. Women and girls carried jugs of *tella* and baskets of *dabo* on their heads.

A ritual procession began near the church in the middle of the gathering. Men moved around in a loose circle, raising their *dulas* high and chanting a monotonic song. The women, in a tighter circle within the men's circle, moved in the opposite direction and sang the song with more fervor and melody than the men. In the center were the mother and grandmother of the dead boy; they were beating their breasts and wailing, sometimes loudly and sometimes hardly at all. The women circling around the mother and grandmother shared the loss by making stylized motions of breast beating.

We found *Ato* Eshete Danye and asked if it would be permissible to vaccinate and gather information at the side of the funeral activities. All of us had done this numerous times before, but it was good to get approval from an official or a priest. Eshete approved and agreed to help us. While I was taking a turn at vaccinating, I noticed that the face of the young boy next in line had the distinct pits of a recently recovered case of smallpox. I started asking the standard questions: where did he live, what was his name, when and where did he contract smallpox, who visited while he was sick. The boy became frightened and started to leave but Eshete caught and gently cradled him in his arms and told him it wouldn't hurt to answer a few questions. We only learned that he lived in Dij Ersha, a village down in the canyon near the Rabel-Mehal Meda route. But it was valuable to get location information for a recent case. Eshete released the boy who quickly melted into the crowd.

This was the only new information we gathered, but we vaccinated 80 people at the church. We returned to camp as Temesgen and Demessie returned from investigating below Daier Mariam where they found seven active cases and patchy cooperation. We had a group meeting after dinner to assess the overall status and plan the next steps. We had two weeks of food stocks left and we needed to get back to our vehicles by then. There wasn't enough time to cover Del *mikitil woreda*, and the remaining highlands in northern Gishe, and the canyons, and Antsokiya on the escarpment wall east of the round mountains.

We decided to leave Antsokiya for another time because there were no rumors for that area and it could be reached independently from Kemise on the main trunk road in the Rift Valley. And we decided to split into two groups to cover the canyons and the remaining highlands respectively. The Canyon group was Temesgen, Demessie, Kadir, Makonen, and me. I would trade my horse to Lewis for his more-sure-footed mule. We would take Konjit (Temesgen's mule), Murphy (Lewis's mule), and four of the stronger donkeys, but no panniers. Temesgen and Demessie would return to Addis Ababa when we finished the Kechene canyon. Then Kadir, Makonen, and I would go on to rendezvous from the south with the Highland group in Kai Amba, the administration and market town of Del *mikitil woreda.*

Lewis, Peter, Tariku, Getahun, Haile, and the rest of the animals were the Highland group. They would move north and northwest of Rabel to cover the population on the round-about highland route to Del via Hamus Gebaya near the round mountains. Then they would cover the northern approach to Kai Amba and vaccinate the market there on Sunday, June 2nd. The rendezvous time window was Sunday, June 2nd through Monday, June 3rd. There was no way to communicate, so each group was responsible for its return to the Ashen school if we didn't meet by June 3rd in Kai Amba. But first we would all work around Taj Amba and the Wadyat canyon below Taj Amba, then resupply and vaccinate again at the Rabel market on Saturday, and then split up.

THE CANYONS

On Sunday, May 26th, the Highland and Canyon groups went separate ways after many rounds of heartfelt good wishes. The Canyon group reached Ligah Feet, a collection of compounds about halfway down the canyon wall, in about three hours through a steady drizzle. It rained hard much of the rest of the day and through the night, but became light rain by the time we finished our breakfast of oatmeal, crackers, and tea the next morning. Kadir and I would check villages along the canyon wall to the east, while Temesgen and Demessie went to the west. We left the mules because the rain made the trails too slippery.

Initially we vaccinated most of the children in Ligah Feet and then went to Chuko, which was about an hour away and near the Rabel - Mehal Meda route. Chuko was a collection of maybe 10 compounds about 1,500 feet above Dij Ersha, which was the village of the boy I met at the funeral near Taj Amba who had just recovered from smallpox.

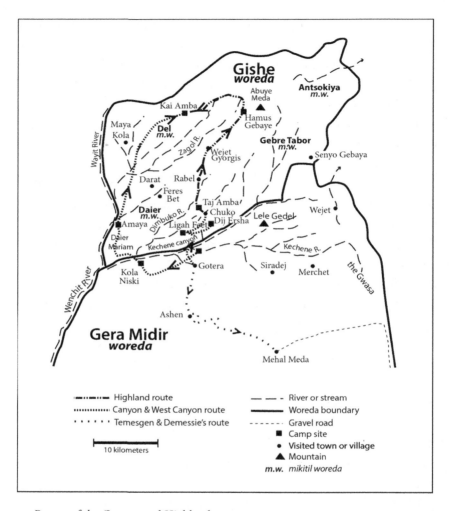

Routes of the Canyon and Highland groups.

People in Chuko said there were no current cases, but we still want-ed to vaccinate since this village was close enough to Dij Ersha to have frequent interchanges with it. When Kadir started explaining about SEP, we were told that everyone from Chuko had been vaccinated in the Rabel market. When I asked if I could see the arms of the children to check that the medicine was working properly, I was told not to trouble myself because it was their business how well the medicine was working.

In a somewhat similar circumstance earlier in the year on the Gera Midir plateau, I asked a skeptical villager how I could convince him and others that we really were working on SEP and that the vaccine really would provide protection without danger of harm in the process. He thought for a moment and then said that many people needed time to get to know an outsider, especially a *ferengi*, and to get familiar with a new idea. He said it might help if we were introduced by an *atbia danya* or a governor who was well-liked, and if they had seen an official letter. I asked him how long he thought it would take to build sufficient trust if the other conditions were met, and he said maybe only a few months for some people.

We continued down to Dij Ersha. The first part of the most-direct route was a steep drop through rock ledges that was like descending a 300-foot ladder. The rest of the way was steep, but it was loose, wet, gravelly soil and thorn bushes - and we didn't need to use our hands for any of it. There weren't many people in Dij Ersha when we arrived. We greeted an old man as we walked among the compounds and he was congenial, so we stopped and asked if we could explain why we had come and maybe get some advice from him on how to proceed.

He was amused and said, "*Tadius*," meaning, in this case, "Why not?" After Kadir gave the quick overview, he grinned and said he'd heard something about us and wondered if we would join him for coffee in his house. His wife was not pleased when she saw us enter, but she made coffee as we sat with her husband on the bench-like seat at the edge of the round stone-walled house. The man said he would take the *ferengi* vaccination, so I vaccinated him and he said it wasn't so bad. He called his wife over; she was distressed but complied. Then he told us to relax and wait for coffee while he went outside for a minute. He returned, several times, with squealing children for us to vaccinate.

The old man told us the smallpox history of Dij Ersha. A five-year-old child brought smallpox to Dij Ersha when he returned from Bakele Midir, a village high on the Gera Midir side of the canyon. This occurred after *Fasika* (Ethiopian Orthodox Easter) in mid-April. The boy I met at the funeral, and his sister, both eventually contracted the disease. In addition, the old man said he'd heard there was active smallpox in the nearby village of Aydips.

We thanked the old man for the hospitality and information, and then moved on to the rumored cases at Aydips, a solitary compound around a buttress ridge from Dij Ersha and up a draw. A teenage boy was struggling with a team of oxen and a plow. He took a break when we came near and told us that, yes this was Aydips, and yes the children were sick with smallpox. The teenage boy had fresh pits himself.

We went to the compound gate and called for someone to come out and speak with us. The dog in the compound repeatedly charged the gate, showing fangs and barking loudly. Finally, a woman carrying a young child appeared in the doorway of the house, and then another child looked out from behind the woman and clasped her waist. Both children were well into the pustular stage of smallpox.

Ato Kebede, the homeowner, wasn't around and his wife wouldn't give us permission to enter the compound. So we yelled at each other to be heard across the compound and over the barking dog. Kebede's wife was surprisingly free with information on names, dates, circumstances, and places where smallpox was contracted. At least we could complete the case form, but the information was troubling.

The children at Aydips contracted smallpox from the Dij Ersha kids by variolation, the *Habisha* vaccination. Variolation was performed by transferring pus or scabs from someone with active smallpox to another person through a cut in the skin, commonly at the left wrist. While variolation sometimes induced an immune reaction, other times it caused a full case of smallpox.

The teenager plowing the field was variolated first and came down with the rash about a week later. When he started to bloom, the two younger children were variolated from his pus and their rashes started about another week later. I asked Kebede's wife the dreaded question: "Has anyone from any other village visited with, or been variolated from, her children?" Indeed, she said a young married girl up in Chuko had been variolated recently. Kebede's wife insisted that she and her husband had taken the *ferengi* vaccination at the Rabel market. There was nothing left to do at Aydips, so we thanked Kebede's wife and left to return to Chuko to look for the young married girl and try again to vaccinate there.

We lost the trail several times and had to climb over and around rock ledges. Heavy, cold rain burst on us midway. Once we reached Chuko, we went door-to-door asking if we could shelter inside from the rain, but no one allowed us inside a house. Finally, one woman said we could sit under the thatch eaves at her compound entrance.

Wet, cold, tired, and miserable, we sat on the wooden threshold of the compound entrance, which gave little shelter. About half an hour passed before the rain let up to a drizzle. A woman from another compound brought us freshly made *injera*! Kadir and I virtually inhaled it. Then the woman who had given us permission to sit at the compound entrance came out and asked why we had come to this village and why we hadn't left yet.

Kadir explained we had come to find smallpox and vaccinate people for their own protection. She wasn't convinced and repeated her questions. I asked her about the young married girl who had been variolated. The woman said the girl didn't have smallpox, but she had been in a fever for the last couple of days. According to the information we were given at Aydips, it had been about a week since she received the variolation, and a couple of days of fever before the onset of the rash was classic smallpox.

Kadir asked the woman where the girl in question lived, but she said she didn't know. Then I asked the other woman, who brought us the *injera*, if she knew where the girl lived. She wouldn't say and I could tell from her pained expression that she felt betrayed by being put on the spot in front of her neighbor after extending the generous food gift to us.

We offered thanks and good wishes and then tried one more time to persuade people at Chuko to take the vaccination. Most people ignored us. One man told us not to worry about it since everyone in the village was healthy. Another told us, with a wide grin, that the young married girl we were trying to find had just run from the house we were coming to next. When we went to that house, the people wouldn't open the door. With a fresh case starting in a fairly large village, there was a chance that others would contract and pass the disease so it could continue through-out the rainy season, especially with variolation so popular in this part of the canyons.

We had no choice but to return to camp. The day had gone about the same for Temesgen and Demessie. In a twisted way perhaps, this was a bit reassuring for me in the sense that all of us met with a lack of coop-eration, not just the *ferengis*. On the positive side, Temesgen thought it likely there were no active cases to the west end of the canyon complex. But he said that many people in Gishe really believed we had come to suck their blood, or take their blood back to Addis to cook into a dark-art potion, or steal their land, or poison their livestock. Clearly, they just wanted to be left alone.

On Tuesday morning, May 28th, we moved to Dij Ersha in two groups. The night before, when Temesgen and I discussed what happened in Chuko on Monday, Temesgen said he would like to go to Chuko with Kadir to try his luck at vaccinating, and then take the steep, direct route to Dij Ersha. So Demessie, Makonen, and I and all the animals followed the Rabel – Mehal Meda route to the level of Dij Ersha and then traversed to the village. Camping at Dij Ersha placed us near the only trail access to Lele Gedel from that part of the canyons. Lele Gedel was the mountain end of a long plateau finger that started near the head of the Kechene canyon and then pinched out in the middle of the canyon.

Unfortunately, Temesgen and Kadir's side trip to Chuko was for naught also. The girl who had been variolated ran away, again, as they approached. The few people who would talk with them said that everyone in Chuko had been vaccinated in the Rabel market. So it goes.

On Wednesday, May 29th, our objective was to search and vaccinate at Lele Gedel. Temesgen, Demessie, Kadir, and I got up early and left camp together in a cold gusty drizzle. We descended to the river and then climbed about 2,500 feet to the populated level of Lele Gedel. Magnificent views down the canyon expanded as we gained elevation.

Temesgen and Demessie searched and vaccinated the north side of the mountain while Kadir and I similarly worked the south side. It was a long day with little success. There were children with fresh scars from smallpox in every village but few people would talk to us and no one took the vaccination on the south side of Lele Gedel. Frequently we were told to go away before we could finish our introduction.

Temesgen and Demessie found active cases and vaccinated 23 people on the north side of Lele Gedel and, like Kadir and I, they also found many recent cases. Apparently we had arrived as the outbreak that raged on this mountain for months, aided by variolation, seemed to be abating. Even so, the possibility of new cases coming from currently active cases remained, and it was extra frustrating that people in the canyons, where we were finding active cases and variolation, seemed most opposed to taking the vaccination.

On Thursday, May 30th, we crossed the Kechene river on the main Mehal Meda – Rabel route and climbed about half-way up the Gera Midir wall. Temesgen had ridden ahead for the last portion of the trip. When we caught up with him, he was sitting on a rock with a jug of *tella* and several drinking gourds he had purchased at the nearby village. So we had an impromptu farewell party before our teams split up. We reminisced about events over the previous three and a half weeks. And we toasted each other, and the other expedition members, and our animals as we drank gourds-full of cool refreshing *tella* and strained barley husks with our teeth.

After the *tella* was gone and we lingered over yet a few more good-byes, Temesgen and Demessie took two donkeys with their provisions and headed over to the nearby village. They would check the Gera Midir wall to the east as far as they could find villages. Then they would return to the Ashen school, leave the donkeys with the teachers, and drive back to Addis in order to meet prior commitments the following week.

Kadir, Makonen, and I had the remaining two donkeys and the two mules. We would search and vaccinate westward along the Gera Midir wall, then cross back to the Gishe side and continue along the western edge of Gishe to Kai Amba in Del *mikitil woreda* to rendezvous with Peter and Lewis. Then, all together again, we would swing by Abuye Meda near the northernmost point of Gishe, follow the top of the escarpment along the eastern edge of the plateau, and eventually retrace our steps through the

Gwasa and return to the Ashen school. That is, to end the expedition, the "west Canyon" team was beginning a full circle tour around Gishe from a position only a few hours from where we started the expedition 24 days before.

Friday was an easy day of checking villages on our way to Kola Niski, which was located near the river at the west end of the Kechene canyon. But on Saturday, June 1st, we were on the trail almost continually all day. Our plan was to head generally northward, searching and vaccinating as far as we could get on the canyon wall on the west side of Gishe. In particular, Temesgen had asked me to check Arada when we got to this area because it was near the village where he found seven active cases not far below the Gishe plateau at Daier Mariam.

Soon after leaving Kola Niski, we crossed the Kechene river and picked up the trail again on the Gishe side. We rounded a bend and dropped down to the gravel bed where the Dimbuko tributary flows into the Kechene. There was no apparent trail on the other side. But there was a man resting on a rock nearby. We exchanged greetings with the man who asked where we were going. Defying all odds, he too was going to Arada. And here we came upon him, as if he were waiting for us, at the very point where the trail disappeared. All this on market day at Rabel during which we met no other travelers between Kola Niski and Arada. The man suggested that we travel together and, of course, we agreed.

No trail was apparent because the bed of the Kechene river was the trail there. Eventually we left the river bed and started climbing. We climbed for about three hours until, maybe 800 feet below the plateau, we reached Arada where compounds were distributed about a bowl that connects the Daier Mariam table top with the Daier plateau finger. We thanked our guide for his help and I offered to pay him for showing us the way, but he wouldn't accept payment.

Nearly everyone from Arada had gone to the Rabel market. Our group stopped to rest between some compounds at a rock that served as a bench. We snacked on the last of our packaged dates and drank water from my canteen that had been sterilized with iodine pills and smelled and tasted like industrial chemicals.

An old man came out of a nearby compound. He leaned forward on his *dula*, adjusted his *gabi*, and studied us and our animals. I asked if he had heard of any smallpox in the area. He asked if I meant the *ferengi* smallpox or the *Habisha* smallpox. I said we were interested in all kinds of smallpox. He chuckled and said there wasn't any kind of smallpox around anyway. And anticipating my next question, he said that everyone in Arada was already vaccinated. So much for finishing the vaccination buffer around cases that Temesgen had found.

I asked if the man knew where we could buy *tella* in Arada. He said no, but we could have some *karare* if we wanted it. *Karare* is called "second *tella*" because it comes from leftovers from the *tella*-making process. When a batch of *tella* is ready, it is poured into earthenware storage jugs through cloth to filter out barley husks. The filtered residue is mixed with water to make *karare*. *Karare* doesn't taste very good and is mostly given to children because it is something to drink and they won't get drunk from it. The man called for his wife to bring us *karare*, and we took turns drinking the extremely sour liquid from a gourd.

We thanked the man and his wife, and I asked the man if he could show us the trail back down to the canyon crossing on the way to Kai Amba in Del. He led us up the path from the village to a saddle half a mile away. We could see parts of trails in the distance but the angle made it difficult to set a course with confidence. The man drifted back to Arada while giving non-answers to our questions about specific directions.

We could see Del mountain in the distance. Still, we knew it would be easy to start with an apparently promising, but incorrect, trail that would lead to a round-about route and extend the journey considerably. I told Kadir and Makonen to rest at the saddle while I went to a point jutting from the Daier Mariam table where I could get a commanding view of the Wenchet canyon complex and maybe see a route to Kai Amba.

In the raw geography of high plateaus and deep canyons, it was clear that the canyons were once filled with continuous rock layers that eroded and were carried to the Nile from these source tributaries. And the brooding dark clouds in the distance were bringing monsoon rain - the source of summer floods that miraculously nourished Egyptian desert agriculture with Ethiopian silt from those eroded rocks, and enriched the pharaohs for more than a thousand years.

At closer range, I could see a trail that passed down to patches of farmland in the lower half of the canyon. Afternoon shadows were lengthening. We still had a long descent to the next village, Amaya, where we could camp. And it would be another full day's journey the following day to get to Kai Amba.

After reaching Amaya and making camp, we spread the word that we would like to hire a guide to Kai Amba the next day. We found a man later that evening who said he would guide us for the very good *ferengi* rate of E$2. But the next morning, Sunday, June 2nd, he refused to join us. We followed the well-worn trail along a route that stayed fairly level across a low shelf with similar experience at each village we passed: no guide, no smallpox, no vaccinations. Then the trail turned upward and we climbed steadily to a village on the side of a buttress ridge. People in the village said the main Rabel-Del route was on the other side of the ridge.

We followed a clear trail out of the village in that direction, alternating rides on the mules, traveling in silence, pretty well burnt out from four weeks of camp living and continual motion. The trail wound ever northward and rose about two-thirds of the way up the canyon wall. Below us the canyon narrowed and a long plateau finger between Del mountain and the Gishe plateau complicated the picture because none of us knew exactly where Kai Amba was on Del mountain or where we should descend to cross the river. The trail we were following didn't feel right, but there were no apparent alternatives.

At the next village, we were told there was a path that dropped down to cross the river at the point where the long plateau finger ended in the canyon. On the other side of the river, we were to follow a canyon to the west and start climbing where the third stream came in from the right. They said we could reach Kai Amba by dark.

We moved on. We were getting even with the end of the plateau finger. It looked like there was a trail down a steep draw ahead. But the trail we were following continued traversing the canyon wall. I guessed we should take the high trail a bit farther, but Makonen thought we should follow the trail dropping down. The issue was left hanging and we kept moving.

I was riding Murphy about 30 yards in front of our group when I reached the trail dropping down. Feeling then that Makonen's guess was probably more reliable than mine, and being impatient to start descending, I dismounted and led Murphy down the trail. I continued for about 10 minutes before turning to see how the others were doing. No one was following me.

I sat on a rock to rest and wait. A few flies circled around. Time passed, probably another 10 minutes. I was vacantly waving away flies with my hand when one slipped by and got caught between my glasses and my left eye. I was so irritated that I jumped and shouted an angry outburst as if by reflex.

All the while I had been loosely holding the reins to Murphy who stood resting in front of me. When I suddenly jumped off the rock and shouted, Murphy reared back, jerking hard on the reins. Caught off balance, I pitched forward to my knees, banging and scraping myself on some rocks. The pain and my awkward position shocked me into realizing that I had to regain focus.

I made a quick assessment: my name is Warren; this is Lewis's mule Murphy; I must get up from the ground; I must find Kadir and Makonen; it is clear they are not on this trail; there is still a long road ahead to Kai Amba; time to move – now!

I stood up and recognized that Murphy was very uneasy – and undoubtedly tired, thirsty, and hungry. I told him to relax, but he didn't. His eyes were fiery. I turned to start back up the trail, expecting that movement would be calming for both of us. But in two steps the reins went taut. Murphy was holding his ground. My emotional reserves were exhausted. I begged: "Please Murphy. Just place one foot in front of another and we'll be on our way."

I tried tugging at the reins a few times but he pulled his head back and locked his legs in a stand-off stance. Then I could feel the frustration rise unreasonably and a few circuits blew. I started yelling at Murphy and

Tight canyon area of the Zagol River crossing en route to Kai Amba, June 1974. Photo by the author.

moved up close and then, to my horror and shame, I whipped him at the ears with the ends of the reins. Murphy threw back his head and reared. The leather strap that went behind his ears and connected with the bit ripped apart and I could feel the reins go slack in my hand. Murphy was watching me closely and holding still. I was watching him closely and holding the reins gingerly. If he backed off again, the bit would slide out of his mouth and I would have no control over him. I was scared.

We stared at each other for perhaps a minute, flies buzzing around both of us. I slowly waved a hand in front of my face and Murphy held still. I needed to get close to him and reset a bridle of some sort. A couple of more minutes passed. Then I started sweet talking in a soft voice and moved slowly toward him. We were watching each other closely in a locked gaze that was holding us together while the reins were worthless.

Murphy let me get close. I stopped even with his head and calmly kept saying: "Oosh, oosh," like Makonen did when the donkeys got ornery at loading times. With both reins in one hand, I slowly raised my free palm below his chin. Murphy liked to be scratched in the soft spot under his chin and between his cheekbones.

As I cooed and scratched him, Murphy lowered his head and the fire left his eyes. I slowly reached for the coil of spare rope slung over the saddle horn. I let go of the reins and put a loop of rope into his mouth and over his nose. He stood still while I slipped the bit out and brought the loop down under his chin. I crossed the rope, closed the loop fairly tight, and brought the two ends of the rope (the new reins) back behind his head. Cautiously, I mounted, strapped the bit and old reins to the back of the saddle, and took a deep breath. I patted him gently on the neck, hoping we could be buddies again. He started walking with a little coaxing from my heels. Up we went. A voice in my head said *"Tadius,"* meaning, in this case, "Imagine that."

We returned to the higher trail and followed it northward. I could recognize Kadir, Makonen, and the animals ahead as we traversed around the next buttress. They were beyond shouting distance, but it was a great relief to see them. Soon we were back together and we figured out the mix-up. About the time that I took the downward trail, Kadir and Makonen had passed some travelers returning from the market at Kai Amba who told them to stay on the high trail past the next ridge where they would find the trail down to the river crossing we wanted.

It was a steep trail down the side of the ridge. At the river we let the animals drink their fill. When it was time to continue, I climbed onto Murphy for the river crossing. I pulled on the right strand of rope to direct him into the water and then felt the rope come loose and dangle freely in my right hand. Murphy had chewed through it. This, and the reins earlier, and Lewis's encounter with the donkey tail, played as recast déjà vu of the Land Rover gear-shift shaft breaking loose in my hand the day we drove up to begin the expedition.

For a few moments I felt disconnected from the physical setting while sensing an interwoven fabric of meaning and circumstance. Battle-weary soldiers wandering lost and found in deep maze pathways through the heart of Abyssinia, homeland to Ethiopia's royal descendants of Solomon and Sheba. But before I got totally lost in my reverie, Murphy started following Konjit who Makonen was riding across the river. The now-defunct improvised reins were no longer needed.

The rest of the day was simple endurance, a drill we knew well. After about a mile of easy travel on the floor of the canyon, we turned right and started the long climb to Kai Amba near the flat top of Del mountain. With a steady stream of marketgoers returning from Kai Amba, we always met people to point out the route. Also they told us there wasn't any active or recent smallpox on the southern end of Del mountain.

As we entered Kai Amba, several children came up to us and asked if we wanted to meet the other *ferengis* in town. *Tadius!* And soon the Highland group and west Canyon team were back together. A quick exchange of summaries for the last week confirmed no finds of active smallpox outside of the Kechene canyon and the southwest edge of the Gishe plateau, so we could shift our attention from smallpox to the trip back to the Ashen school.

Later that night, sitting on my cot drinking tea spiced with the last of our cinnamon, and writing by candle light as the bright moon cast shadows outside, I savored the richness of the experiences I'd been privileged to share with my expedition companions and others encountered along the way.

REACHING THE END

Monday, June 3rd, was a day to rest and prepare for the journey around the northern and eastern edges of the Gishe highlands. But we had to modify our plans after we received an urgent summons to meet with the *mikitil woreda* governor, *Balambaras* Bereded Mashile, who had been informed of a smallpox outbreak in Maya Kola (southwest of Kai Amba) by the *atbia danya* of that area. Bereded read an official petition ordering us, as government workers in his *mikitil woreda*, to investigate the rumored outbreak.

It seemed ironic that, as we were about to leave after spending three weeks in Gishe (sometimes frustrated over government inaction), the government in Gishe was formally ordering our expedition to cooperate. Furthermore, we were skeptical because we heard no rumors of cases for that area during travel in the region by the west Canyon team, or while

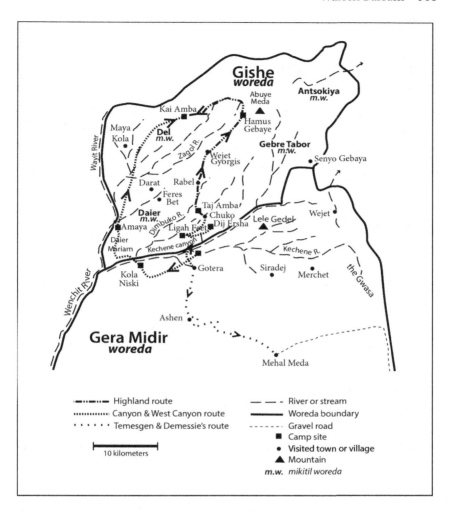

Return routes to the Ashen school.

working the Kai Amba market by the Highland group. Regardless, we needed to remove doubt about an outbreak.

Taking the whole caravan by a route via Maya Kola would have been a repeat of the first-day canyon-descent disaster many times over. Peter volunteered to check the rumor with Tariku and Haile. They traveled light and fast with only two mules. But there was no outbreak of smallpox - or chicken pox or measles. Rather, the *atbia danya*'s wife was seriously ill, perhaps with typhus or flu, and he had hoped a *ferengi* doctor could cure her. Lewis and I, with Kadir, Getahun, Makonen, Orion, Murphy and the donkeys made the highland traverse more or less as planned. The Maya Kola team and Befekadu (who finished his rounds of Gera Midir without finding new cases) were already at Ashen when our caravan arrived.

We thought that the expedition had found all the then-active cases in Gishe. And, with new vaccinations, we had added immunity overall beyond what local variolations and recovered cases provided. So it was at least possible that smallpox transmission would be interrupted in Gishe with the help of the summer rains and the difficult terrain. And the records and reports we provided to SEP could be used to expedite follow-up operations.

IN CONCLUSION

A few thoughts on how Peace Corps experiences influenced my life and career:

I grew up in Chicago with little outdoor, nature experience. I entered the Peace Corps right after college, attracted by idealism and curiosity about different cultures and far-away places. Actually I was a PCV in Malaysia for two years (TB Control with the Department of Aborigine Affairs) before rejoining to work with the SEP in Ethiopia. I rejoined because I didn't have a clear idea yet of a career direction, but I looked forward to working again with a traditional culture that was largely uninfluenced by western culture, and to having back-country experiences and challenges perhaps analogous to extended treks in the jungle.

By the time of the Gishe expedition, it had finally dawned on me that I wanted to learn the stories behind different landscapes and the wildlife that inhabited them. So my plan after returning from Ethiopia was to move out west (Idaho) where I could take a few classes in geology and wildlife (with great examples nearby) and then head to the jungles and mountains of South America to try freelance natural history photojournalism. But soon I was hooked on geology especially (leading to a PhD), and Idaho in general (where I've lived most of the time since 1975). With the PhD, I did a little wandering in government and consulting before settling in academia as a research professor. Along the way I've looked for international opportunities such as leading several treks in Nepal and working on international research collaborations, including hosting post-docs on fellowships from Germany, Switzerland, and Italy.

That is, from my Peace Corps experiences I finally recognized a general direction that really interested me. Also I've been comfortable making mid-course adjustments as the picture and implications progressively clarified (fundamental Peace Corps skill). And I regularly draw on the understanding that "different" does not imply better or worse, but does offer the opportunity to broaden perspectives and enter additional dimensions. And the lure of different cultures and far-away lands continues.

•

15

Meeting Ciro and Doing Smallpox

by Michael Santarelli

In mid-August 1972, I was in the small town of Welkite, looking for anything with four wheels that would take me north to Addis Ababa, the capital of Ethiopia. The long monsoon season was winding down, as was my two-year Peace Corps Volunteer (PCV) service. Within a short time, I had to decide whether to extend for another year or go back to California.

I had been living with the Gurage (Gu-rah-gee) people deep in the bush country of southwest Shoa province, serving as an Agricultural/Rural Development (AG/RD) Volunteer.

The Gurage people, like other Ethiopians engaged in subsistence living, had a limited offering of food. Their staple crop, *ensete edulis*, commonly known as the false banana plant, was their principal source of nutrition. From the trunk of *ensete*, the Gurage would make a bread-like substance called *qoch'o*, which served as their primary food. While *qoch'o's* nutritional value may be questioned, its cultural and social value cannot. The Gurage culture revolved around the planting, nurturing and harvesting of *ensete*. Friends, family and neighbors would come together during certain times of the year to plant, transplant, prune and harvest the *ensete*. The labor became a social event, allowing family and friends to share in the latest gossip and clan news. After eight years growth, involving no less than three transplants, the false banana plant was harvested and made into *qoch'o*. It was believed that one false banana plant could provide enough *qoch'o* to sustain a family of six for a few weeks, which, when considering the time and energy involved, did not provide much bang for the buck. Even so, due to the widespread availability, and long-term storage capability of *qoch'o*, hunger may have been ubiquitous, but famine was not. My purpose as a PCV was to supplement *qoch'o* with additional foods.

After moving into the village of Gofrer, I lived with a growing family of ten in a two-room, tin-roofed house and started introducing vegetables, good egg-laying chickens and meat producing rabbits. In addition, the Gurage villagers supported a trial demonstration of growing four types of grain in virgin soil that was turned over and broken up by hand-held, two-pronged digging sticks. When the soil was ready, we sowed corn, sorghum, wheat and *teff*, the indigenous grain of Ethiopia, giving half of each plot an application of synthetic nitrogen fertilizer.

Those efforts ended with varying degrees of success . . . or failure, depending on your point of view.

For instance, after our extensive and thriving vegetable garden was flattened by baseball-sized hail, we learned to plant only root and tuber crops, like beets, carrots and potatoes, for they would still produce a crop if it hailed.

We could not, however, stop the nightly visits of hungry hyenas that simply terrified the outdoor, hutch-enclosed rabbits. That fear caused the rabbits to eat their young upon birth.

The egg laying chickens did well, but cats slowed down their propagation by picking off the small chicks, one by little one.

Of the four-grain trials, the only one that did well, actually, did very well, in the virgin soil was *teff*, the indigenous crop, but it needed fertilizer.

Through it all though, my two-years living with the Gurage in Ethiopia was an incredible experience. There were some difficulties from time to time to be sure, but the innate hospitality and generosity of the Gurage more than compensated for any trials and tribulations endured. And when you're living out in the bush for extended periods of time, without electricity, running water, or much to eat, trials and tribulations would indeed arise. However, the Gurage's native camaraderie, along with their energy and humor, as well as their cohesiveness of family, village and clan, not to mention their looking out for me, always lifted my spirits. Spirits that needed lifting especially after nights of sweating through hallucinatory fevers or days of diarrhea caused by gut wrenching intestinal parasites.

Over the two years of my assignment, my weight had dropped below high school levels and chronic fatigue had settled in. My 26-year-old body was inclined to go home, but my mind was not. I was learning more than I was teaching by coping with the daily challenges of living a self-reliant life in an African country — a country populated by strong, hard-working people in a topographically diverse environment full of lakes, mountains, deserts and forests.

One could not help but admire the people, enjoy the temperate weather, be interested in the culture and want to see more of the country. Furthermore, after living so long in the bush, I became well conversant in the national language, Amharic, which greatly facilitated my daily interaction with the people. The enchanted Empire of Ethiopia ruled by His Imperial Majesty, Emperor Haile Selassie the First, Conquering Lion of the Tribe of Judah, King of Kings and God Elect, was a great place to be young and adventurous. It would be hard to leave.

HITCHING A RIDE TO ADDIS ABABA

So, there I was, trying to get out of Welkite, while figuring out my life's next step.

I had arrived in Welkite mid-morning after hoofing the two miles from my Peace Corps village, Gofrer, on my way to the market town of Emdiber where I hoped to find transport to Addis. Since there was no bus service from Emdiber to Welkite, private entrepreneurs filled the transportation gap with old, well-used Toyota pickup trucks and Land Rovers. The entrepreneurs did not provide regularly scheduled service so no one ever knew when, or if, a passenger-carrying vehicle would come into town. You just had to sit and wait and hope.

Remarkably, after only waiting a couple of hours, a pale-green, long wheelbase Land Rover chugged into town overloaded with passengers eager to disembark. The driver told me he would return to Welkite if, and only if, he had another full load of passengers.

A couple of more hours passed before the Rover finally filled beyond capacity with travelers determined-to-squeeze-in, tightly wound over-sized bundles, terrified chickens . . . and me. After a cozy, cheek by jowl, 40-minute ride, where everyone got to know each other a little better, we arrived in Welkite, cramps and all.

Aside from some *buna bets*, (coffee houses) that offered limited hot food and, on a good day, some lukewarm beer, Welkite had the one and only postal service within many miles. When here, I would collect a month or two of mail from friends and family and read about their seemingly over-whelming concerns with faulty electric garage doors, clogged plumbing, and the incredibly exasperating "ring-around-the-toilet." The highlight of the mostly machine stamped collection of envelopes was always from an old friend in L.A. who tried hopelessly to beat me in chess. We had been playing chess by mail for a few years and he still could not penetrate my Sicilian Defense. In another move, I would have the advantage and be able to close in on his king. I was saving that letter for last.

Walking north away from the commercial stalls, I found some splotchy shade offered by a struggling acacia tree and sat down, hoping to catch a ride. It wasn't looking good. The road in either direction was as empty as a beggar's cup, and as silent as a lion on the hunt. Furthermore, the sun's position in the equatorial sky indicated the so-called "Jimma bus," coming up from the south, would have already gone by. So, my chances of reaching Addis by the end of the day were limited to flagging down a late-running short haul bus to the next town where more transportation was available, or hitching a ride.

Half of the mail remained unopened when I heard the faint sound of a motor approaching from the south. Cocking my head, I heard the distinct sound of tires scrunching the rocky roadway. A minute later, I could see a fast-moving car coming my way. I jumped onto the road and readied myself to flag it down. As it approached, I flung my right hand high over my head and waved it back and forth, but the vehicle flew past me like I wasn't even there. As it sped by, I caught a glimpse of two male foreigners sitting in a long wheelbase Land Rover with windows rolled up, enjoying the air conditioning.

As they made their unconcerned high-speed run north, I yelled out some choice Amharic insults, which, unfortunately, lose a lot in the English translation, *"What kind of people are you? Where's your father?"*[1]

As I was ranting and raving, a Gurage passerby gave me a strange look.

"Those are bad people," I told him, and he didn't seem to disagree.

There was nothing to do but return to the filtered shade, where I continued to dwell upon the choice I had to make. To stay in Ethiopia or not to stay . . . that was the question. Compounding my decision was the fact that I had grown accustomed to village life and had made a strong connection with the villagers and the family I lived with. If I left and went home, not only was I sure I'd miss Ethiopia, but I'd miss everyone in Gofrer, and the many social activities with which I had become familiar.

I would certainly miss the sunrise gatherings for the preparation of homegrown *buna* (coffee), in which we sat together watching sleeping embers stirred to life. We'd stare as eucalyptus cuttings strained to catch fire, all the while hearing fresh coffee beans being pounded into course, flavorful bits just outside the door. With the fire established, a large clay coffee pot, the *jebena*, holding liters of water carried from afar, would be set over the climbing flame. As steam blew from the raging boil, handfuls of fresh *buna* grounds were dropped into the *jebena*, followed by a fistful of hard rock salt. After 5 to 10 minutes, the piping hot, black brew would be served all around in small *sini* (handleless cups) and the 15, or more, of those of us assembled would drink until the *jebena* could pour no more.

I'd also miss the informal evening assembly, the *sebseba*, that usually began after sundown and was attended by the head of household, who was village chief and clan arbitrator, along with nearby villagers and any house guests. We would sit around the dim light of a single kerosene candle and talk about that day's AG project, or the *tukul*, (hut) being built for my future residence, as well as plans for the morrow while munching

---

1 Note: italics are used for all translations of Amharic conversations.

on enough *qoch'o* and roasted barley to cheat starvation for yet another day. It rarely failed that a bottle of *areki* (the local brew), would make its appearance. *Areki* was a strong alcoholic beverage distilled from *gesho* leaves and fermented barley and served in shot glasses. Two shots gave a nice buzz; four shots and the drinker developed a thick, but loose, tongue. More shots after that and you would wake up the next morning wondering if the tribal name, Gurage, had any connection with how you felt.

As I sat in the sparse shade along the side of the road, going over the pros and cons of staying or going, I heard the faint sound of a vehicle once again. Soon a short wheelbase Toyota Land Cruiser appeared racing up the road towards me. I tried waving it down, but it shot past me like a black mamba snake on a mission. Once again, two people had the whole car to themselves with plenty of room for a third. As it sped by, the *ferengi* (foreigner) riding shotgun gave me a quick look then turned all the way around to stare at me. The vehicle was going so fast I couldn't tell who it was, but since it kept moving, what did it matter?

"What kind of people are you?" I yelled, as the car sped away.

"Bad, terrible people!" I said, answering myself using insulting Amharic vernacular.

I was not happy.

But just as I was returning to the shade, I saw brake lights! The car was stopping! Then it started coming back in reverse at almost the same speed it passed me! I grabbed my backpack and started moving towards the fast-moving vehicle. When it stopped, there was my friend and fellow AG/RD PCV Russ Burkey grinning ear to ear through the rolled-up window. The car skidded to a stop just as Russ jumped out.

"Get in! Get in! Quick! Quick," Russ yelled, pulling his seat forward.

No one had to tell me twice. I dove into the backseat headfirst while shouting out the national greeting.

"Tenayistilegne, Russ!"

Russ slammed the seat against my knees and jumped back inside, just before the Cruiser jerked forward.

"Tenayistilegne," Russ said, turning my way with a full-faced grin.

"Thanks for picking me up," I yelled, over the accelerating engine noise.

"Not a problem," the driver yelled back while giving me a quick glance.

"This is Ciro," Russ said, pointing to the driver, who turned my way with a broad smile.

"And this is Mikael," (my name in Amharic) Russ continued. "Mikael is an AG/RD guy too."

"Nice to meet you, Ciro, I really appreciate this ride."

"No problem."

"Ciro is from Brazil. He's doing smallpox eradication work here in Ethiopia," Russ explained.

Ciro looked my way while keeping his right foot pressed on the gas and said, "You and Russ are friends?"

"Yeah, we're in the same Peace Corps group, thirteen, that trained in Awassa."

"So you have been in Ethiopia a long time, too," Ciro said, pushing his long brown hair back.

"Yeah, same as Russ."

"Russ is going home," Ciro announced.

"Russ, you're going home?" I asked.

"Yeah," Russ explained with that deliberate Midwest tone, "Gotta get back to the farm in Nebraska. Need to get the beans and corn in this year. What about you?"

I swayed towards the window when the car swerved to avoid a donkey cart overloaded with forage. "I'm not sure. Hate to go, but maybe?"

Russ nodded. "I know what you mean. It's a good country. Great people. I wouldn't leave, but I have to."

"I'm not keen on leaving either, but I am a little worn out."

"Why don't you do smallpox?" Ciro interjected, looking at me through the rear-view mirror.

"Do what?" I asked.

"Do smallpox! There are many Peace Corps in the program now. We have openings."

"Well . . . I don't know. What's 'doing smallpox?'"

"Just look for smallpox and vaccinate the people," he said with a grin.

"That's it? Sounds pretty simple."

Ciro turned my way and waved a hand in the air. He then briefly explained that the Smallpox Eradication Program (SEP) had begun the previous year and that they were still looking for vaccinators. The SEP had begun in Addis Ababa and in the four southwest provinces of Illubabor, Welega, Gemu Gofa and Kaffa. They never expected that 26,000-plus smallpox cases would be recorded in the first year alone, and now realize just how widespread smallpox was.

"We need more people," Ciro said.

After hearing Ciro explain the SEP, I was interested, but not convinced.

"There is a big problem up north," he continued. "The villages are far apart from each other, and we cannot get into some areas because of difficult terrain, and when we do, the people don't want to be vaccinated. That is a big problem," he reiterated. "We need a plane or something."

"I can fly a plane," I blurted out.

"You are a pilot?" Ciro asked.

"Well, I've got a private pilot's license and have flown in Ethiopia."

"OK, you can be the pilot! Come to the office tomorrow," he told me, just like that!

"Well . . . I . . . uh . . .," I looked to Russ for help.

"Ciro is one of the directors. He can hire," Russ said.

I looked back at Ciro, but before I could say anything, the Cruiser came to a skidding stop and the driver's door flew open. The next thing I saw was the back of a blue shirt streaking across the road, then pushing its way into thick bushes until it disappeared.

"What's up with him?" I asked Russ.

"He's got the trots."

"I'd say he's got the gallops!"

"He's had diarrhea since yesterday. We've already stopped twice."

"I can empathize, believe me."

Russ nods, "Oh yeah."

Russ and I caught up on Ethiopian exploits and agricultural endeavors while waiting for our driver to return.

Minutes later, Ciro walked up, still tucking in his shirt. "When you gotta go, you gotta go."

With that, he piled back behind the wheel, fired up the Land Cruiser, punched the pedal to the metal and we surged forward.

"Let's see if we can make it to Addis this time," Ciro said as the Toyota raced forward.

"So, you're going to be our new pilot?" Ciro said, turning to me.

"Well, I don't know? Tell me more about 'doing smallpox.'"

"I will tomorrow. Come to the office in the morning and we can talk then."

"OK, where's the office?" I asked, not sure if I would go.

"In the Telecommunications Building." Russ chimed in.

After one more unscheduled, sudden stop along the roadside, we arrived in Addis where I was dropped off at a common PCV crash pad located away from the downtown area.

After Russ and I said our last goodbyes, Ciro said, "See you tomorrow," with complete confidence.

"Yeah, and thanks again for the ride."

TRANSFER TO THE SEP

By mid-morning the next day, I found myself standing in front of the multi-storied Telecommunications Building. I rode the elevator up a few floors, walked down a narrow hallway and found the smallpox office.

Ciro saw me as soon as I opened the door.

"Good morning. Glad you made it. Come, follow me."

Ciro brought me into the office of Dr. Kurt Weithaler, the Director of the SEP in Ethiopia and Senior WHO Advisor, and introduced me — to my astonishment — as the "pilot" for the smallpox program. Dr. Weithaler greeted me with a strong accent and stronger handshake.

"So you can fly a plane?" Weithaler asked.

"I've got a private pilot's license and have flown in Addis a few times while here," I replied.

Dr. Weithaler nodded, then proceeded to explain the smallpox situation north of Addis in somewhat similar terms as Ciro's, saying Ethiopia was a huge country with many villages far from one another and that they were finding a lot of smallpox in that area. Aside from the problem of the people being resistant to vaccination, too much time was spent getting to those distant villages. The Program needed a faster way to get into those areas, search for smallpox, vaccinate, and get back out. Air transport would do the job.

"What kind of plane do you suggest?" Ciro asked.

"It must be bigger than the Cessna 150s I've been flying around here," I replied. "You would need more power to compensate for the high elevation."

"We have been thinking of one like this," Ciro said, showing me a photo of a Piper Cherokee 235.

I examined the photo and the specifications, and realized I would have to take some additional flight lessons on this larger aircraft. "OK. That looks good. I can get checked out in that plane when I'm back in the States."

"Checked out?" Dr. Weithaler inquired.

"Yes. I see this plane has a constant speed propeller and more horse-power than what I've been flying, so I need to be rated for it. I'll just need a half dozen solo hours flight time, and then I can get signed off on it."

Dr. Weithaler and Ciro look at each other. "Sounds good," Weithaler exclaimed.

"So when can you start?" Ciro asked.

As soon as I get back."

"Ok, we will call Peace Corps and tell them you are now with small-pox."

And so they did.

To this day, when people ask me how I got started in the SEP, I tell them: "I was hitchhiking in Ethiopia one day, when this Brazilian doctor with the runs picked me up."

LEAVING GOFRER

By the time I walked into the Peace Corps office, everyone already knew I was extending for another year. The staff welcomed me with genuine enthusiasm and a short stack of bureaucratic papers to sign. With that done, the staff wanted to make a reservation for my 30-day home leave break given to all PCVs between their second and third years of service, but I asked them to wait on that. I had to go back to my village first.

When I got back to Gofrer, the all-encompassing clouds were breaking up, which hinted that warm spring weather was soon on its way. During that night's *sebseba*, and after a couple *arekis*, I broke the news that, yes, I was going to stay in Ethiopia another year, but I would be working in another area for the SEP. They responded quietly and seemed to understand . . . then poured another shot.

When the day came for me to leave, some prominent elders and village friends gathered in the large, conical-shaped, thatched roof *tukul* that was built for my residence. We spoke light-heartedly about the good times we had, the change in the weather and the condition of the false banana crop. They thanked me for coming to Gurage country with new ideas, and I thanked them for showing me what life is all about. They wished me well, and a long happy and healthy life, while I encouraged them to continue growing beets, carrots and potatoes and to try sowing *teff*.

It wasn't easy packing up my things, but I was holding up pretty well until I stepped outside and was surprised to see hundreds of men, women and children standing like statues along the dirt roadway. I saw men I knew and others that knew of me; men who were helpful and others that could have been more so. I saw men from villages, near and far, who turned the soil, planted crops and brought in the harvest and other men who feared I would take their land. I saw women, strong women who hauled water, collected firewood, scrubbed clothes, went to market, bore the children and fed the family. And I saw women who lost a child from disease, or to the hyenas. I saw children, bare-footed and barely clothed, that tended the livestock, ran constant errands and ran from the scary PCV. They all stood motionless, not making a single sound, silently saying goodbye while staring at me . . . as I looked at them . . . and looked . . . and looked . . . as my life with the Gurage passed before my eyes. When I finally slipped back inside, nursing a wounded heart, I felt like I had just attended my own funeral.

HOME LEAVE

September and October are the best months to be in Northern California, especially if you find yourself in San Francisco. The depressing fog and annoying drizzle that haunt The City during the cold summer months of June, July and August, give way to clear, stunning days and pure, unadulterated, warm sunshine. My Peace Corps leave began by simply getting over jet lag and devouring anything resembling food on a plate.

After adjusting to my new California circadian rhythm, I started taking flying lessons in a single-engine, fixed wing Piper Cherokee at Half Moon Bay Airport. I started with a Piper 140, quickly moved up to the Piper 180 and after a few more solo hours, got into the Piper 235, the plane in the photo Ciro had showed me. After another half dozen hours of solo flight, the instructor signed me off and I was ready to fly for the SEP.

CHANGE OF PLANS AND NEW ASSIGNMENT

Days later I arrived back in Ethiopia and after adjusting to the 11-hour time change and 8000-foot elevation of Addis, I was ready to report to the SEP headquarters.

When I walked into the office, Ciro jumped up and greeted me with an enthusiastic handshake and sparkling smile. "Welcome back, Mikael. How was your trip? I see you gained some weight."

"It was good. Yeah, I gained 20 pounds!" I told Ciro. "I also got some good flying time in on that plane you showed me so I'm ready to go."

"Good. Come with me."

As soon as we entered Ciro's office, he told me right up front that the plan had changed. Rather than use a fixed wing aircraft to get into the countryside, they had decided to use a helicopter instead.

"There are no airfields up north where we have to go," Ciro said. "But a helicopter can land almost anywhere."

"Really?" I said, not expecting to hear that.

Ciro could see that I was a bit disappointed. And I was . . . to a certain extent. But from my previous flight experience in this mountainous terrain, I knew full well, that flying in Ethiopia was not going to be easy. There were frequent unexpected downdrafts, and even updrafts, to deal with, and tricky crosswinds during take-offs and landings were not that unusual. So although I was ready, able and willing to shuttle smallpox vaccinators around the country, perhaps it was for the best? But what was I going to do now?

"We still want you in the program," Ciro said. "You can have your choice of provinces to work in and we will give you a new Land Rover. OK?"

"OK. That sounds good," I replied.

I knew exactly where I wanted to go, "How about Gemu Gofa?"

"Sure. You got it." Ciro said. "We think we stopped smallpox there, but there are areas that might not have been searched. You can do that."

"Thanks."

During the next day, I received training on smallpox and information about the SEP. I was shown the clinical stages of smallpox, from rash to pustules to the last scab falling off. I learned about the typical centrifugal distribution of smallpox lesions and that smallpox lesions appeared on the palms of hands and soles of feet. Those clinical observations would help differentiate smallpox from chickenpox. If I wasn't sure about the diagnosis, I was to treat the case as smallpox and start containment procedures by isolating the case and vaccinating the nearby population. The training included how to reconstitute the freeze-dried smallpox vaccine; how to vaccinate using the multiple puncture technique with a two-pronged, bifurcated needle, which reminded me of the Gurage digging stick, and how to sterilize the needles after use. When I asked how I would treat a smallpox case, I was told there was no cure, the disease had to run its course.

After the training, Ciro updated me on the program in Gemu Gofa. I already knew that the SEP started the year before, but didn't know anything about the epidemiological situation or the staffing. He told me they were still finding thousands of cases in Ethiopia, mostly in the north, and that outbreaks were widespread. The staffing situation was improving because volunteers from Japan and Austria were supplementing the PCVs. As for Gemu Gofa, Ciro said that the previous PCVs had done a good job down there and left believing smallpox transmission had been interrupted. But since Gemu Gofa bordered the Sudan and Kenya, where cross border migration was common, it was still an important province that required surveillance and vaccination until it was declared smallpox-free.

He said I would be working with two government sanitarians, Girma Tiluhun and Kassaye Tessema, and another PCV, named Mark Weeks, all of whom were already down there. In addition to conducting smallpox surveillance and vaccination in the countryside, we were to visit all the schools, markets and clinics asking whether anyone had seen smallpox. In the field, even if smallpox was not found, we could still vaccinate the people in order to raise the overall immunity level. This was particularly true with the many nomadic tribes who roamed about and were difficult to locate. Once a month we were to send in a report. If no smallpox cases were found, we were to report the number of vaccinations performed and where. If we found smallpox, we were to include in the report the number of cases and deaths and the name, age and sex of each case. We also had to find out the smallpox history of the outbreak, meaning, where the first infected patient came from. "**Most important**," Ciro said, "**Any report or rumor of smallpox must be checked out, no matter what, because who knows if anyone will ever go there again? You could be the only one**."

With training complete, Ciro gave me the keys to a brand new 1972, blue Land Rover and a smallpox vaccination on my left arm for good luck. He also gave me a letter from Emperor Haile Selassie commanding the people to assist me in my smallpox eradication endeavors by providing food and accommodation. I was all set and eager to get started. Early the next day, I drove down to Gemu Gofa ready to experience a whole new series of adventures.

SMALLPOX HOUSE

I arrived in Arba Minch, the provincial capital of Gemu Gofa, near the end of day, exhausted from the eight-hour drive. After asking around for the *ferengi* (foreigner) doing smallpox, I was led to a small house in Sikela, the lower section of the two-tiered capital. I knocked on the painted door and was greeted by a short, thin, barefoot white guy wearing wire-rimmed glasses, shorts and a green t-shirt. He didn't have a scraggly beard like me, but his hair was long, like mine, and framed with long sideburns.

"I'm Mikael, here to do smallpox."

"I'm Mark, c'mon in."

Mark led me into a small single-story, two-bedroom house with bare wooden floors. He showed me my room and then gave me a semi-cold beer.

"Welcome to Gemu Gofa," he said.

After taking a long swig, Mark told me that because of the incessant rains and impassable roads, his smallpox surveillance was limited to checking the schools and nearby markets. Now though, with the rains over and me arriving, he was sure we could explore the whole province and find smallpox, if there was any.

Then we went into the living room, where I saw a huge map of the African continent hanging on the wall. It had to be four feet wide by nine feet tall! It almost covered the whole wall. Looking closely, I could see that someone had perfectly pieced together three individual maps of north-east, north-west and central Africa, made by the French company, Michelin, without any overlap of country borders. That map was full of details about all-weather surfaced roads, partially improved earth roads and unmarked tracks. It showed hydrographic features such as rivers with or without car-carrying ferry services, location of lakes, dangerous waterfalls and possible flood areas. It had terrain elevations, estimated distances between towns and cities and known obstacles such as bridges liable to flood, as well as roads "under construction." All this valuable information was demarcated in intuitive colors: blue for lakes or waterways, green for forests or highlands, light brown for semi-arid savannah and rolling hills, white for arid desert and yellow for country boundaries. Furthermore, the map pointed out such things as hotels and restaurants, safari bungalows (with and without food), camping sites, petrol stations, mechanic stations, airfields, forts, palm groves, oil wells and good water holes, as well as things to see, such as known architectural ruins. I was completely amazed at this incredibly descriptive, mesmerizing map of all of Africa.

"And here I thought Michelin only made tires," I told Mark.

"Now look at this map," Mark said. "We call it the 'smallpox map.'"

I turned, facing the other side of the room and saw another map taped to the wall. This one was much smaller and only showed Gemu Gofa province. It had the two Rift Valley lakes, the muddy, red Abaya and dark blue Chamo, with Arba Minch and the thick jungle nestled in between. The names of noteworthy towns, such as Chencha, Jinka, Gidole, Gardulla and Konso, were written in appropriate locations as well as the route and approximate distances between them. However, although there was a scattering of other names, representing small villages, there were still large areas of uncharted real estate on the map, which was intriguing.

We sat down and Mark gave me a short history on the house. He said the previous PCVs, who initiated the smallpox surveillance program the year before, used this house as their base. Hence everybody knew it in Amharic as the *fentata bet* . . . the "smallpox house." Each time one of the smallpox Volunteers came back from the bush, they added the places they visited and the route taken to the smallpox map.

After giving the map a thorough look over, I had to admit, it was good. "Those guys did a good job down here," I said.

The smallpox map was a great idea, one that had to be continued. It would help us because we could rightfully assume that any demarcated town or village had been previously searched and the population fairly well vaccinated. Of course, we would do follow up when passing those areas, but with this information, we could focus our time and energy on those vacant areas of the map that had no road or village markings.

With the rainy season over, Mark and I went searching for the dreaded pox that ravaged humankind through the millenniums. Sometimes we went together, sometimes we teamed up with a sanitarian, and sometimes we went out alone. We would go on 10- to 20-day surveillance forays into the interior, stopping at every town, village, school and market and ask if anyone had seen any smallpox. We would check the left arms of everyone we met to see if they had a vaccination scar, if not, we'd see if we could vaccinate them. Each and every smallpox surveillance outing was different and an adventure in itself. I chased the elusive pox until the next year's torrential monsoon began eight months later, and during that time, I had many memorable experiences, three of which have never escaped my mind.

DOING SMALLPOX: TADESSE'S VILLAGE

One such experience occurred when I set off alone trekking through the Rift Valley on the eastern side of hippopotamus and crocodile infested, Lake Chamo. That area was devoid of any village or town markings on the smallpox map so it seemed like a place that needed to be checked out.

I prepared for the trip by loading my small backpack with vials of vaccine, containers of bifurcated needles, a flashlight, matches, an extra t-shirt and four cans of Norwegian sardines in case I found myself with no food. After stuffing my white, all cotton *gabi*, (traditional Ethiopian light blanket), a gift the Gurage had given me, into my pack, I was set to catch the ferry that crossed the lake.

The ferry was small, slow, carried no vehicles, and only ran once a week on Saturday mornings. It left around 8:00 and got to the other side of the deep, dark blue Lake Chamo in about three hours. It was a peaceful, uneventful ride although the questionable condition of the ferry and the sound of hippos and sight of crocs, as well as the occasional venomous black mamba snake swimming far from shore, kept me alert.

When the ferry arrived on the other side, a few Ethiopians stood waiting to board to go to Arba Minch, but that was all. There were no huts, no stalls, no other people, just miles of semi-arid savannah on rolling hills. I took a quick swig from my canteen then started trekking upward and due east.

Upon reaching the hill's summit, a young man called out in Amharic, asking where I was going. I told him, optimistically, to all the villages in the area. He replied saying he knew where all the villages in the area were, and for the right price, he could guide me. Looking around and seeing nothing but empty hills, I figured I could use a local guide.

"*What's your name?*"

"*My name is Solomon,*" he said proudly.

"*By day, how much do you want, Solomon?*"

"*I want ten dollars,*" he said.

I laughed and said, "*You will never get that. One dollar per day is enough.*"

Solomon thought about it, then said, "*Ok, let it be.*"

Even though he didn't show it outwardly, Solomon was happy to be hired. He offered to carry my backpack for no extra charge and promised that he would find us food as we went along. When I asked what he was going to do with the money he earned, he said he was going to buy his first pair of shoes.

For the next few days, Solomon and I covered a lot of ground, visiting a minimum of two villages a day, sometimes three, depending on the distance between them. Each village reacted to my presence with excitement and curiosity, as if I was the first *ferengi* they had ever seen . . . which I probably was.

Being quite the circus attraction, large crowds followed me on the way to the chief's *tukul*. Once there, I would introduce myself, show him the Emperor's letter, (whether he could read Amharic or not) and ask if he knew of any *fentata*, in the area. All the chiefs knew what *fentata* was, but they didn't know of any on-going outbreaks. When I told them I had *medhanit* (medicine) that would prevent them from ever getting *fentata*, they always wanted it and so did the villagers. When word spread about the *ferengi hakim* (foreign doctor) who had *fentata medhanit*, the Ethiopians flocked to be vaccinated. After everyone who came up was vaccinated, I would go through the village, with an open ampoule of vaccine, checking for smallpox or a vaccination scar on those I found.

We stopped our work just before sundown to look for a place to sleep. Solomon always had a friend or relative he could count on, while I usually was invited to stay with the village chief who would provide roasted grain for nourishment while letting me sterilize the used needles in boiling water. Once that was done, I'd lay down on an animal skin or a banana leaf, wrap up in my gabi and fall asleep to the serenade of blood seeking mosquitoes.

By the end of the fifth day, I had searched numerous villages, finding no smallpox, but blanketing the population with vaccine anyway. However, on the sixth day, as I was vaccinating another smallpox-free village, a bare foot, middle-aged man wearing long pants and a long sleeve shirt, came up and said in Amharic: *"My village has smallpox!"*

I looked the man over as I poked vaccine-laden prongs into another left arm.

"Where is your village?" I asked.

"Over there," he said, pointing east over the hills.

"Is it far?"

"It is far," he replied.

"By foot, how many days road is it?" I asked.

"Three days."

"Three days! That is very far!"

"If we go very fast, two days," he said.

"Did you just come from there?"

"No. Now I am returning. A month ago, I went to another village. I was afraid of smallpox."

I asked Solomon if he knew of any smallpox in that village or anywhere in that direction. Solomon said no. I asked him if this man's village was indeed that far away and he said yes.

"There is a lot of smallpox. Let's go now," the man shouted.

I wasn't sure what to do. Up until then, I hadn't seen any trace of smallpox in any of the villages and no one said anything about smallpox. There were no visible pockmarks, recent or otherwise, on anyone and no one even had a rash. Therefore, I wondered if the man was reporting an outbreak of severe chickenpox. Three days from where I stood meant at least a 20-hour trek, a trek that could be leading me away from a real smallpox outbreak in a nearby village. Then, I remembered Ciro telling me during training that every rumor or report of smallpox had to be checked out because **"Who knows if anyone will ever go there again?"** He emphasized that once you get to some distant place you have to investigate all reports because it just might be smallpox and, he warned, **"You could be the only one."**

With those memories, my plan of catching Saturday's ferry back to Arba Minch had vanished.

"*What's your name?*" I asked.

"*Tadesse.*"

In Amharic, the name meant to renew or rejuvenate . . . something I wanted to do.

"*OK, Tadesse, I'll go,*" I said, which produced a wide smile.

"*However, it will be necessary to enter every village along the way.*" I explained to him.

Tadesse's joy was now tempered. He wanted us to race non-stop directly to his village, and maybe I should have, but I wasn't sure about his claim of smallpox and I didn't want to return on the same route I would use to get to his village. I wanted to make a loop and search new territory and new villages, on the way to the ferry. I had to be sure there was no smallpox in any of the villages we passed. It didn't make sense to rush past villages without searching them if I wasn't coming back the same way.

It only took two days to check out and vaccinate the villages found along the way. By the third day, we reached Tadesse's village and as soon as we did, he started running around yelling in his native vernacular as loud as he could. Immediately, anxious people rushed towards me from every direction, surrounding me, all crying "*medhanit, medhanit!*" I was stunned and had to step back as even more crazed people rushed up.

Both Solomon and Tadesse saw my plight and moved toward me, trying to hold back the frenetic crowd.

"*Stop, stop, please stop,*" I yelled. But they didn't stop.

"*One minute, one minute, please,*" I begged them.

Tadessa and Solomon held the demanding crowd back so I could pull vaccine from my backpack and reconstitute it. Then I fished out a container of sterile needles and went to work.

"*OK, OK, now I can,*" I yelled out.

As soon as I said that, Solomon and Tadesse eased up, and the crowd pushed forward, and the three of us were engulfed once more. The village men used their strength to force their way through the raucous mob and be first to bare an arm. As soon as one man got vaccinated, another forced his way against me. Some wanted the *medhanit* so badly they pleaded for a double dose! There was no time to say hello . . . how are you . . .what's your name; all people wanted was to be vaccinated, and vaccinated right then and there!

I continued vaccinating people with rapid puncture strokes as fast as I could change needles, but the crowd still grew larger. Solomon and Tadesse tried to calm people down, slow people down, but their efforts were wasted. The people were adamant about being vaccinated. All I could do was look down, dip a fresh needle in vaccine, grab someone's left arm and apply the multiple puncture technique, one person after another. The process stalled each time I had to get a clean needle, so I gave the container to Solomon and told him to shake 'em out and hand 'em to me! The procedure became automatic, no thinking required: Dip needle, grab arm, apply puncture. Faster and faster I went: needle, arm, puncture, needle, arm, puncture. They kept coming from all directions, yelling "*medhanit, medhanit*," so I dug out more vaccine and more prongs as the madness continued and then started all over: Dip, grab 'n jab. Dip, grab 'n jab. Dip, grab 'n jab.

This frantic process continued on and on until I latched onto this one guy's arm, ready to jab him, but stopped when I saw pustules. I looked up and saw pustules scattered on his face. I asked him to remove his shirt, and doing so revealed pustules on his abdomen, but not as many as on his lower arms. When he pulled up his pants, I saw patches of pustules, mostly below his knees. From head to foot, all the lesions appeared uniform in size and development. To complete the field diagnosis, I turned his hands over and found pustules on his palms. The guy had smallpox!

I yelled at Tadesse, "*Take this man to his house and wait for me.*"

He agreed and pulled the man from the crowd.

"*I will come later. Don't let him go!*"

Tadesse was right . . . his village did have smallpox. No wonder these people were so crazy for vaccine. I wanted to search for more cases and start containment, but by then the women had me surrounded, demanding "*medhanit*" so I went back to my rapid "dip, grab 'n jab" procedure to arm after extended arm until I thought I was done. But then, another wave of arms came my way as the women who were vaccinated returned, pulling their frightened children with them.

The author administering smallpox vaccination, Gemu Gofa, 1973. *Photo by Mark
Weeks.*

With a semblance of delicacy, I vaccinated the small arms of terrified children, who couldn't help but cry out loud, until the last grateful
mother walked off.

I thought it was over, but then I saw fathers, carrying their last born,
the infants, and I knew the crying was going to get a whole lot louder.
Along with the babies came the old and infirm, struggling with their
canes or leaning on a relative. I waited patiently as they deliberated how
best to bare their arm.

Sometime after mid-day, the clamor for vaccine was over. More than
300 people took vaccination leaving me with a raw index finger.

Solomon led me to the man with the case of smallpox whom I had
sent home and I found him lying down, and being cared for by a female
who was shedding smallpox scabs. He would go through another week,
or more, of misery but would most likely survive.

Over the next day and a half, I conducted outbreak containment
throughout the village, recording over 30 smallpox cases, with no deaths,

Young man with smallpox, Gemu Gofa,
1973. *Photo by the author.*

and performed another 70 or so vaccinations. The cases were suffering
through all stages of the disease from macule rash to well-developed
pustules distributed centrifugally over the body. Each case had pustules
on the palms of their hands and soles of their feet. Some cases had fully
recovered, but could be identified by their depigmented skin or fresh
pockmarks.

As I went from hut to hut searching for smallpox and making sure
everyone had been vaccinated, I was welcomed with offerings of roasted
sorghum or corn along with the ever-present Ethiopian coffee.

When Tadesse caught up with me, I thanked him for his help during
the frenzy and apologized for not believing his claim about smallpox.

"*Not to worry*," he said, and shook my hand.

With containment complete in Tadesse's village, Solomon and I
turned westward towards Lake Chamo, continuing to search every new
village along the way. We found many people to vaccinate, but none
suffering from smallpox. When we reached Chamo, I paid Solomon for

his invaluable service, and told him to get a good pair of shoes. I then boarded the ferry back to Arba Minch.

DOING SMALLPOX: THE BORANA

On some smallpox surveillance treks, a public health student, Berhanu, accompanied me. Berhanu used his school vacation time to get experience working in public health and was assigned to me by the provincial medical officer. We usually worked in the cooler, highland terrain of Gemu Gofa, trekking from sunrise to sunset, climbing over steep mountains and wading across clear and cold streams. Although the long treks were demanding, Berhanu never complained about the rigorous pace, shortage of food or lack of good sleeping accommodations. He would always keep up and go anywhere . . . except once.

We had been in the highlands, southeast of Gidole, well south of Arba Minch, for five or so days, when we came to a mountain bluff that overlooked a large tract of Rift Valley savannah. I stood and gazed long and hard looking for any sign of hut or human, but saw only miles and miles of dried grassland and thorn bush. As I was looking for a path to descend the steep escarpment, Berhanu said he was not going down there.

"*What*," I asked.

"*I'm not going down there.*"

"*Why aren't you going?*"

"*There is a problem.*"

"*What kind of problem?*" I asked.

"*A big problem.*"

I stared at Berhanu. "*Please, Berhanu, what's the problem?*"

"*The people who live there are tough and dangerous,*" he said.

"*Who lives there?*"

"*The Borana.*"

"*The Borana. So?*" I said.

Berhanu told me the Borana were dangerous because before a Borana man could get married he must kill another man to prove his manhood and strength. He could kill a lion or elephant instead, he explained, but it was easier to kill a man, so they did. Furthermore, afterwards, the victim's scrotum and penis were cut off and displayed at the tip of a spear to show as proof.

I had heard the Borana were fierce nomads who often fought with neighboring tribes, but hadn't heard about that emasculation thing. Up until then, I thought "scalping" was a bit over the top!

As we sat overlooking the endless savannah below, I wondered if this was the marrying season.

The silence was broken when Berhanu suggested we search our way back to Arba Minch. I gave it some thought, believe me, as I scanned that dismal desert, but we were so far out in the bush . . . and I thought of Ciro and his admonition: **"Who knows if anyone will ever go there again? You could be the only one."** I doubted if anyone had ever been down there. In addition, the smallpox map indicated this region had yet to be searched. Somebody had to do it.

"Berhanu, you stay, I'll go."

Berhanu understood, somewhat. Then, after some thought, tried to console me by saying that maybe since I have white skin there won't be a problem. That didn't quite cheer me up.

"Maybe that person will get two wives for me," I joked.

We both laughed.

It was settled. Berhanu was to stay right there and wait for me. If I didn't come back by nightfall, he was to go back to the last village and find shelter. If I didn't come back the next day, he was to go back to Arba Minch and let them know. Then I gave Berhanu two cans of my emergency sardines and half of what was left of my canteen water. I took all the vaccine and needles and started negotiating my way off the cool plateau down to the desert bottom below.

By the time I landed on the savannah floor, it was 30 degrees warmer and shade had all but disappeared. I started walking in a southeasterly direction past tall thorn bushes and the occasional acacia tree, looking for any sign of human activity, but found nothing. With such thick bush, visibility was limited, but I kept walking, looking, listening, and stopping only to quench my thirst. I continued my Moses-like wanderings over savannah sand for at least another hour, hoping to get some clue of hab-

Young Borana woman offering water,
1973. *Photo by the author.*

itation of man, or beast, until I realized it was pointless. Seeing no one and hearing no one, I rested in the half shade of a thorn bush, thinking about the way back to Berhanu.

Suddenly a young Borana woman appeared from around a thick bush and stopped right in front of me. I couldn't believe my eyes. Where did she come from? Was this a mirage, an apparition? I was spellbound.

She too, was stunned at seeing me, but she held her ground, looking proud and elegant. She was young, healthy and wore a long, desert-brown, gathered skirt with similar cloth draped over one shoulder. Her hair was tied in braids, similar to Jamaican dreadlocks, and she wore several beaded necklaces and a string of gold-colored bracelets that sparkled in the desert sun. She cradled a large yellow gourd in her left arm that I assumed held water.

I stuttered some traditional Amharic greetings that did not elicit a response from her. Then I pantomimed my thirst and the need for water and she understood.

She pulled out a metal bowl, filled it with water and offered it to me. Water never tasted so good.

Again, I pantomimed using hand signals, asking to follow her. That seemed to work, for she put the bowl away and started walking. I kept up with her brisk pace through savannah scrub for over ten minutes until she led me straight to an old man crouched in front of a small makeshift *tukul*.

He also was surprised to see a *ferengi* out there in his world, but he too kept his poise, and with the hospitality common to all Ethiopians, offered me a place to sit.

Hoping he knew some Amharic, I slowly explained what I was doing there.

He nodded his head, but I didn't know if it was in recognition of what I said or just to be polite, so I asked, "*Is there any smallpox here?*"

He raised his right hand, and uttered "*fentata*" while shaking his head no.

I nodded back, understanding his negative response.

Turning around, I noticed his was the only form of habitation within view. There were no other structures, permanent or temporary and he was the only male Borana in the area.

"*No other people?*" I asked.

He didn't answer, he just looked forward.

A moment later, the young woman returned with a small basket of roasted sorghum, which the old man and I shared.

When the shadows started to lengthen, I had to decide if I should stay the night and sleep on the desert floor or head back to the plateau. My thoughts were then interrupted by a commotion coming my way from the south. The shrill sound of men's voices ululating as if in celebration, came through the bush. I strained my eyes through the bush camouflage and saw a band of Borana men jumping up and down, punching spears skyward. I couldn't tell what it was all about, but then I remembered what Berhanu told me, which gave me pause to think. Knowing that discretion is the better part of valor, and knowing too that no one could dance like a Whirling Dervish if they had smallpox, I thanked the old man for his generous hospitality and quietly crept off at a determined pace.

DOING SMALLPOX: THE LOWER OMO VALLEY AND THE MURSI

Then there was the time Mark Weeks and I were sitting in the smallpox house staring at the smallpox map. We were reminiscing about all the towns, villages, schools and markets we had been to, searching for the scourge of smallpox. We both had spent much time in and around the established towns of Chencha and Jinka, in the west, as well as Gardulla and Gidole, in the south and everything in between. I had blanketed the savannah side of Lake Chamo with vials of vaccine and Mark had done the same north and west of Arba Minch. We were confident those areas were smallpox-free, and when considering the work done by the previous PCVs, we believed immunity levels were very high. Aside from that out-break in Tadesse's village east of Lake Chamo, we found no evidence of smallpox in any of the towns, villages, schools or markets we had searched. But absence of evidence is not evidence of absence. This was no time to stop searching for smallpox.

While focusing on that homemade map we noticed a vast vacant tract of land southwest of Arba Minch that neither of us had searched. It was located west of Konso and south of Jinka, two towns we knew well, but there were no other towns or villages marked in that area.

"Maybe we should check that area out?" I said.

"What's out there?" Mark asked.

I didn't know, so, hoping for more information, we turned around and examined the Michelin map. Again, that region was barren of any towns or villages. There was a small village named Tertale, but that was 30 miles south of Konso and, according to the Michelin, it was in Sidamo Province. Due west of Konso, there was nothing, not even markings indicating road tracks of any kind. That large expanse was part of the Great Rift Valley and it was depicted as wide-open, unexplored savannah, mostly flat with some low rising contours. This depiction of barren landscape went from Konso all the way to Kelam on the Omo River, a long way away. Mark and I were intrigued.

The next day, we met up with Girma and Kassaye, the two sanitarians who knew some English and inquired whether anyone had searched that area between Konso and Kelem. They knew that region as the Lower Omo Valley, but couldn't recall if it was ever searched. They also heard about a nomadic tribe called the Mursi, who inhabited that valley but didn't know where they would be.

"Maybe we should find out," I said. "Could be some smallpox out there."

Then Girma warned us that the Mursi could be dangerous and violent. They raided other tribes for livestock, and carried out revenge killings, so it might not be a good place to go.

We talked about that for a while, before the four of us agreed that the Lower Omo Valley had to be searched. Girma and Kassaye said they would go with us, so Mark and I returned to the smallpox house and started organizing a four-man expedition to find the Mursi tribe.

We figured we needed to make a 10 to 14 day trip into that remote area, and we would have to bring everything required to get there and back: food, water, petrol and vaccinating supplies. In addition, we needed tents, cots, and cooking gear.

After compiling the list, it became obvious we were going to need more transport than the Land Rover.

The next day we rented a six-wheeled lorry and hired a driver along with it. The lorry driver suggested that we bring along a mechanic, and after inspecting the truck, we agreed it would be a good idea. Now there would be six of us, instead of four, which added to the supply list.

A few days later the provincial medical officer advised us to take along a police officer for security. He knew of someone who had been there to investigate the Mursi, and so he would send him to us.

Late the next morning, a short-haired, clean-shaven man in his mid-thirties walked up, showed his police I.D. and said he had been assigned to us. We knew better than to object. We now had to plan for seven expedition members . . . and then eight, as the officer rightfully pointed out that we needed someone to organize and cook the food.

After a week of assembling supplies and material, the lorry was loaded down with two 50-gallon drums of petrol, two drums of drinking water, two large tents with sleeping cots, two spare truck tires, a propane two-burner cooktop with a 20-gallon tank, mechanic tools and various other items. We stored our backpacks in the back of the Land Rover, along with our 35 mm camera equipment, while the officer kept his revolver and carbine within reach. I also packed some extra soap, razor blades, and cigarettes and matches as possible gifts, if not tribute.

The day finally came when both vehicles were loaded, gassed up and ready to roll.

I put the Rover in four-wheel drive and headed south to our expedition jump off point at Konso. Mark, Girma and the officer rode with me, while Kassaye, the mechanic and cook, jumped in with the lorry driver. The dirt road leading immediately out of Arba Minch was good enough for any cross-country vehicle, but within five miles, the lack of regular maintenance became all too apparent. Nevertheless, it was hard packed and open, so we couldn't really complain. Past Gidole, however, the road deteriorated into a less recognizable dirt track forcing us to slow down and watch for washouts. We pulled into Konso during the hottest part of the day and parked in front of the only *buna bet* in town where we found nourishment and accommodations.

The next morning, after saturating ourselves with strong coffee, the officer led us just outside of Konso to our jump-off point, which was nothing more than a beaten down footpath. However, the landscape ahead looked okay, so we forged ahead. As the morning wore on, we found ourselves driving across barren, dry scrubland and savannah grass while avoiding the occasional decrepit tree. At times, we had open views of the lay of the land, allowing us to plan our route for a half a mile or so. Other times, we just plowed along in first gear wary of falling into a hole or breaking down.

Geographically, our position was latitude five degrees north of the Equator, so as soon as the first sunbeam pierced the air, the nighttime, already-warm temperature rose like a rocket, reaching well above code red by high noon. It became so hot that if you curled a finger ever so slightly, a bead of perspiration would emit from the crease in seconds. In most places, the wind would help cool the air down, but there, in the Omo Valley, we dreaded any light breeze for it felt like it was coming out of a

Mark Weeks (right) and sanitarians, Lower Omo Valley, Gemu Gofa, 1973.
Photo by the author.

blazing furnace, able to cremate us alive. To keep going in the scorching
heat was insane, so by late morning-early afternoon we stopped and lay
in shade provided by the vehicles and sweated gallons.

Each day offered the same routine: wake before sunrise, eat and
drink, answer nature's call, start our search, quit by mid-day, seek shade
and bear the unbearable heat. After five days of hard travel we still had
not seen a single person, Mursi or otherwise, and were wondering if we
ever would.

To break up the monotony, we asked one of the sanitarians to drive
the Rover while Mark and I grabbed our cameras and hopped in the back
of the lorry, accompanied by the officer. The driver waited while we loaded
a roll of 35 mm slide Kodachrome and locked in the oversized 200 mm
telephoto lens. When done, the lorry lurched forward with our cameras
held over the railing, ready to shoot some big game. Unfortunately, we
didn't see any big game, nor any small game for that matter, most likely
because of the loud noise coming from the lorry.

We were hanging over the side, with our cameras at the ready, when all of a sudden the lorry came to a jarring stop. We looked around and saw 30 or more nomadic warriors surrounding us. They were tall, muscular and wearing nothing but a rifle or a spear. I mean, they were buck naked, standing there unwelcoming and uncircumcised. Although they didn't point their weapons our way, it was clear they had us by the short hairs.

"Are these guys the Mursi?" Mark asked, under his breath.

"Could be the lost Long-Dong tribe, for all I know," I whispered.

"*It's the Mursi*," the officer said, clearing the air.

I told everyone not to make a move . . . especially the officer with his revolver. No one did and no one said another word, neither them nor us. Time passed much too slowly and finally I suggested we put our cameras down, inside the lorry, for who knows what they thought those long lenses were.

As soon as the cameras were down, the Mursi changed their previous posture and spoke a few words amongst themselves, in a language unbeknown to me. Seeing them relax a bit, I tried out some Amharic: "*Hello, you guys all right? Everything OK? Your cattle are good? When will the rain come?*"

Maybe they knew some Amharic, maybe they knew only some syllables, I didn't know, but my speech seemed to ease the tension so I kept it up. "*We are from Arba Minch. It's a long ways. Is this good country?*"

There was no reply, but some of the younger men strayed over to the shade of a tree and sat down while the older guys stayed around the lorry. Sensing an easing in the awkward tension, I carefully climbed off the lorry and stood amongst them.

"*How you guys doing?*" I blurted out.

There was no verbal response, but they did become more relaxed, as did all of us. Those Mursi closest to the lorry meandered to a nearby shady spot and rested there. They kept a watchful eye on me as I walked over to the Land Rover and grabbed the bag with all the gifts. I returned and casually sat among them. They watched with curiosity as I opened up a pack of cigarettes.

"*Who wants a smoke?*"

Author checking Mursi arms for smallpox vaccination, Gemu Gofa, 1973. *Photo by Mark Weeks.*

The younger guys didn't take any, but the older guys held out their hands. After figuring out how the wooden matches worked, the oldest looking Mursi lit a cigarette, took a drag and blew enough smoke to cover his face. Others just put the cigarette in their mouth and held it like a toothpick. While this was going on, I was checking to see if they had been vaccinated, but all their arms were completely unblemished.

More time went by before I asked, *"Do you know smallpox?"*

One Mursi warrior turned his head towards me. As with first learning any language, it's always easier to understand than to speak, so I thought this guy might know some of what I was saying. I continued my monologue by using the word *fentata* whenever I could. Then I told them about the *medhanit* that would stop *fentata*. That same Mursi warrior watched me speak then spoke to the others, who, in turn, responded with unfamiliar short sounds.

While this was going on, Mark and the officer climbed down and leaned against the lorry. Mark was in no hurry, nor was the officer, so we

Mark Weeks vaccinating Mursi warriors, Lower Omo Valley, Gemu Gofa, 1973. *Photo by the author.*

handed out our gifts of soap, and amused them by pantomiming how to use it. We did the same with the razor blades . . . being careful not to cut anyone.

Eventually we felt comfortable enough to bring out the vaccine and bifurcated needles. The Mursi watched with intense interest as I reconstituted a vial and then shook out a needle. To show them how it worked, I vaccinated myself, yet again. Then I vaccinated Mark and even persuaded the officer to roll up his shirt.

"*Nothing to it. It's easy. It's doesn't hurt,*" I told the Mursi.

The Mursi examined my arm, touched it and showed amazement.

I pointed to the guy who understood me the best and pulled out another needle. Gesturing what I wanted to do, and seeing no objection, I leaned forward and jabbed his arm multiple times. He watched every puncture without flinching. There was a tiny speck of blood at the site, but he stayed strong.

"*That's good. You are a strong person,*" I told him.

Mursi warriors, Gemu Gofa, 1973. *Photo by the author.*

He looked me in eyes, then shrugged his shoulders as if to say, "Is that all there is?"

With his acceptance and tacit approval, we were able to vaccinate all the warriors who were there that day and when they left, they seemed to be proud about it.

We stayed in the Lower Omo Valley for another couple of days and found more Mursi in the bush and in a market area. It was still *de rigueur* (customary) for the men to appear without clothing, but the women, being somewhat modest, covered themselves below the waist. We were surprised to see the women wearing clay plates in their lower lip and earlobes in order to stretch them. They would increase the size of the plate until the lower lip stretched out past their chin and the elongated earlobes almost rested on their shoulder.

Although there was a language barrier, we asked about smallpox as best we could, but no one knew of any *fentata*, nor looked like they were ever exposed to the virus. We vaccinated everyone we found, every Mursi man, woman and child, naked or not, for **"Who knows if anyone will ever go there again?"** Frankly, I doubted it. But if they do, I hope they bring some extra trousers.

DOING SMALLPOX: DONE

My "doing smallpox" days in Ethiopia ended in mid-June 1973, when the relentless monsoon rains converted the roads into vehicle-trapping bogs and quagmires.

No other smallpox outbreaks were ever detected in Gemu Gofa, which led to the province being declared smallpox-free at the end of the year.

On my last day, I gave Mark the keys to the Rover and a healthy hug goodbye, not knowing that a few years later I would be chasing the dreaded smallpox with him again in Bangladesh and Somalia.

Eight adventurous months had passed since I had last seen Addis Ababa, but it had not changed a bit. The city was still heavily forested, the air clean and crisp, and the citizens welcoming.

Nor had Ciro changed. He still had his goatee, long hair, sparkling eyes and infectious smile when I walked into smallpox headquarters. He grabbed my hand and shook it until I pulled loose.

"Good to see you!" he said. "It's been a long time."

"But a good time," I replied.

After catching up, I explained that with the monsoon starting and no smallpox in Gemu Gofa, I was heading home. Ciro understood and had no problem with that. When I told him I was going to begin graduate school in three months, he was genuinely happy for me. We had a good laugh when I recalled how we met that day on the road in Welkite . . . and how sick he was. As I left, Ciro wished me well and I the same for him.

Looking back, had not serendipity stepped in on that fateful day in Welkite, and I had not met Ciro, I would never have had such incredible experiences doing smallpox eradication, not only in Ethiopia, but later, in Bangladesh and Somalia as well. Nor would I have ever met the group of unforgettable, dedicated people who did smallpox, which was an experience in itself. Sure, back then, I was eager to stay in Ethiopia, but without Ciro's charismatic personality that made me feel so welcome, so important, I'm not sure I ever would have, or been inspired to join the SEP. Meeting Ciro was good fortune that provided me with a treasured past.

•

ACKNOWLEDGMENTS
The author is grateful to the editors, Jim Skelton, Alan Schnur, Gene Bartley and Scott Porterfield, for their time and effort in reviewing this chapter and for their constructive comments and suggestions. The author also wants to recognize Jim Skelton for his editorial expertise and persistent patience without which this story may never have been written.

16

Buna, Tej and Smallpox Eradication in Kaffa Province

by Vince Radke

As I sat in the airport in Addis Ababa, Ethiopia in April, 1974 with fellow Peace Corps Volunteer (PCV), Don Piburn, who was there to witness my departure to the United States, I wondered if my three and a half years in Ethiopia had been worth it. It was only many years later that I came to understand how valuable those years were to me and to Ethiopia. I had been fortunate to have been part of the global Smallpox Eradication Program (SEP).

Five years earlier, in the spring of 1969, I was finishing my junior year at Michigan State University, and had begun to wonder what I was going to do with the rest of my life after my senior year. The war in Vietnam was ongoing. Protest against the war was in full swing across many campuses in the United States. Against that backdrop, I decided to talk to job recruiters who were on campus during the final weeks of the spring semester. I was hoping that by talking to them I might figure out what I wanted to do.

    I stopped by the Peace Corps booth and spoke to the two guys at the table. We talked for a while, and they handed me an application. Little did I realize that filling out that application would totally change my life. I wanted to do something positive with my life, and I remembered that one of the criticisms from my parents and others towards young people at the time was that we seemed to be opposed to many things, but not *for* something. How was I going to make the world a better place and help myself?

Months later I filled out the Peace Corps application and mailed it.

During the spring of 1970, just prior to graduation, I was thinking that I might go to graduate school after working for a year. When I got back to the house where I rented a room, a housemate told me that the Peace Corps had called.

It was late, so I called back the next day. The person on the other end of the line said the Peace Corps had reviewed my application and thought a smallpox vaccination program in Ethiopia might be of interest to me. The caller asked me if I would be interested in going to Philadelphia to attend a program to introduce me to the country of Ethiopia and the smallpox program. I immediately said "Yes," even though I had no plans or direction for my life at that time. The Peace Corps person said they would send me a plane ticket, and make a hotel reservation for me, and that I should plan to spend two days in Philadelphia.

As soon as I hung up the phone, I made a beeline for the library because I had no idea where Ethiopia was located, and I had no idea what smallpox was. The librarian was very helpful, and I was able to borrow a few books on both Ethiopia and smallpox.

I made my way to Philadelphia at the appointed time. There were about 30 other guys going through the same introduction to the smallpox program in Ethiopia. Hanging on the walls of the meeting room there were some beautiful looking tourist posters of Ethiopia, and I had a chance to meet some Ethiopian Peace Corps trainers. The possibility of being in the country, and working in the smallpox program seemed like a great adventure to me. At the end of the two day introduction, one of the members of the Peace Corps staff asked if I would still be interested in going to Ethiopia, and I said "Yes." He said that the Peace Corps would contact me later in the summer.

That summer went by fast, but I had a chance to visit with friends and tell them I would be going to Ethiopia soon. Most of my friends were excited for me, but my parents were a little concerned. My mom worried I would get sick there — which I did multiple times. My dad was worried that my education and career would be lost — but they weren't.

I received another call from the Peace Corps in September, 1970, asking me to report for training at the Communicable Disease Center (CDC) in Atlanta, Georgia. I would be in Atlanta for two weeks and then off to Ethiopia so I was supposed to pack up my bags for the next two years.

I arrived in Atlanta from my home town of Detroit. I met the other PCVs in what the Peace Corps designated as Ethiopia Group XIV, all of whom would be in training with me. It was unknown to me at the time that most of these guys would become my brothers in the fight against smallpox, and lifelong friends.

The two weeks of training at the CDC was the finest training I have ever had in my 47 years of public health service.

After the CDC training, I was on my way to Ethiopia with my fellow PCVs. We arrived in Addis Ababa, the capital of Ethiopia, after stops in New York, Rome, Athens, Beirut and Asmara. The flight from New York to Rome was on one of the first TWA 747 flights. My PCV odyssey had just begun.

TRAINING

After clearing customs and passport control in Addis Ababa, we were greeted by a Peace Corps staff member. We loaded our luggage and ourselves into a couple of vans and headed into the city. The smell of burning wood and eucalyptus filled the air. Looking out the van windows, I saw many people walking on the side of the road. Most people were carrying wood or something, and a few were walking with mules. As the van slowed because of heavy traffic, I noticed a man urinating on the side of the road. I did a double take to make sure. Indeed he was urinating. As we drove, I noticed others doing the same. At that moment, doubt came into my mind if I would be able to adjust to this new culture and work there. At the same time, I remember all the "don'ts" the Peace Corps trainers had told us about — "Don't drink the water." "Don't eat anything raw," etc. Eventually, as the days, weeks, months and years passed, I would be the one urinating in the open, drinking the water and eating the raw meat.

Just a week or so into our language and culture training, we were told to report to the Ethiopian Ministry of Health (MOH). The Emperor Haile Selassie had declared there was a cholera epidemic in the country and all people were to be vaccinated, and our Peace Corps smallpox eradication training group was to be part of that effort. We had brought with us from the U.S. some "jet injectors" for use in the smallpox program, but the jet injectors could be used for other immunizations as well. Part of our training at CDC had been on the use, maintenance and sterilization of the jet injectors. We were instructed to use the jet injectors to vaccinate the Ethiopians against cholera.

The plan was to spend a week in Addis Ababa vaccinating its population, then we would be sent to the provinces to vaccinate the people there. I was assigned to work at the horse racing track in Addis Ababa. Our Ethiopian health team vaccinated more than 50,000 people that week. For the next two weeks, I was assigned to Kaffa province in the southwestern part of Ethiopia. I vaccinated in the provincial capital of Jimma, as well as the towns of Agaro and Bongo.

Following the vaccination against cholera campaign, the Peace Corps resumed our training. We went through the in-country language and culture training in grand style, and saw many parts of Ethiopia over the next three months. The smell of the roasting *buna* (coffee) and eucalyptus became a treat for me each morning, and I was finally learning a language (Amharic) and using it.

Near the end of our training we were introduced to the World Health Organization (WHO) Smallpox Eradication Program (SEP) team. The Ethiopian SEP was led by Dr. Kurt Weithaler, an Austrian physician who had left his position as the physician to the Emperor's Imperial Body Guard to join the SEP. Another person we were introduced to was Dr. Ciro de Quadros, a Brazilian epidemiologist, who would be our field coordinator and supervisor. Ciro had been an epidemiologist with the successful smallpox eradication program in Brazil. As part of the introduction process, we went around the room and each person told a little about themselves. Ciro spoke to us, but his command of English was not very good, and he did not speak Amharic. When he finished, I leaned over to fellow trainee Marc Strassburg and asked if he understood anything Ciro had said. Marc said he hadn't, and then added, "If he is in charge of the field operations this smallpox eradication program is in trouble."

We quickly discovered how wrong this first impression turned out to be.

For a variety of reasons, the WHO staff decided to begin the program in the southwestern part of Ethiopia. Because I had already been to Kaffa province, I requested to be assigned there, and Marc Strassburg ended up being assigned to Kaffa province, too. We were given a new Land Rover for our work. It was very rare for PCVs to have such a vehicle. We went shopping for supplies and then headed for Kaffa province, where I would spend most of my next three years.

WORKING IN KAFFA

When we arrived in Jimma, we reported to the provincial health officer, Dr. Hugo Neimer, a Dutch physician. Over the next two years, I would come to know the Neimer family very well. Also, during our first week in Kaffa we met our Ethiopian counterpart, *Ato* Fekada Gebre Selassie, an Ethiopian sanitarian assigned to the SEP in Kaffa province. The three of us, Fekada, Marc and I, would be in charge of the smallpox program in the province. It was decided early on to split Kaffa into three sections: Marc would take the northern part, Fekada would take the middle part, which included Jimma, and I would take the southern part, which bordered on the Sudan.

I spent most of my time operating out of the small town of about 4,000 people called Mizan Teferi. The only practical way to travel into and out of Mizan was by Ethiopian Airlines DC-3 or C-47 airplanes. The road from Jimma to Mizan was good for the first 60 miles, and then it was terrible for the next 100 miles. The Italians had built the road from Jimma to Mizan in the late 1930s and early 1940s, but the Ethiopians were only able to maintain the road for the first 60 miles. The one and only time I drove to Mizan I busted two axles on the Land Rover, and had to order the two replacement axles to be flown to Mizan before I could drive out of there.

Most of my days with the SEP were spent walking with pack mules looking for cases of smallpox and vaccinating. In order to do my smallpox work, I needed the mules to haul my equipment and supplies as I would be gone for weeks at a time.

During one of my extended stays in Mizan, it was the *buna* harvest season, which presented a problem. The best *buna* I ever had was in Kaffa province. I drank a lot of *buna*, and most of the time I drank it black with nothing added. Occasionally, like many locals, I would add a little salt, or red pepper.

The problem was that during the *buna* harvest all available mules were used to haul and transport *buna*, so it was very difficult to rent any mules for the SEP. When I tried to rent mules either none were available or the rental was three times the normal rate.

I was working with an Ethiopian dresser, *Ato* Metaku Letta then. For almost three years, Metaku and I would be joined at the hip doing our SEP work. One day, while Metaku and I sat in the *buna* shop planning what to do next without mules, Metaku mentioned that he had heard there might be mules for sale in the market. I knew we could pay for renting mules from SEP funds, but I did not know if the WHO would approve the purchase of mules.

First, Metaku and I went to the market to see if indeed mules were for sale. We found a merchant who was willing to sell his two mules to us. Next, I radioed the SEP headquarters in Addis, explained the situation, and asked if I could purchase two mules. I was told they would have to check with WHO headquarters in Geneva. After a few days, the answer came back, "No, WHO is not in the business of buying mules."

I was not happy with the answer because I knew the WHO was in the business of getting rid of smallpox, and the only way for me to get rid of smallpox in southern Kaffa province was to buy mules. So, I took my monthly Peace Corps allowance, went into the market and bought the two mules.

I figured I would get my money back when I sold them, that is, if the mules didn't die first.

I made arrangements with the health officer in Mizan to keep my mules in the health center compound while I was in Mizan. Also, I hired the former mule owner as a guide and to take care of the mules when we were out in the countryside looking for cases of smallpox and vaccinating.

I took good care of my mules while in Mizan, feeding them carrots and grain that I bought in the market. My mules became like my pets. They would recognize me as I came down the path to the health center and meet me at the edge of the fenced-in compound, and thanks to them I learned an important skill, of which I'm very proud, how to pack a mule.

One of the big problems in remote Ethiopia was getting safe water to drink. Most of the time, I would filter the water, then either boil it or use chemicals to disinfect the water. I believe most of the time this provided safe water for me to drink. There were occasions, however, when this boiling or disinfection technique was not possible, like when I was offered water to drink by a local chief after a long and difficult trek.

There were many times and places during my travels when I would partake of the honey wine, known as *tej* in Amharic. The honey to make the *tej* came from the "honey gatherers" — a unique group of men and boys who would go into the woods, climb up the trees, place hollowed-out logs in the trees and wait for the bees to do their thing. After waiting weeks to months, the honey gatherers would return to the trees having the hollowed-out logs, climb back up the trees and collect the honey. They would scoop up the honey, honeycomb and all, and place it in a small pouch. They would do this activity while bees were flying about and stinging them. The honey gatherers would return to the markets and merchants and sell the honey, which would eventually be used to make *tej*. Most of the *tej* was sweet to semi-dry, depending on the fermentation process. After much practice, I became a connoisseur of *tej*. I preferred the semi-dry to the dry kind. In fact, I enjoyed the *tej* so much I would put it in my canteen instead of water. Sometimes I would drink too much, but most times I would walk it off.

In 1971, the first year of the SEP in Ethiopia, the SEP team recorded over 26,000 cases throughout the country, with most in the southwestern part of Ethiopia.[1] By comparison, in 1970 there were only 722 cases reported in all of Ethiopia.[2] In the previous 10 years, only a few hundred cases were reported each year. In my three and a half years in Ethiopia, I saw thousands of cases and vaccinated tens of thousands of people.

Occasionally, I would return to Jimma for meetings with Marc and Fekada and to resupply. Upon my return to Jimma at the end of June 1972, I received a memo from the Peace Corps office in Addis, which was addressed to "All Peace Corps Volunteers & Trainees." It was rare to get any correspondence from the Peace Corps office.

The memo was from the new Peace Corps Country Director, John Mills, who didn't even bother to introduce himself, but instead expressed his concerns about what he had seen and heard about the appearance and behavior of many PCVs in Ethiopia. Specifically, he complained about the unkempt appearance (long hair and beards) of a number of male Volunteers. The part of the memo that bothered me the most was the order that all male Volunteers were to keep their beards "trim, short and neat." I took personal offense because I had a beard. There were two reasons I had a beard. First, because it was very difficult to shave or even bathe frequently, given the lack of water in remote areas of Kaffa province. Another reason I grew a beard was the respect that was shown to the elders in Ethiopia, and many elders had beards. I believed that my beard made many Ethiopians think I was older than my years, so it helped indirectly with my work. Therefore, I prepared a response to the memo from Mr. Mills, and told him about the culture and respect shown to the elders in Ethiopia and the importance of having a beard. I put my letter to Mr. Mills in the envelope along with all the hair from my beard, which I had cut earlier in protest of his new policy, and mailed the letter on July 4th. Then, I returned to Mizan and continued my work.

---

1 D. A. Henderson, Smallpox, The Death of a Disease: The Inside Story of Eradicating a Worldwide Killer (Amherst, New York: Prometheus Books, 2009), 219.
2 Ibid. at 220.

A few months later, I was in Addis for a smallpox meeting and a physical exam at the medical office at Peace Corps headquarters. While sitting in the medical waiting room, Mr. Mills walked in and started to introduce himself to the PCVs sitting there. When he came to me, he held out his hand, introduced himself and shook my hand. I told him I was Vince Radke. He held the handshake a little longer than normal, and said, "Mr. Radke, I've been waiting to meet you ever since I received your letter." He continued, "When you finish your exam, please see me in my office."

I thought, *well that's it, I'm on the next plane out of Ethiopia.*

After my exam, I made my way to the director's office. The secretary showed me in.

He offered me a cup of coffee and spoke about his introduction to Ethiopia and its culture. He said he appreciated my letter, but did not appreciate having my beard fall out of the envelope all over his desk. As he spoke, I was waiting for him to hand me my plane ticket out of the country. Instead, he explained that he should have understood the Ethiopian culture better before writing his memo. He thanked me for my service and encouraged me to continue my good work for the SEP.

Before I headed back to Mizan Teferi, I did some shopping in Jimma to get supplies and pick up half a dozen radios and batteries. I would use the radios and batteries as gifts for local chiefs in the rural areas to thank them for their cooperation and help. Radios and batteries were hard to come by in southwestern Ethiopian.

A few times a chief would offer me a gift in return. The gifts I received included a bull's horn, a spear and a goat. I was able to get the spear and bull's horn back to the United States, and I still have them. I cooked the goat and shared it with the local chief and his family.

I almost always had good cooperation from the local chiefs. In addition, I received good cooperation from Ethiopian local government officials, the police, army and missionary folks. I always carried my Ethiopian MOH ID, and papers signed by the Minister of Health and the Emperor himself, which stated that people should give me full cooperation.

After arriving back in Mizan, I heard about some cases of smallpox, and headed out as soon as I got my mules. After walking for two days, I arrived in the area where smallpox had been reported and immediately met with the chief of the area. He confirmed that there were cases of smallpox in his area. He decided to send his son with Metaku and me to see the cases and to vaccinate. His son would not only act as our guide, but also as a translator. The chief's son, who was educated, spoke Amharic and the local language and I welcomed his assistance. Many times in my travels I desperately needed a translator because there were 70 different languages in Ethiopia and more than 200 dialects.

We saw a number of cases of smallpox and vaccinated the contacts and others in the immediate area. All cases of smallpox were recorded (handwritten) on a form we called Form #1. Some folks would refer to it as a line list. This was the same method Ciro de Quadros had used in Brazil. Every case of smallpox in Kaffa province was recorded on a Form #1.

That evening, we returned to the chief's *tukul* (house) and had dinner with him and his family. I asked the chief if we had seen all the cases of smallpox in his area; he said we had. I told the chief I had heard of smallpox cases in another area, and I would need his help in getting to that area. The chief said that was not a problem, and, in addition, he had heard about cases of smallpox in a third area. The chief wanted all of his people to get vaccinated before we left. He wanted to send word to all of his people to come to the village for smallpox vaccination the next day, and I agreed.

The next morning, I was awakened by noise outside our tent.

There I saw hundreds of people — men, women and children — sitting on the ground waiting to be vaccinated, so Metaku and I started to vaccinate them.

While we were vaccinating, out of nowhere, Ciro de Quadros rode up on a mule. He had flown into Mizan two days before to see how the work was going. To say the least, I was a little surprised to see Ciro — it was the first time I had seen him outside of Addis or Jimma. He was worried that I might not be locating all of the cases of smallpox and thought I might be focusing too much on performing vaccinations. I explained to him what Metaku and I had done the day before — I showed him our Form #1s — and that after vaccinating the people here, we were going to the two other areas that might have smallpox cases. I believe Ciro was assured that I was doing a good job. After vaccinating the people, we all had something to eat with the chief. Then, Ciro headed back to Mizan and I traveled to the other area with possible cases.

Due to our vaccinating duties that morning, Metaku and I arrived in the new area late. The chief of this area had us set up our tent next to his *tukul*. He invited us for dinner, and we ate *doro wot* — a spicy chicken stew, *injera* made from corn and teff. That evening Metaku and I returned to our tent to sleep.

After being asleep for a few hours I felt something on my face and brushed it off before trying to go back to sleep. After it happened again, I reached for my flashlight near my sleeping bag, turned it on and pointed it at the top of the tent, which was totally black. I thought that was strange, given that our tent was green. As I brought the light down to the front of the tent and onto my sleeping bag, I realized the black was moving. It was ants . . . we were covered in black ants.

I poked Metaku with my flashlight to wake him up and showed him the top of the tent. He swore in Amharic. We slowly unzipped our sleeping bags, but it was not easy. We did not want to disturb the ants. Metaku got to the front of the tent to open it. We were covered with ants by this time, and some of the ants had started to bite. We got out of the tent and started to knock the ants off of ourselves. The noise we made woke the chief and his family, and he had a good laugh watching Metaku and me jump up and down knocking the ants off our bodies. After a few minutes, we managed to get rid of the ants, so the chief invited us into his house and asked his wife to make some *buna*. After an hour or so, we returned to our tent. The ants were gone, and it seemed like they had never been there.

We finished our work in one area and moved onto another . . . and so it went for the next two years. We moved from area to area in southern Kaffa province getting rid of smallpox.

Towards the end of this period, Metaku and I arrived early one evening at a small *woreda* village (75–100 people). The police said we could set up our tent in the police compound, which we did. The next morning, Metaku and I walked to the *buna bet* (coffee house) a few hundred meters from the police compound. We were wrapped in our *gabis* (large, thick white cotton shawls), part of the Ethiopian national dress, because it was cold that morning. We were covered from our heads to our knees. As we walked, a man walking in the opposite direction greeted us and we returned the greeting. After having some *buna* and bread we headed back to the police compound to get ready for the day. We would be working a large market asking about cases of smallpox and vaccinating the people.

On our walk back to the police compound the temperature was a little warmer, so we lowered the *gabis* from our heads, leaving our faces uncovered. The same man who had greeted us as we walked towards the *buna bet* was about to pass us again. This time he stopped and was surprised to see that one of us was not an Ethiopian. We laughed. He had thought from our greeting earlier in the day that we were both Ethiopians. At that moment, I felt like an Ethiopian.

We stayed in the village for a few days working the market and planning our next trip. One evening, the *woreda* governor invited us for dinner. We had *doro wot*, *injera* and *tej*. After dinner, we returned to the police compound.

During the night, a servant of a French Catholic priest who had a house and a small church nearby, asked us to come to the house of the priest with any bandages, alcohol and antibiotic lotion we might have because one of the farmers in the area had injured himself. When we arrived, we found the priest and a man who had accidentally cut his lower leg along the calf with a machete. The cut was more than 5 inches long and deep and it was bleeding badly. The priest was going to sew the wound with thread used for stitching clothes along with needle that normally would be used for leather. We used the alcohol to soak the thread. We flamed the needle and cleaned the wound as best we could, and then held the wound closed while the priest sewed the wound. We used some of the bandages to soak up the blood, and we applied the antibiotic lotion as the priest sewed the wound while the priest's servant held a gas lantern. After we finished, the priest asked the farmer to stay in his house. We had a drink of *tej* with them and headed back to the police compound.

I never found out what happened to that farmer.

MY LAST YEAR IN ETHIOPIA

The number of cases of smallpox had dropped to near zero in Kaffa province by the end of 1973.

We had taken Kaffa province from the list of those places having the highest incidence of cases in the world in the first half of 1971 to near zero in less than three years. Our surveillance system was very good, and our vaccination coverage, even in remote areas, was very good as well. Additionally we had trained many Ethiopian vaccinators, and to the benefit of the country, some of them went on to become health workers.

All of the other smallpox PCVs with whom I had started in Group XIV during the fall of 1970 had left by the beginning of 1973. I remained in Ethiopia through March of 1974.

Most of my last year was spent training new PCVs for the SEP, and helping out in a famine relief camp in northern Ethiopia.

It was fun to train new PCVs to become surveillance officers for the SEP because I had a chance to pass my knowledge and skills along to others. By 1974, volunteers from Japan and Austria also had joined the effort.

I was asked to assist in the famine relief camp in northern Ethiopia in late 1973 and early 1974, and it was difficult work. Many times, small children with severe malnutrition would come into the camp and never leave. I was in charge of sanitation and burial teams.

For the last couple of months before I left Ethiopia, I headed back to Kaffa province to finish where I had started. I wanted to see Fekada and Metaku one last time, and make sure that the new PCVs, Don Piburn and Stuart Gold, were doing well.

There was a rumor of smallpox not far from Jimma, so Metaku and I went to investigate. The case turned out to be chicken pox, but we stayed and vaccinated people in the marketplace.

Later that day, Metaku and I were hassled by some students for allegedly being part of Emperor Haile Selassie's repressive government. During the beginning of 1974, Emperor Haile Selassie was starting to lose power. Some units of the military and some high school and college students went on strike.

On one of my last nights in Kaffa province, in Jimma, my Ethiopian SEP colleagues threw a party for me. They gave me the entire Ethiopian national dress (outfit) from head to toe. They also gave me a ring that was made of gold. Metaku had obtained the gold during a trip we had made near the Sudanese border. The ring had the raised image of the country of Ethiopia with the initials "S. E. P." in the middle. I was deeply touched. These gifts were from my brothers in the fight against smallpox. I will never forget my Ethiopian colleagues and PCVs who I worked with, suffered with, cried and laughed with. They will always hold a special place in my heart. They were the best.

And I will always remember and be grateful to Ciro de Quadros and D.A. Henderson for their inspiration and belief that we would get the job of eradicating smallpox done.

Ciro was instrumental in my decision to make a career for myself in public health. He had taught me the importance of data collection (Form #1) and how to use that data to measure my work and how to improve my work. These are skills I still use today for my work at the Centers for Disease Control and Prevention. Presently, I'm passing these skills on to other young public health workers.

I stayed in touch with Ciro and D.A. over the years. We had a bond that would last a lifetime. I had that same bond with my fellow PCVs and Ethiopian colleagues who worked on the SEP. We were warriors in the battle against smallpox.

By March 1974, it was time for me to leave Ethiopia. I traveled around Europe for a few months before heading back to the United States to start my Master's degree in Public Health in September, 1974 at the University of Pittsburgh. Before I could finish my degree, D.A. called and asked me to join in the fight against smallpox in Bangladesh, which I did. Later, after I finished my degree, I served again in the SEP in Kenya. D.A. knew the good work we had done in Ethiopia and he would call on us to help out. You could not say "no" to D.A. As the years passed I occasionally saw Ciro and D.A. at meetings or conferences. It was always good to see and talk with them. I miss them. They were my heroes.

•

17

The Ethiopian Experience
Shaping a Career

by Marc Strassburg

It has been over 45 years since my Ethiopia days, and since that time I have experienced a variety of Proustian remembrances[1] related to my two years in Ethiopia. I frequently come across events that activate such recollections. A common trigger is meeting someone of Ethiopian descent here in Los Angeles. When I say, "*Tenayistilegne*," the standard greeting in Amharic, they always respond with a big, friendly smile. This was also true during my work in Ethiopia. The Ethiopians are a dark-skinned, proud, and diverse people, both from the standpoint of their culture and their unique racial mixtures (there are over 80 different ethnic sub-groups in Ethiopia). They are also a very sociable people who enjoy close family ties and making new friendships. It seemed strange for many of us new Peace Corps Volunteers (PCVs) that in Ethiopian society male friends commonly walked together holding hands.

An even stronger trigger is the Ethiopian cuisine, which has a very unique aroma due to the use of spices and butter in their cooking. Now,

---

1. *Remembrance of Things Past* is a novel by French author Marcel Proust in which a series of common events triggers memories of long ago.

whenever I come into contact with a potent cooking aroma, even if not Ethiopian, my mind immediately goes back to those incredible dishes I enjoyed then. Those smells remind me of *ghee*, a clarified butter used in the cooking that is also commonly used as hair dressing in much of Africa. Women would keep *ghee* in their hair as a conditioner for many days!

Ethiopians are a very hospitable people, so much so that even when visitors arrived unannounced in remote areas they were always welcomed. This was especially true of the friendly children who might not have seen a fair-skinned *ferengi* (foreigner) before. In many respects, working in Ethiopia was like going back in time, where villagers lived simply, many with livestock living in their homes, which were covered with tin roofs or straw atop mud-walled structures called *tukuls*. There was a saying that Emperor Haile Selassie took his people out of the 14th century and put them into the 15th century. Regardless of the conditions in which they lived, there was always a feeling of calmness and composure in these good-natured people.

The smell of smoke (particularly from burning charcoal) inevitably evokes those times when we entered a village to look for a case of smallpox. Smallpox had existed for thousands of years, as evidenced by pock marks on mummified remains found in Egypt. Throughout history this disease has been responsible for millions of deaths, and even today, more than 35 years after its eradication, it is still feared as a possible agent for use as a bioweapon. Thankfully, a mild infection in humans contracted from cows, known as cowpox, provided the basis for a vaccine that resulted in immunity against this deadly smallpox disease, and eventually led to its elimination from the world.[2]

U.S. PEACE CORPS APPLICATION

In 1969, I was living in Los Angeles, and was a Philosophy of Science major with plans to obtain a doctorate, and become a professor. At that time, the Vietnam War was going on in full force. It was the last year of my undergraduate work, and I was in possession of a student deferment.

---

2. Edward Jenner observed in 1798 that milk maidens who contracted cowpox rarely came down with smallpox. He is considered the father of the smallpox vaccine.

Unfortunately, the word was out that graduate student exemptions were going to be difficult to obtain.

So, I decided to file an application with the U.S. Peace Corps — just in case I would be called up. There was a section in the application related to job/work preferences and I selected "health related" as I didn't want to teach English.

Later that year, on December 1, 1969, the Selective Service System of the United States conducted a lottery to determine the order of call to military service in the Vietnam War for men born between 1944 and 1950. Even today, I can see with my mind's-eye a number of my friends, all potential draftees, sitting around listening to the radio as the ping pong balls were selected — each ball had a number 1 through 365, corresponding to January 1 through December 31. The order in which those ping pong balls were picked would be directly related to our fate. It was generally felt that those with a number of 200 or higher would not be called for duty. Luckily, I received a high number (205) and thus continued my school work, forgot about my Peace Corps application and expected to start graduate school in the fall of 1970.

A CALL TO DUTY

In the summer of 1970, I received an unexpected call from a Peace Corps recruiter asking me if I was interested in working with the World Health Organization (WHO) in Abyssinia (Ethiopia) to eradicate smallpox.

My initial responses were, "Where?" "Doing what?" and, "Don't need that deferment now, thanks," in that order.

The recruiter was patient and said, "Why don't you come to Philadelphia to hear more about the program?" Having not seen much of Philadelphia before, I agreed to go to that Peace Corps Pre-invitational Information Session (PRIS) in Philadelphia. Once I heard more about the program, especially the part that mentioned a Land Rover and being in the "wilderness," and, with my graduate advisor assuring me that there would be a spot for me upon returning, I decided to join up. Thus started a new chapter in my life that would eventually lead me away from philosophy to a career in public health.

PREPARING FOR THE ADVENTURE

I had about six weeks to prepare before leaving, and decided it would be best spent taking a course in infectious diseases in a summer session at the UCLA School of Public Health. The course covered the basics of infectious diseases and epidemiology and, most importantly, how they related to disease control. This introductory knowledge would serve me well in my upcoming work on smallpox. After a brief Peace Corps training visit to the Centers for Disease Control and Prevention (CDC) in Atlanta in October, 1970 as a member of Ethiopia Group XIV to learn some eradication basics, and also on how to service jet injectors,[3] we were off to Ethiopia. At that time, there were 18 of us in the smallpox section of Group XIV who were destined to work in the Ethiopian Smallpox Eradication Program (SEP).

ARRIVING IN ETHIOPIA

The shock of living in a developing country struck us all to varying degrees when we Group XIV trainees arrived in Addis Ababa. For me, I wondered how, in this modern era . . . the 1970s, could so many people be without so much, especially when it came to basic needs such as health care.

Our three-month in-country training session was to include further training in disease control techniques and language skills, however, this was interrupted by a cholera epidemic for which we were asked to assist in providing vaccine to the population. This unforeseen activity thrust us into the field for a month, and it turned out to be a great chance to be immersed in the culture and to see first-hand the types of problems we would be facing for the next two years. Unfortunately, the cholera vaccine available at that time was not a very effective vaccine, which contrasted with smallpox vaccine, a highly effective vaccine.[4]

---

3. A jet injector uses a high pressure narrow jet to inject a liquid, such as a vaccine, instead of using a hypodermic needle for mass vaccination. It is usually powered by a hydraulic foot pump system, using compressed air through a pressure hose.
4. Smallpox vaccine is highly effective with one dose providing immunity for years and for some over a lifetime. Although there may be rare severe reactions to the vaccine leading to disability and death, the cost-benefit when smallpox is a threat was always strongly in favor of using the vaccine.

OUR FIELD ASSIGNMENTS

We were all assigned to various places to begin our work on eradicating smallpox. Unfortunately, I was assigned — via a flip of the coin — to the capital city of Addis Ababa, which at the time was not the most appealing location to work in, and further, I had some doubts as to whether this program was right for me. Also, I believed there were many educated and competent Ethiopians living in Addis who were capable of doing this work.

To the rescue came a fellow PCV, Gary Urquhart, who readily gave up his field position to make me feel more comfortable in what I thought I came to do . . . which was to "work in the field." This act of kindness did the trick for me, and I was off and running with a field assignment to Kaffa province and never looked back.

Gary was a very mature individual, although only one or two years older than most of us. He always seemed to know what he wanted, so it made no difference to him where he was assigned. Gary went on to have an outstanding career in public health. He worked additional years in smallpox and later finished his career as a Branch Director at the CDC in Atlanta, overseeing Immunization Registry support systems. He has remained a close friend over the years.

OUR STRONG LEADERSHIP

For the most part, the PCVs were made to feel like "warriors" in a war against the smallpox virus. It would be unusual to find us sitting around philosophizing with regards to the suffering or unfairness of the world, or, for that matter, whether it was even possible to eradicate a single disease like smallpox from the face of the Earth. Basically, we all just tried to do our job the best that we could.

To that end, we were very lucky to have excellent support from the WHO, especially from our field supervisor, Dr. Ciro de Quadros, who was from Brazil. Ciro was a strong leader who became a great friend and mentor to us all. Ciro turned out to be a rare genius of public health: he was knowledgeable in the science of disease control, and possessed keen administrative, management, and organizational skills. Ciro was a man of vision who was able to develop strategies quickly to achieve his goals.

Ciro de Quadros, center, with the author, at left, in Teppi, Illubabor Ethiopia, 1970. *Photo by James Siemon.*

His "troops" all felt that he was indeed a "field general" in charge of the war being waged against this virus. A technique he used, which always amazed us, was that he would show up unannounced in the most remote and difficult to access locations — just to make sure we were doing our job correctly.

After smallpox was successfully eradicated, Ciro decided that the world should eradicate another disease, polio. Thanks to his efforts in the Americas, by the time of his passing in 2014, polio was well on its way to being globally eradicated. Polio will be the second disease to be successfully eradicated from the world after smallpox. During his stellar career in global public health, he employed many former Ethiopia PCVs, his trusted troops, to work with him in various initiatives related to vaccine preventable diseases. After he became the Director for the Immunization Program at the Pan American Health Organization (PAHO) in the 1980s, I was privileged to work for Ciro on a variety of assignments over the next thirty years.

DOING OUR JOBS

Ciro's incredible work ethic rubbed off on all of us. Before we knew it, we were all doing the activities needed to find where the smallpox virus was circulating (we called this surveillance) and to control it (known as ring containment). As work progressed, my instinctive feeling for organizational activities came into play. Together with my PCV partner, Vince Radke, and our local counterparts, we built a surveillance system and control response teams in the southwestern province of Kaffa over the next two years.

In a way, it is odd that the same advisor, Professor Vick, who told me that he would hold a place in graduate school for me, had once made a prognostic comment at the end of one of my term papers. After indicating a few missed points on the ontological argument for God, he went on to say, "But, you have a gift of clarity." That "gift" has served me well in the many disease control programs subsequently worked on.

Even in Kaffa, our team attempted to create a simplified manual for smallpox activities. Later, I would coordinate the writing of manuals for polio eradication, measles, and neo-natal tetanus elimination for PAHO. It was Ciro who taught me that when instructions/directions are provided in a straightforward and simplified fashion there is a better chance that field workers will understand them and be able to carry out the activities successfully.

A word or two on my incredible partner, Vince Radke, who took to doing the smallpox work and adapting to the local culture like a fish does to water. No place was too remote, too rough, or so difficult that he couldn't get there to do his job. Sometimes, he was just a bit too "local" in that he would not worry about the food or the water, and he would suffer for that. One time he was so sick, probably from eating or drinking something he shouldn't have, the SEP team had to send a helicopter to pick him up to take him back to the capital for emergency medical treatment. But typical of Vince, even when he was on the stretcher (during a refueling stop for the helicopter), he was saying something along the lines of "don't worry I will be right back" — and he was! Vince did indeed live on — after Ethiopia, he went to graduate school in public health and had an outstanding career in environmental health services in public health, and, like Gary, became a life-long friend and ended up working for the CDC in Atlanta.

STARTING TO SEE PROGRESS

As our work progressed, despite many obstacles, we all started to understand how effective the WHO strategies were for controlling the spread of smallpox. A sense of satisfaction, and a feeling of "accomplishment" came over many of us. That is, if we did our jobs right, by making sure populations at risk were appropriately immunized, we would be preventing smallpox from occurring.

In a short period of time, we were reporting something like 10% of the world's smallpox cases from our relatively small province of Kaffa in southwestern Ethiopia. The Global Chief of the smallpox program, Dr. Donald A. Henderson, who was based in Geneva, and whom we had met on only one occasion, sent a telegram to our SEP Director, Dr. Kurt Weithaler, in Addis Ababa, with an inquiry along the lines of: "Are they sure that they are not seeing chickenpox cases?"[5]

In fact, after a short period of time, he came personally to our province to check us out. It was indeed a thrill to have the global WHO SEP Chief make an appearance in our somewhat remote, and hard to reach, province. He not only knew us by name, but he knew a lot about our backgrounds as well!

D.A., as he was known, turned out to be yet another fantastic leader and mentor to many of us. I know it sounds a bit hackneyed, but yes, he was another public health genius.

There is a story to the effect that at the press conference held in 1981 declaring smallpox officially eradicated, D.A. was asked, "What will be the next disease we have to eradicate?" Without hesitation he responded, "Bad management!" Further, he would often emphasize it is not for the

---

5. Chickenpox was another common viral rash disease, which was much milder and less dangerous than smallpox. At its worst, chickenpox might resemble smallpox to varying degrees, but it was rarely fatal. The most virulent strain of smallpox, variola major, could be fatal in up to 30% of cases. In Ethiopia, however, the less potent strain, variola minor, was prevalent, killing less than two percent of its victims.

lack of tools or technology that programs fail, but due to poor administration and management.

He went on to continue his outstanding career in public health, as Dean of the Johns Hopkins School of Public Health, and as a science advisor to Presidents. I was privileged to work with him on many technical advisory committees over the years, especially those related to polio eradication and measles elimination. As an adherent to the Law of Parsimony,[6] a hallmark of his thinking was that no matter how complex an issue was, it could always be broken down to a practical, workable solution.

OBSTACLES WE FACED

Thinking of obstacles we faced in getting our job done, one can make a long list of candidates, including different culture, spicy food, inadequate housing (at times just our field tents), being wet for hours/days at a time, multiple languages in use, and rugged and muddy terrain during the rainy season. In addition, the work was hard — sometimes 24/7 with miles to walk, not to mention having to deal with the occasional local bureaucracy.

With regards to language barriers, in many of the provinces like Kaffa, multiple languages were spoken, most as different from each other as English is to Spanish. We once hired a worker to be a translator, who claimed he spoke thirteen languages, but, unfortunately, he spoke most of them poorly. This same translator had to be fired for selling aspirin on the side. An important rule we all had to live by was that we could not be side-tracked from our primary mission, which was to do only those activities that contributed to the eradication of smallpox. Requests for medical assistance or help in transporting the sick for the most part usually had to be declined, even though that was at times very difficult because we all felt badly about the suffering that was around us.

Despite this somewhat long list, for the most part I didn't really think of them as obstacles, with one important exception - transportation. However, there were solutions.

---

6. A scientific principle expounded by William of Occam that the simplest solutions are usually the best, or in Occam's words, "The assumptions introduced to explain a thing must not be multiplied beyond necessity."

Land Rover backing off wood bridge,
Bonga, Kaffa province, 1971. *Photo
by the author.*

THE ULTIMATE DRIVING MACHINE —
THE LAND ROVER

They say that adversity makes you stronger . . . then surely trying to get around in Ethiopia to do smallpox work must clearly be a good example of that. In order to successfully complete the smallpox eradication work we were doing, we had to reach all the places where suspected cases were being reported and check them out. There were three seasons in Kaffa province: generally, from September to February was the long dry season; followed by a short rainy season in March and April; and the long rainy season from June to August. Travel was not so bad during the dry season, but when the rainy season, known as the monsoons, arrived, and as it always did, getting anywhere could be a major challenge.

Most roads were built with loose gravel, rocks, and dirt, and the best vehicle to get the job done on such roads was the Land Rover. We often had to drive through very rough terrain including climbing over two to three-foot boulders in the middle of what was supposed to be a road,

Land Rover driven by the author fording a small creek below that wooden bridge, Bonga, Kaffa province, 1971. *Photo provided by the author.*

fording creeks, and making one's way through thick mud or over rocks. The photographs displayed give a good idea of the road conditions we faced. Both photos were taken within a 24-hour period. The first photo shows our Land Rover stuck on a muddy, wooden bridge with no railings. The previous night it had been raining "cats and dogs."

After almost slipping off the side of this wooden "bridge," I attempted to back off, but got stuck. Luckily, several Dutch Roman Catholic priests came to our aid the following morning. The reason we had attempted to use the bridge the night before was that the water in the creek below was too high to pass. There was a general rule we followed: never ford a creek or river if the water line was above the vehicle's distributor, which provided electric current to the spark plugs. The following morning when the second picture was taken, the rain had stopped and the creek was low enough to cross.

DC-3 somewhere in Kaffa province, 1972. *Photo by the author.*

THE ULTIMATE FLYING MACHINE — THE DC-3

Roads only covered a small proportion of our assigned territory. Therefore, on occasion, we also had to make use of one of the world's most stable and dependable aircraft. That plane, being the Douglas DC-3 (most of these aging planes were left over from WWII duty), a fixed-wing, two motor propeller-driven aircraft that was so noisy you could hardly hear yourself think. Such planes could land almost anywhere, including in cow fields/patches, not to mention that they could fly well with only one engine working, and even at times when neither engine worked (at least for short periods of time!).

WHY I PREFERRED HOOFING IT TO MULES AND HORSES

In a rural province like Kaffa, we were frequently faced with locations that were unreachable by plane or vehicle, especially in the mountainous areas. In order to reach such places, we had the option of hiring horses

The author getting his shoes shined.
Ethiopia. *Photo by James Siemon.*

or mules. Between the two, mules were steadier on treacherous narrow mountain passes, and, to some degree, smarter. I'd been told that if you happened to get thrown or slip off, the mule was less likely to kick you in the head! Overall, however, I preferred walking over riding because riding always made me sleepy and sore. During my two years in Ethiopia I used a pair of burgundy-colored boots that I brought from the U.S. I kept them well polished and even employed two *listros* (shoeshine boys) at a time to keep them shiny . . . to no end of amusement for the local population.

THE IMPORTANCE OF MAPS

Obviously, a complement to having good transportation was having good maps, but in the beginning we did not have good maps. In fact, we were told that the best maps of our area were those that the Italians drew up during their occupation during WWII, and that turned out to be true. If there is a take-home lesson from this chapter, it is that good maps are

Mobil Road Map of Ethiopia
and Addis Ababa, 1970. *Photo
by the author.*

essential for field work. In the 1970s, GPS was not widely available as it is today. One of the first things I did upon arriving in the country was to buy a road map sold by Mobil Oil Company.

However, this map showed only the main roads and did not give us a very accurate picture of how to get to 98% of the areas in our province, all of which were located off of the two main roads. So, without any knowledge of cartography, we started drawing some reasonably accurate maps depicting locations, roads, mountain passes, distances, impediments, and walking times. We even added contour lines and circles to indicate approximate altitudes. Within a short period, we had pieced together a comprehensive collection of maps depicting our province in detail, all of which we posted on the wall of our SEP office in Jimma, the capital city of Kaffa province.

Now you would think that was an important accomplishment! However, there was a moment when we thought otherwise. One day, the General of Haile Selassie's Southern Army came knocking at our door, and I was indeed worried to see this well decorated military man at our threshold. It turned out that he had heard that we had been putting together such maps and wanted his staff to see what we had done. We became fast friends and from that time forward the Army was always

A local chief pointing out on my newly-drawn map where I should not be going that day. Northeast Territory, Kenya, 1975. *Photo by the author.*

ready to help us in our efforts to vaccinate affected areas, which was a good use of local resources.

The importance of map-making stayed with me on other assignments as well. To use my dramatic license here, for one assignment it might have meant the difference between life and death. In 1976, I was assigned by WHO to go to the Northeast Territory of Kenya to determine if any smallpox cases were coming into the country from nearby Somalia, which, at that time, was experiencing the final cases of smallpox in the world. While patrolling the area, I relied on the maps I had drawn. In this case, such maps were very important to avoid any landmines that either the Ethiopian or Somali armies had buried on the Kenyan side.

WORD ON THE FOOD – HOT!
Many of the PCVs who joined the program came from sheltered lives . . . at least where culinary experiences were involved. For myself, probably the spiciest food my mother would make was chili, and that was from the

can. Therefore, you can imagine the shock for some of us when we were served, especially in the field, a steady diet of very spicy Ethiopian food. Ethiopian cuisine includes a great variety of excellent dishes, but most notable are the stews, especially the chicken stew (known as *doro wot*). Such stews were often extremely spicy, especially for the uninitiated. In the field, we ate what we were given, and I was okay with that as long as my meal was accompanied with a gallon of water. The stew is served with a pancake-like bread called *injera* (usually made from *teff*, a grain found only in Ethiopia at that time). *Injera* is prepared by a fermenting process and results in a somewhat sour and acrid taste and, for some of us, it was a bit malodorous. However, after about two to three months, most of us ended up loving the food, and I no longer needed that gallon of water by my side because I had learned to like it hot. My wife and children in Los Angeles were subsequently introduced to Ethiopian food, and they also love it.

In anticipation of our limited ability to adapt to the local food, and in case we got stuck in the middle of nowhere, the Peace Corps obtained a supply of U.S. C-rations (ready-to-eat meals in cans) to take with us on our field trips. Such food got old quickly, although I personally found certain items to my liking, such as the peanut butter and the biscuit bar, which was loaded with nutrients/vitamins that probably exceeded the amount in today's power bars.

In Ethiopia, there were a number of missionaries who could be found in the provinces providing medical services or "looking for converts." Although I could not condone or agree with those missionaries who heavily proselytized, and whose main aim seemed to be saving and converting as many souls as possible, I did see them at the same time doing beneficial projects for the local populations. I clearly recall being warned by a narrow-minded group of missionaries that I was entering into an area of "evil" and needed to be very careful. To my delight, the area known as Jangero on the Kenyan border, was inhabited by some of the most pleasant people on Earth. Apparently, their only transgression was that they were animists, who good heartedly believed that plants and other inanimate objects had souls.

Many times, after walking and working for 12 to 14 hours in a day in a remote area, I would come upon a small mission post and would be welcomed and offered a wonderful hot meal. I made good friends with many of the less aggressive priests and pastors, who, luckily, were assigned to our province, usually from the Netherlands.

MY IRON STOMACH – NOT THIS TIME

In fact, it might have been those C-rations that gave me the worst case of food poisoning I experienced during my two-year stay. I was helping fellow PCV eradicator, Jim Siemon, in a very remote area when a strong stomach ache hit me. What he told me afterwards was something along the lines that he thought I was going to die, and if I was dying, what he would do, and how he would get me out of there. Luckily, 24 hours later, I recovered enough to walk out.

Not every smallpox PCV ended up with a career in the field of Public Health, although a surprising number did. Jim, who always sounded scholarly and seemed to know more about grammar than the rest of us combined, ended up as an accomplished author and Shakespeare professor at Boston University.

I was usually known as having an iron stomach, but, in reality, I was very careful about certain foods (such as avoiding salads not prepared with filtered water, raw meat, etc.). There were many times in the field when I met a local chief of a village who would generously offer me a nice cool glass of fresh milk (probably obtained from the local cow that may or may not have had bovine TB). I always accepted the offer, but would ask the chief whether it would be possible to boil the milk as that was my favorite way to have the drink prepared. It worked every time, and if sugar was available, I had that added to my drink as well. In general, I tried my best to follow the old adage, "keep hot foods hot and cold foods cold." I also treated all my water in the field with iodine tablets. This was not the most favorite disinfectant because of its bad aftertaste, nevertheless, its sterilizing powers were greater and quicker than chlorine tablets, which were the alternative.

A small girl with smallpox, Teppi,
Illubabor, 1970. *Photo by the author.*

With regard to treating the water, I recall my first assignment to check out a suspected case of smallpox in a very remote area called Teppi in Illubabor province. In order to reach that town, it was necessary to walk for about 15 miles (6-7 hours) along hot, remote trails. About two hours into my trip, my canteen of filtered water was empty, and I was ready to obtain water from a local well and add my iodine tablet. To my surprise, the little bottle I kept my iodine in was missing – it must have fallen out from under the canteen cover flap where I usually kept it. Given the late hour of the day, there was no time to stop and boil water, so we pushed on without drinking any water. Luckily, about half way through the trip, we came upon a cold, fast flowing stream, so I stripped off my clothes and sat in it. This was probably not the best idea from an infectious diseases point of view, but it did revive me enough to get me to the town where we found active cases of smallpox.

Upon arriving in Teppi town, we discovered a small clinic with a diesel-powered refrigerator. When the local nurse saw how parched I was,

The author vaccinating a small child
in Teppi town, Illubabor, 1970. *Photo
provided by the author.*

he told me to help myself to the beers, filtered water, and Coca Cola. I
chose the Coke, but after a large gulp I spit it out and went for the water!
I guess I will not be doing Coke ads any time soon.

Clearly, one of the most rewarding aspects of the SEP work occurred
when I returned to villages after an outbreak and saw the villagers' healthy
smiling faces – that was reward in and of itself.

AFTER ETHIOPIA

After completing my PCV assignment in Ethiopia, I returned to my school-
ing, but instead of studying philosophy, I chose to study public health,
specifically epidemiology. During my two years in Ethiopia, I was able to
learn more about infectious diseases, especially vaccine preventable ones,
and it was clear that epidemiology was the science behind how we prove
what works and doesn't work in medicine and in public health. Returning
to Los Angeles, I obtained a Master's degree (MPH) and then a Doctorate

The author returned to check village
children to make sure that their
vaccinations were successful, Teppi,
Illubabor, 1971. *Photo provided by
the author.*

degree (DrPH) in epidemiology at UCLA. I ended up having a career as
an epidemiologist for the County of Los Angeles Department of Health
Services, and continued to work, when time permitted, as a consultant for
WHO, mostly in immunization programs, consulting in over 20 countries.
I also became an Adjunct Professor and taught epidemiology at UCLA
for over thirty years and at USC for fifteen years. In 2012, I was inducted
into the UCLA School of Public Health alumni's Hall of Fame, partially
based upon my international work with WHO.

CONCLUSION

My experiences in Ethiopia provided me with such an excellent introduction to public health that it is not hard to understand how I would
spend the next 45 years in that career trying to make a difference. The
memories and lessons I learned from my first public health experience in

Ethiopia stayed with me for my entire career. In particular, I understood the need to be hands-on and to go in-person to areas where there were problems to solve. My advice for many of my students who wanted to "help people" was to try to participate in a field project or volunteer in an area in which they are interested—and that experience just might help to focus or jump-start their careers.

•

my further endeavors in two other subsequent SEP country programs, would lead me to work in the newly created WHO Expanded Program on Immunization (EPI) in 1979. The EPI was the vision of Dr. Donald A. Henderson, the Global Director of the WHO SEP. In 1974 he prepared a memorandum to the then director of the WHO, Dr. Halfdan Mahler, expressing his views on this new program, which would become a legacy of the SEP. But for me, it all started in Ethiopia.

My Peace Corps training group (Group XVII) received excellent training in contact tracing (as used in the U.S. Sexual Transmitted Disease Program) and differential diagnosis of rashes similar to smallpox at the U.S. Centers for Disease Control (CDC) in Atlanta before our departure, and it served me well.

Before boarding the plane to fly to Addis Ababa, I had prepared a collection of the music that I wanted to have with me. I carried two albums, the Rolling Stones' *Sticky Fingers* and the Grateful Dead's *Skull and Roses*, and some cassette tapes. This music would keep me company, provide me comfort and keep me grounded in my culture.

When I arrived in Addis Ababa in July of 1972, as a PCV assigned to the WHO's SEP, I had no idea that I would be involved in and witness the historic eradication of a disease while working with the Ethiopia's Ministry of Health (MOH) and my PCV brethren.

Fortunately, my experience living in Quito, Ecuador for almost one year in 1960, when I was just 10 years old, provided me with the type of mental toughness that I needed to face the sharply different culture that Addis Ababa and the rest of Ethiopia served up every morning.

The poverty that I encountered in Ethiopia, even in the first few weeks of Peace Corps language training, was extraordinary and heart-breaking. In Bahar Dar, our training site, the large number of beggars, both young and old, was almost overwhelming. As I wrote in a letter to my parents on August 30, 1972, many boys had left their homes because their parents could not support them. One young boy wanted me to support him, but at that time, as a trainee, I could not. But then again, for a boy whose stomach was empty, it was very difficult for him to understand or accept my decision. I would later support a student when I took up residence in Welega province, my first assignment with the Ethiopian SEP.

After our in-country Peace Corps language training, quite frankly, it was exhilarating to get started and I felt like I was ready for the experiences that Ethiopia would provide every day, whether I was walking in the Awash Valley lowland desert, or scaling the mountain sides in the Ethiopian highlands, searching for smallpox cases and undertaking vaccination activities.

YEAR ONE: 1972 – 1973

I was first assigned to work in Welega province (now referred to as the Oromia Region). I met Alan Schnur, who was a fellow PCV, assigned previously by WHO to eradicate smallpox in this province. Alan was a teacher, and he guided me and provided me with advice in my first few months as I undertook my work as a smallpox surveillance officer. Eventually, another PCV, Steve Reiber, joined us.

We divided the province among the three of us, and, with our MOH sanitarian SEP team members, we set out to search for smallpox and to vaccinate. My field trips averaged 14 to 17 days each, during which I drove to the parts of the province that had not yet been searched or from where we had received information (rumors) of possible transmission of smallpox. I soon realized that those areas of the province that could be reached by a Land Rover or Land Cruiser had already been searched, and what was left untouched by the previous SEP surveillance work were those areas that could only be reached on foot where only mountain peaks and valleys could be seen in the horizon.

The WHO epidemiologist, Dr. Ciro de Quadros, a Brazilian, was our field coordinator for the SEP activities; some would state very accurately that he was our "field general."

When I visited his office in Addis, he would ask me to point to his map and show him the places I searched, and he would place red or white pins to show where cases of smallpox, or no cases, had been found. He was also a fine mentor and schooled me in other diseases and rashes. I

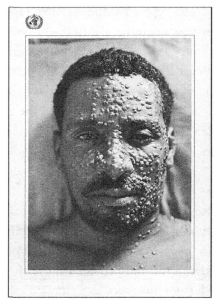

Picture of a smallpox recognition
card. *Photo provided by the author.*

remember one of the first trips we made together, which was the result of
a rumor of a possible smallpox case. It turned out be a case of syphilis in
a woman who provided sexual services. She was in the secondary stage
of the disease and had developed scabs, which were the reason that her
case was reported as a suspected case of smallpox.

SEARCHING FOR POSSIBLE CASES OF SMALLPOX
Like other SEP field staff, I often visited schools and sought permission
from teachers before asking the students if they had seen possible cases
of smallpox in their villages. As most of my SEP colleagues would agree,
our disease recognition cards and posters were very effective in eliciting
information from the students and teachers about the existence of recent
smallpox cases or ongoing transmission. Based on any information provided by the students and teachers, I would set out, by Land Rover or on foot,
to find the villages and families where smallpox cases had been reported.

Outside of Nekemte, the capital of Welega province, there were very few villages that offered acceptable, if any, hotel-like accommodations in 1972. Therefore, our British-supplied tents and cots offered the warmest and best accommodations out in the bush.

I quickly discovered in the highlands, however, that I often had uninvited guests in my sleeping bag — fleas. In some places, they were so bad that the fleas would jump onto my socks and hitch a ride into the tent and then into the sleeping bag.

Eventually, I got wise and would place dog flea collars inside my sleeping bag, or at the foot of my bed at home, to prevent waking up various times in the middle of the night with my flashlight to hunt down those little no-good critters!

The search for smallpox cases in the rural areas in the highlands of Welega served to educate me quickly about the other health problems that were viewed by the local population as a higher priority than smallpox, impacted the people on a daily basis and could result in premature deaths.

One of the health conditions affecting young and old were respiratory infections. I remember very clearly the infant who was brought to me when I was searching for smallpox cases in a village west of Nekemte in the highlands. The infant was laboring to breathe and was suffering from substantial nasal congestion. The father stated that the baby would not take milk from his mother. The parents requested me to provide them with medicine (penicillin) for the infant, but I had none. I did offer to vaccinate the child because of the possible presence of smallpox cases in the area, but the parents politely refused. I continued my search and went on to the next village. On my return to find my Land Rover a couple of days later, I stopped by the same village and inquired about the infant. Regrettably, the father told me the infant had died.

Months later, in the highlands of Welega, where I was searching for cases and vaccinating, I was asked to transport a person to the closest hospital. I asked what the person was suffering from and the villagers stated that the gentleman was severely constipated and had not evacuated himself in almost three weeks. I asked what had caused this condition and they informed me that he had tried clean himself with a stone after going

Land Rover underneath a tree while waiting to meet a *balabat* to request his support. Because it was such a long wait, the sanitarian started to kill flies. Our Land Rover was full of flies, I mean really a lot of flies. He would grab a fly using the palm of his hand and vigorously shake it and send the fly smashing against the window or dash board of the Land Rover. This resulted in the fly being killed or incapacitated since it could not fly. My interpreter and I soon found ourselves doing the same thing. After some time, the sanitarian stated, "We should pursue the eradication of flies after eradicating smallpox." He explained that all Ethiopians should be instructed to do this simultaneously on one day. We all laughed.

Where the local *balabat* was well-liked, or, in some cases, feared, by his tenants, he could command many people to come to the smallpox vaccination site. In one memorable vaccination event, the crowd of persons was almost overwhelming. In these cases, I used the Ped-O-Jet injector, which we called the jet gun, and it was very effective for vaccinating crowds of up to 500 or more people at one site within four to five hours. The jet gun suffered from breakdowns with some frequency, however, and had to be serviced often. My SEP colleagues often complained about the jet guns and would avoid using them, but I found them to be strategically useful because I had been trained in their maintenance and repair.

Like most of my Peace Corps SEP colleagues, we spent our nights in our tents in faraway places. I had the pleasure of viewing some very beautiful sunsets. The nights in the highlands of Welega were cold, but in the mornings freshly made *buna* tasted great and seemed to break the cold air of the highlands.

Some PCVs stated that one of the most difficult things for them to deal with was the loneliness. Fortunately, I owned a short-wave radio, and at night in my tent it was very helpful. Tuning in to the BBC and the U.S. Armed Forces Radio Network station in Asmara provided news, information and sports and a contact with the culture that I had left behind.

The Ethiopian culture and environment was a stark contrast to my Chicago upbringing. Welega, located west of Addis Ababa, was both a physically rugged place and so different culturally. Sometimes, I heard people refer to it as the "wild west." Leaving Addis Ababa, the road was asphalt, but, after a short distance, the road turned to gravel and got rougher as it extended to the Sudanese border. For me, all these differences provided the trappings of a great adventure. In addition, the process of searching for smallpox cases presented opportunities for experiencing many unique adventures.

One day in the highlands of Welega, I found myself walking from village to village going from house to house showing the smallpox recognition card attempting to obtain information. In one village, I cannot remember the name, a villager informed me that there was a "witch" who might have some information about cases of smallpox. I was told that the witch could converse with cows also. It seems that the witch had "spooked" the villagers, and she also had the reputation of drinking a lot of alcoholic beverages, such as homemade *tella* (Ethiopian beer made from barley) and *tej* (honey wine). When I asked where she lived, the villager pointed up to the slopes on the side of the large hill in front of me, so, I proceeded to climb uphill with my interpreter.

When we reached her hut, I introduced myself and showed her the smallpox recognition card. She stated she had not seen persons with this disease. After a few minutes, I indicated to her that we were about to leave, but she insisted that we stay and have a glass of her *tella*. I accepted and she walked to the corner of her hut where she had been fermenting her *tella* in a clay earthen jug. She broke open the mud seal and poured out the brown beer into a tall glass. As we drank the cool, good tasting *tella*, using my interpreter, we conversed about her witchcraft. After drinking one glass, we departed. When I walked outside into the nice warm sunlight, I realized that I was a bit high from the witch's strong brew, but I easily managed to get down the hill.

Not all villages were receptive to my visits, however. In one village, the house owners put their dogs outside their doors or compound gates where the dogs howled and announced their displeasure with me with their ferocious, loud barks. Needless to say, I didn't knock on the doors of those houses.

One critical practice that all SEP field staff had been instructed to do was to follow-up in villages that had reported cases of smallpox to determine if transmission of the smallpox virus had ceased after vaccination of the surrounding area. During these follow-up visits, we would also evaluate the "take rates," or the rate of successful smallpox vaccinations. One time, Ciro de Quadros and I returned to a village in which I had found an outbreak of smallpox. We found one boy who had been vaccinated, but he had one classical smallpox pustule on his forehead. We determined that the boy was vaccinated while in the incubation period of the disease, which had greatly reduced the rash. His case increased our case count for this outbreak.

SEARCHING FOR SMALLPOX CASES IN THE BLUE NILE GORGE

Of all the great adventures that I experienced in chasing down smallpox outbreaks, there are a few of them that stand out in my mind. One was my field visit to the Blue Nile River in the northern part of Welega province.

We drove to the edge of the plateau the day before and slept in our tents. The next morning the *balabat* had organized our visit with chiefs of villages in the sector of concern in the Blue Nile gorge. He had organized guides for our trip, but I found out the sanitarian who was with me could not travel because of a bad case of the "trots." That meant I had no interpreter with me for this visit. *What to do?* It was decided that I would go by myself as everything had been organized and the villagers were waiting. Everybody was informed of the purpose of my visit and who I was, so I packed a donkey with a tent, a cot and sleeping bag, smallpox vaccine, tubes filled with bifurcated needless, and a small backpack, which contained my spare shirt, underwear, socks, jeans, medicine kit and a very small portable Swedish stove that ran on kerosene, plus a small aluminum container that held extra kerosene.

The descent to the bottom of the gorge took a bit more than five hours. Over the course of my many excursions, I had found that going down a steep mountain incline was more difficult than going up, but it was a beautiful descent as I peered across to the other side of the gorge and watched how the Blue Nile River got closer and closer. I reached the bottom of the gorge where the village was located high on the river bank.

The chief of the village was waiting and escorted me to the hut where he had arranged a bed for me. The bed was made of split bamboo slats and was set up almost three feet above the ground.

To my consternation, a chicken had already taken a comfortable position on the bed, which made me worry about lice. During my field trips over the two years, I had experienced a couple of lice infestations. During one field trip, I had to have my shirt and underwear boiled, which was the only way to kill the body lice that made their home in the stitching of my shirts and underwear.

The chief and I communicated by sign language and my broken Amharic. After supper, he came into the hut where I was resting comfortably. He was accompanied by a young, well-fed woman who had put on a new coat of red okra over her almost naked body. Her hair was nicely braided, resting on the top of her head. Her jewelry was a nose bone and a necklace of crockery. Using his hands and fingers, the chief made a motion to offer her to me. I quickly thought about it, but I politely refused. The chief accepted my decision and left the hut with her.

Some of my friends, to whom I have related this event, have commented that I should have taken advantage of the experience, which would have given me what they called "total cultural immersion." At the time of visit of the chief and the young lady, I had reached a lightning quick conclusion: I wanted to make sure I could leave the village. I was very concerned that if I had taken her into my bed, I would never have been permitted to leave and I would have been asked to marry her. I even wondered if I could have left after the wedding.

The next day, I proceeded to vaccinate the villagers, young and old. An elderly woman had traveled some distance to see a white man for the first time. As she approached me, she reached out and grabbed my arm and put it next to her arm. She wanted to contrast the color difference between our skins. To the best of my understanding, the villagers informed me that I was the eighth white man to have visited this region, as far as their history and memory were concerned.

The ethnic group that inhabited that area of the Blue Nile River were of Bantu lineage. I had been informed that these people had migrated from the Sudan centuries ago. The Amharas and Oromo used a word to describe the peoples of darker skin and of Bantu origin. The term they used was *shankilla*, which meant persons of lower class or even slaves.

At the end of the day, after vaccinating villagers from both sides of the river, I went down to the river to take a bath and was followed by many persons. As I stood on the bank of the river looking onto the shallow, fast moving, clear waters of the Blue Nile, a man came up to me and pulled on my shirt to peer down to see if I had breasts. I did have long hair, but not too long, and perhaps my decision not to accept the kind offer of the young lady's love was a cause of doubt. My audience watched me bathe in the warm waters of the Blue Nile as the sun began to set behind the mountains that crowned the gorge.

The following day, I woke up and consumed a good breakfast before proceeding to climb back up to the plateau. Before I departed, I vaccinated a few more persons. It was about 8:00 a.m. or so when we began our ascent up the escarpment. I would regret eating such a large breakfast about a quarter of the way up as I "heaved ho" my breakfast. I would climb more than six hours before reaching the top.

Near the top, my guide took me to another village about an hour along the escarpment, where I pitched my tent for the evening. I was dead tired. As the sun set, the fading sunlight painted beautiful warm colors on the walls across the gorge.

The family that lived in the only hut where I was camped provided me with one of the best Ethiopian meals that I ever had, which was *ayib* (fresh cheese curd) with *injera*.

That was definitely a field trip to remember. I eventually returned to my Land Rover safely and we drove back to Nekemte.

THE VALLEY

Just an hour or so outside of Nekemte, traveling west on a gravel, all-weather road, lived two Rural Development PCVs, Tim and Dennis. They had established a fabulous training/demonstration project for teaching farmers how to use more modern farming and irrigation techniques to produce better crop yields.

They had built their own accommodations, which were quite sparse. Since it was very hot in the valley, they each built their own one-room house from bamboo slats. The bamboo slats were spaced two to three inches or so apart, which provided perfect air conditioning. Each house had a tin roof. A platform bed, raised about five feet off the ground, to prevent snakes from climbing into the bed, occupied most of the interior of each house. There was a table and two chairs on the other side of the room, and next to it was another table with a two-burner gas stove. Each house also had its own toilet. When I went to avail myself of his commode, I yelled out to Tim, "Where is the toilet paper?" He replied, "Tear the pages from the paperback book," which was lying next to the commode. Tim confirmed that he would read the pages while sitting on the commode and then use those "read pages" for cleaning himself up. Now that's what I call rugged.

They were dedicated individuals and they were making a difference. I went to the demonstration plots to see for myself what they had built for teaching modern farming techniques. When I arrived with Tim at the demonstration area, we found several men who were part of the project who were smoking their own home-grown tobacco underneath a huge tree that provided shade against the pounding hot sun. They offered me the calabash water pipe. Before I smoked it, I looked at the ball of tobacco lying next to the pipe. It was as black as coal tar. Boy, it was strong smoke — so strong that the eyes of the farmers were bloodshot red.

There were a few other PCVs in the province, like Jamie and Tony who were school teachers. These PCV brethren were not only our comrades, they also served as an extension to our informal surveillance network for gathering information on any suspected cases of smallpox.

The Welega SEP team advanced with its searches and vaccination operations and taking containment action in the face of smallpox cases. By the end my first year, in July 1973, between the SEP Team in Welega and the WHO in Addis Ababa, we were able to ascertain that there was no transmission of the smallpox virus in Welega. Therefore, Ciro de Quadros pulled me out of Welega and stationed me in Addis to support operations in the Awash Valley and the highlands north of Addis Ababa.

YEAR TWO: 1973-1974 — WINE, GUNS AND EL DUCE

When traveling from Addis Ababa north through the mountains, one enters a tunnel just after Debra Berhan to head towards the town of Dessie and other points to the far ends of northern Ethiopia. Coming out of the tunnel there is a spectacular view . . . below lies the great Awash Valley and to the left a huge escarpment formed by the mountains of the Ethiopian highlands.

If one were to look back toward the stone retaining wall after coming out of the tunnel and proceed to descend into the valley, one could see the fading insignia carved into the face of the wall in remembrance of Benito Mussolini . . . el Duce. Today, I don't know whether the wall still shows the insignia; it may have been resurfaced or replaced by now, but back in 1973, the wall stood as a bad memory of the Italian invasion of Ethiopia and the forced labor used to build the roads. Yet, the history of the Italian occupation also left cultural footprints.

Addis Ababa had good Italian restaurants, which PCVs would seek out for a change of cuisine. There was also a wine industry started by the Italians, which had taken root and continued under the Ethiopians and Italian expats. The chianti-shaped bottles of Ethiopian wine were a hit or miss affair, but when we found a good bottle of wine we enjoyed it.

Almost everywhere I traveled when looking for smallpox cases, men would carry World War I-era single-cartridge breech-loading European/ Italian rifles. However, it appeared that they possessed very few bullets. I never saw any ammunition belts filled — normally they carried only five to eight cartridges.

I would spend many of my months between July 1973 and July 1974 in the Awash Valley with the nomads of the Afar and Issa ethnic groups, searching for smallpox cases and vaccinating the people.

The approach of selecting search areas not previously searched and collecting rumors from different sources was viewed as the "best practice" for the Ethiopian SEP program in 1973. However, I'm sure that today's widespread availability of mobile phones and a myriad of digital social networks and apps would offer much more information, and would

Ismael (far right) standing next to two nomadic women and a man. *Photo by the author.*

probably afford the epidemiologists a way to filter all the information to better pinpoint active transmission of the smallpox virus.

Detailed logistics planning was the prerequisite to staying out in the desert for 14-plus days at a time searching for or following the nomads, or for any excursion beyond 14 days where a vehicle could not traverse the terrain.

I carried as much drinking water as possible in my canteen, in addition to carrying jerry cans of gasoline. I also took iodine tablets for when I ran out of drinking water. Canned tuna, rice, tomato sauce and noodles were the staples.

My Land Rover could cross the desert floor of the valley, and only acacia tree thorns impeded my progress when their needle-sharp points punctured the tires.

Identifying a trusted guide, who also spoke the tribal language, was an indispensable element of my plan. For me, this was Ismael who was from the region, and he spoke good English. He guided me as I drove my

Land Rover; he knew where the nomads would be so that we could seek out their camps, which were mainly along the Awash River.

The nomads were very amenable to being vaccinated. Despite our intensive searches, we could not find active transmission of smallpox among them even though we were constantly seeking more information.

One rumor that we obtained from the health system turned out be associated with a meningitis outbreak in adults. When I arrived at the area, I found adults who were bathed in purple iodine and had developed scabs, which was a hideous combination. They were being treated by government health workers. The sick were suffering from meningitis, a communicable disease, and hence were in very poor health. Some were delirious and some were so weakened that they could not walk. Since I already knew about a possible meningitis outbreak in the area, I had brought sufficient penicillin to treat myself in case I became infected.

By and large, the nomads were quite healthy despite their Spartan life style, and they willingly helped me find encampments and facilitated vaccination efforts.

One evening, out of nowhere, Ismael asked if I wanted to hunt some wild boar. I said yes, although I didn't know quite what I was getting into. He got into the driver's seat and I assumed a sitting position on top of the Land Rover. It was quite dark out and we needed the lights of the Land Rover to spot a wild boar. After a time, we stopped about 35 feet from a wild boar who was devouring grass, I aimed the World War II issue rifle that Ismael carried in the Land Rover and felled it with one shot.

We gutted the boar, and I asked for help from some villagers to carry it across a small river to a house where we could cook it. After carrying the boar across the stream, I noticed that the young men who had carried it started jumping back into the small river. I asked why they had done this and was told that, as Muslims, they were not supposed to touch the boar.

Oh, no, I said to myself, and I pleaded my innocence and apologized. I took over handling the boar, and cooked it over an open fire. (It would be about 15 years later, in Cuba, that I would again enjoy such a succulent portion of pig meat as I experienced that evening.)

The next day I met up with a Dutch WHO smallpox worker and I asked him if he could take two of the legs of the boar to the PCVs in Addis Ababa, and he kindly obliged. About two weeks later an entourage of about five PCVs from Addis came down to hunt wild boar. Unfortunately, they returned to Addis Ababa without a wild boar for their dinner table.

Later that week, Warren Barrash, a fellow PCV/SEP, met me in the Awash Valley. I had previously arranged to meet him at a seasonal camp of some people of the Adal ethnic group. Warren had brought several jerry cans of additional fuel for my Land Rover because I knew that this current trip was beyond the capacity of spare gas that I could bring myself.

Warren decided to stay and join me in the search for smallpox transmissions. That night, we set a campfire to cook one of the boar legs we had brought with us . . . and it was as succulent as the other boar-leg meat I had eaten earlier in the week.

We retired to our cots with full bellies, but within a few hours after falling asleep we were awakened by the whooping noises of hyenas. I peeked out of my tent and saw that the fire had died down and two hyenas were attacking the boar's leg. When I woke up in the morning I saw that the boar's leg had been almost totally consumed by the hyenas.

Later, as I was dressing, I peered into my boots and saw that a scorpion had booked a room in one of the boots, so I made sure it checked out immediately. Such is life in the desert of the Awash Valley.

The rigorous work in the Awash Valley offered some beautiful memories as I searched for cases of smallpox.

At one point, I contacted an American missionary who knew the region and stated that he could accompany me to find the encampments of some nomads. We arrived at an encampment just before the sun set. We pitched our tents and ate some food from our rations. A full moon lit up the surrounding scenery and a beautiful deep blue sky. As I set myself into my cot for a good night's sleep, I heard singing voices of women in the distance. I listened carefully again and decided to get dressed and investigate from where the beautiful voices were coming.

I walked under a full moonlit sky toward the singing and came upon a group of women standing or sitting around a large drum made of wood and covered with cowhide. Their voices were enchanting. I asked what they were doing and I was informed that the adult women were exorcising the devil from a young woman. Their singing mesmerized me. I returned to my cot and fell asleep to their singing. To this day, I regret not having a voice recorder then.

Life in the wild desert, like anywhere else was challenging and tough.

In another of my searches, I came upon an encampment at midday and was invited to dine with the men from the clan. They had just slaughtered a camel, an animal known to be highly prized, owned by one family of their clan. Because I was a guest, I joined the elders who were served first, and who are so revered they were given the best part of the camel meat. I selected my meat, which had been stewed in pure camel's fat. I asked why they had slaughtered the camel, and I was told that the camel was killed as punishment to the owner for not watching his infant child . . . a hyena had crept into the encampment and made off with the child and killed it.

One of my last trips into the Awash Valley led me to a natural hot spring about which the nomads had told Ismael. It was an oasis in the middle of the desert and was surrounded by vegetation and palm trees. I jumped into the warm thermal waters and thoroughly enjoyed a moment of a separate reality against the sunlit blue sky.

By mid-1973, a very large portion of northern and eastern Ethiopia was overcome by a massive famine. I joined forces with the Oxfam workers, who were providing flour and other foods to the nomads and other people who had settled in the valley. I must thank the Oxfam people for their good will in allowing me to vaccinate the people as they received their food donations.

Sitting under an acacia tree, a nomadic woman, who had covered her upper body with a light-weight, black floral shawl, extended her arm to me to be vaccinated. As I proceeded to apply the 15 needle punctures with a bifurcated needle, she abruptly pulled her arm from my hand and exposed her cancerous right breast. There was no skin left on it.

I am not sure about the data, but it is reported by UN Food and Agricultural Organization (FAO) that about 300,000 people, predominantly the northern rural poor, died during the 1973–1974 Ethiopian famine.[1] During that time, I did not record any cases of smallpox, but did vaccinate many people at the Oxfam site in the Awash Valley.

THE GREAT GISHE SEARCH EXPEDITION

In the spring of 1974, Ciro de Quadros called me into his office to discuss plans to carry out a search for transmission of smallpox cases with Warren Barrash and Lewis Kaplan (a British volunteer) in Gishe, a remote subdistrict of Menz and Gishe *awraja* in the highlands north of Addis Ababa. No teams had worked there before, and so SEP had no surveillance information. Warren and Lewis had undertaken a reconnaissance trip to Gishe in 1973, but their efforts were blocked by uncooperative authorities, so the real the situation regarding smallpox transmission there was unknown. As I departed Ciro's office, he said, "Keep the team out there as long as possible."

I will not dwell on the specifics of the Gishe Expedition because Warren Barrash has described that adventure thoroughly in his chapter. It turned out to be a policy changing expedition. When we arrived at our staging site north of Mehal Meda in Menz, all one could view in the distant horizon were huge peaks and valleys, but no roads.

At the end of the 32-day expedition, we confirmed multiple chains of transmission. People accepted being vaccinated, although sometimes it was only after the *balabats* aggressively urged the people to cooperate.

At one point during the expedition, Lewis Kaplan had to perform vaccinations from his cot inside his tent because he was terribly sick with a cold. After 32 days of walking, all of us were tired, but we knew we had accomplished something special. More importantly, after returning to

---

1 See *Perspectivesonafrica.wordpress.com/2012/10/21/why-did-northern-ethiopian-peasants-starve-in-the-1973-1974-famine.*

Addis Ababa and a debriefing with Ciro de Quadros, he realized that there had to be a different approach to ending the transmission of smallpox in this corner of the earth.

Within months after this expedition in 1974, Ciro, Kurt Weithaler, WHO Senior advisor to the Ethiopian SEP, and the WHO office in Geneva had obtained support from various governments to supply helicopters, pilots and additional funds to undertake an assault to stop the transmission of smallpox in these highly inaccessible areas.

LOOKING BACK

I remember very clearly the day in August 1974 when my plane departed the airport in Addis Ababa and headed for Nairobi, Kenya. I reflected on seeing Emperor Haile Selassie I in his car that day that I walked to his palace. The month after I left, Haile Selassie was deposed and taken prisoner, and on August 27, 1975, he was declared dead. Thus, within months of my departure from Ethiopia, the pages of history turned and a new chapter was being written, however recent pictures from 2016 sent to me by some former smallpox PCVs, who had recently traveled to Ethiopia, show that change in the rural areas has been very slow. Also in 2016, Ethiopia had the misfortune of repeating history with another famine. [2]

In August 1976, the last case of smallpox was recorded in Ethiopia in the Ogaden desert among the desert tribes close to the Somali border. As the pages of public health efforts were changing with the eradication of smallpox in Ethiopia so were the pages of Ethiopian history with the demise of the Emperor Haile Selassie I.

Little did I know that this event would lead me to a sequel to my SEP work in Ethiopia by providing me with my last encounter with smallpox in 1977 in Somalia where the last outbreak of endemic smallpox in the world occurred in October 1977 in the region around the seaside town of Merka, Somalia.

•

---

2 See article published in the *Washington Post*: http://www.washingtonpost.com/sf/world/2016/02/22/history-repeats-itself-in-ethiopia/

19

Contributions of Ethiopia SEP PCVs to the Global Smallpox Eradication Effort

by Alan Schnur

Many Ethiopia smallpox eradication Peace Corps Volunteers (PCVs) continued to make important contributions to the global smallpox eradication effort, even after leaving Ethiopia, through their work in other countries. They took with them from Ethiopia their knowledge of the surveillance and containment strategy, experience, enthusiasm, energy, confidence in the program, and can-do problem-solving attitude and abilities, and applied these skills, outlook and approaches to the Smallpox Eradication Programs (SEPs) in other countries.

While the other countries with smallpox had different cultures, levels of development and climatic and topographical conditions, there were also some similarities with the Ethiopia program in terms of the smallpox eradication strategy, work processes and cultural sensitivity requirements. The SEP method of working in Ethiopia required PCVs to show initiative, and plan and coordinate their work with their Ethiopian counterparts, while also often working independently and creatively in challenging conditions. This turned out to be excellent preparation for the SEP work in other countries.

By 1974–1975, the constantly improving smallpox situation in most provinces of Ethiopia proved that the global smallpox eradication strategy of surveillance and containment truly worked. Successes in Ethiopia, even in the most difficult to reach areas, instilled a sense of assuredness and confidence in the global strategy, and in the feasibility of eradicating smallpox when the strategy was properly and creatively followed. This enthusiasm and problem-solving approach was readily transferable to other countries, and enabled the former PCVs to identify and solve problems in a culturally appropriate manner in other countries, based on their experiences in Ethiopia.

According to a 2016 Peace Corps report further updated for this book, a total of 73 PCVs participated in smallpox eradication in Ethiopia, working for periods ranging from a few months to four years. This number includes Volunteers who arrived in 1974, only a few days before Emperor Haile Selassie was deposed, and who accepted offers of early termination.[1] Six Ethiopia Peace Corps (PC) groups included smallpox eradication PCVs. In addition, some PCVs who originally came to Ethiopia for other programs later transferred to the SEP. PCVs served in the Addis Ababa HQ as Operations Officers, and as Assessment or Surveillance Officers based in Addis Ababa and the provinces.[2]

The global SEP leadership monitored competent and innovative workers in country programs and actively looked to mobilize these workers to work with programs in other countries to transfer experiences and best practices between countries. As explained in the book *Smallpox and Its Eradication*, "As working counterparts, WHO staff with prior experience in other smallpox eradication programmes transmitted confidence in the feasibility of eradication and were better able to introduce new

---

1 K. Van Roekel, "The Peace Corps' Contribution to the Global Smallpox Eradication Program," Peace Corps, December 2016, https://s3.amazonaws.com/files.peacecorps. gov/documents/open-government/Peace_Corps_Global_Smallpox.pdf, pp. 50–52; and listing of SEP/Ethiopia PCVs in Chapter 2, beginning on page 26 herein.
2 Source: Records of the author, email correspondence with former Ethiopia SEP PCVs, and the website http://www.ethiopiaeritrearpcvs.org/pages/rpcvs/vols.html (accessed April 16, 2016).

methods . . . ."[3] The use of the term "staff" here also applied to World Health Organization (WHO) short term consultants, like the former Ethiopia PCVs, who were hired by the SEP on three to eleven-month contracts, and normally worked in the same manner as WHO long term SEP staff.

Surveillance and containment was the accepted smallpox eradication strategy from the start of the Ethiopian SEP. PCVs knew no other strategy, and, seeing how successful it was in their day-to-day work in Ethiopia, were fully committed to it. They did not need to be taught from a theoretical basis that the strategy would work; they had already implemented and experienced its suitability and success. Given the PCVs' commitment, and full belief in the strategy of surveillance and containment, they became strong advocates, and never considered that the strategy might fail in other countries. It became a question of how to do it correctly and thoroughly enough so that it could stop transmission in any country. This commitment, and unwavering faith in the strategy, helped to successfully implement the strategy in other countries where there might still be some doubts about the appropriateness of the new strategy, such as India and Bangladesh.

As shown in the table below, 13 Ethiopia smallpox eradication PCVs went on to work with the SEP in one or more other countries, taking their knowledge, skills, experiences, enthusiasm and optimism with them. Former Ethiopia smallpox PCVs worked as WHO short term consultants for periods of three months to more than one year (with contract extensions), or as WHO long term staff, with the SEP in the following countries (with the number of former Ethiopia PCVs working in each country shown in parentheses): Bangladesh (11), India (3), Kenya (2), Pakistan (1), Somalia (4), Sudan (1), Yemen (1), and WHO HQ (1).[4] The PCVs' creativity, and confident, optimistic attitude that smallpox eradication was feasible, and,

---

3 F. Fenner, D. A. Henderson, I. Arita, Z. Jezek, I. D. Ladnyi, *Smallpox and Its Eradication* (Geneva: World Health Organization, 1988), p. 1361.

4 Sources: Personal communications to the author, *Smallpox and Its Eradication* (Geneva: WHO, 1988), *The Eradication of Smallpox from India* (New Delhi: WHO SEARO, 1979), *The Eradication of Smallpox from Bangladesh* (New Delhi: WHO SEARO, 1980), *Smallpox Eradication in Ethiopia* (Brazzaville: WHO AFRO, 1984), and *Smallpox Eradication in Somalia: Report to the International Commission on the Smallpox Eradication Programme in Somalia* (WHO EMRO, 1979).

indeed, inevitable, proved useful in the other country programs where they worked and contributed to the successful eradication efforts. Although the WHO would have liked to recruit some of the former PCVs to work as WHO SEP Epidemiologists in Ethiopia, only one PCV returned as a WHO consultant before the Government of Ethiopia rejected former PCVs proposed for WHO SEP consultant assignments, apparently due to a policy of not allowing former PCVs to return as WHO consultants.

Former Ethiopia PCVs who subsequently worked as WHO SEP staff or consultants

Name of PCV	Countries
Jay L. Anderson	India, Bangladesh
Peter Carrasco	Bangladesh, Somalia
John DeVleming	Bangladesh
James Lepkowski	Sudan
Paul Mongeau	Bangladesh
Don Piburn	Bangladesh
Vincent J. Radke	Bangladesh, Kenya
Michael Santarelli	Bangladesh, Somalia
Alan Schnur	India, Bangladesh, Somalia, WHO HQ Geneva
Robert C. Steinglass	Yemen*
Marc A. Strassburg	India, Bangladesh, Kenya
Gary A. Urquhart	Bangladesh, Pakistan, Ethiopia**
R. Mark Weeks	Bangladesh, Somalia

* Worked as WHO Staff in Yemen.

** Returned to SEP Ethiopia as a WHO consultant, after completing Ethiopia PCV assignment.

Sources: Personal communications to the author, *Smallpox and Its Eradication* (Geneva: WHO, 1988), and WHO publications reporting on the successful country smallpox eradication programs: *The Eradication of Smallpox from India* (New Delhi: WHO SEARO, 1979), *The Eradication of Smallpox from Bangladesh* (New Delhi: WHO SEARO, 1980), *Smallpox Eradication in Ethiopia* (Brazzaville: WHO AFRO, 1984), and *Smallpox Eradication in Somalia: Report to the International Commission on the Smallpox Eradication Programme in Somalia* (WHO EMRO, 1979).

PCVs DEVELOP THEIR OWN SMALLPOX OUTBREAK CONTROL APPROACHES

PCVs and counterparts in the provinces of Ethiopia were left to creatively develop their own tactics and work plans within the overall SEP strategic guidelines. In Welega, the author, along with the other SEP provincial team members, developed an approach of vaccinating around the edges of smallpox outbreaks in areas where the outbreak was heading, but had not yet reached, in order to set up a "wall" of vaccinated and protected people to stop transmission. We then moved the vaccination activities towards the center of the outbreak, and usually found that by the time we reached further into the center of the smallpox activity, the cases were already in decline. The Welega team performed this "ring vaccination" in *woredas* in the central part of the province. Using this approach in Welega, the team could rapidly achieve zero cases in the province, with the last endemic smallpox case in the province occurring in December 1972, 15 months after adopting the approach. The last reported case in the province, in June 1973, was an imported case from Gojam. A similar approach was adopted in Kefa province by Vince Radke and his team. D.A. Henderson mentioned this approach in his book *Smallpox, The Death of a Disease,*[5] and it is also described in the book *Smallpox and Its Eradication*, quoted here:

> One volunteer, Mr. Vincent Radke, has described his own initial surprise at the magnitude of the smallpox problem and the nec-essary adaptations in procedures which field staff had to make. During the training programme, the surveillance teams had been instructed to undertake a planned series of trips through the province for which they were responsible. They were to visit health centres and schools, where these existed, as well as village leaders and, in showing the WHO smallpox recognition card, were to inquire about possible smallpox cases. Any reports were then to be investigated. In the first classroom Mr. Radke visited in Kefa [Kaffa] Province, he obtained so many reports of cases in so many different villages that he did not bother to

5 D. A. Henderson, *Smallpox, The Death of a Disease: The Inside Story of Eradicating a Worldwide Killer* (Amherst, New York: Prometheus Books, 2009), p. 220.

was respectful and there was no mention of forcing anyone to take the vaccination (although it was implied that the team would not leave until everyone was vaccinated). Shortly, the man came down and opened the door so that the team could vaccinate all the remaining unvaccinated people in the house.

After the systematic day and night vaccination work, no further smallpox cases were discovered. Active searches for fever with rash cases were also initiated at markets, and other places where people congregated, within a five-mile radius of the case.[9]

While working as a WHO consultant, Peter Carrasco, a former PCV who worked in Welega and Shoa provinces of Ethiopia, was involved with the investigation and containment activities in October-November 1977 for the world's last endemic smallpox case in the town of Merca in Somalia.

He chased down nomadic contacts of the last case in order to vaccinate them and check that they did not have smallpox. Dr. Isao Arita (Chief of the global WHO smallpox eradication unit following D.A. Henderson), describes the experience in his book: "Since this area was not accessible by car, Carrasco, along with his Somali staff, organised a caravan of fourteen camels and ten donkeys to follow the family of nomads."[10] Carrasco acquired the animals and moved rapidly under difficult conditions, to track contacts of the last case. It is quite remarkable that the organization of the animals, and the containment team, in Somalia had many similarities to the organization of the expedition in Gishe woreda, Shoa province, Ethiopia, in which Carrasco also took part, as recounted in this book in the chapters by Peter Carrasco and Warren Barrash.

MANY ETHIOPIA SMALLPOX PCVs WENT ON TO CAREERS IN THE HEALTH FIELD

As related in several of the previous chapters in this book, many of the former smallpox PCVs were strongly affected by their smallpox work in Ethiopia, and it served to guide them into careers in the health field,

9 Alan Schnur, "WHO Epidemiologist Tour Diary" (Dhaka: unpublished, 1975).
10 Isao Arita, *The Smallpox Eradication Saga, An Insider's View*, (Hyderabad, India: Orient BlackSwan, 2010), p. 109.

either internationally or domestically in the United States. Several of the former Ethiopia SEP PCVs also participated in other international disease eradication/elimination initiatives such as polio eradication, measles elimination, and neonatal tetanus elimination in the Americas, Africa and Asia. As in Ethiopia, they often interacted with Dr. Ciro de Quadros in their future work. It is a conservative estimate (which may omit some former SEP PCVs for whom information is not available), that at least 19 Ethiopia SEP PCVs eventually went into careers in the health field. Considering that some of the previous chapters of this book describe the difficulties of working in the northern provinces of Ethiopia, it is interesting to note that 15 of these 19 PCVs had worked in the southern and southwestern provinces of Ethiopia, while only three had worked exclusively in the more difficult northern provinces. Information is not available on where one of the 19 former PCVs had worked in Ethiopia.

It should be noted that former Ethiopia smallpox PCVs were not the only smallpox PCVs who went on to contribute to the global smallpox eradication effort. PCVs from other SEP programs (e.g. Zaire) also went on to work in other countries as WHO SEP consultants or staff. It should also be noted that Japanese volunteers (Japan Overseas Cooperation Volunteers) and Austrian volunteers also worked on smallpox eradication in Ethiopia, as well as some individuals who volunteered to take part in the SEP while visiting Ethiopia. All of these volunteers made important contributions to the program.

IN CONCLUSION

The work and performance of the smallpox PCVs in Ethiopia substantially benefited not only Ethiopia, but also the global SEP. The Ethiopia SEP, by serving as a training and proving ground for smallpox eradication workers, gave the PCVs the knowledge, skills, attitude and outlook to contribute to the program in other countries. In return, these PCVs also greatly profited from their experiences in the smallpox eradication program. All were changed by the experience, and, for a substantial proportion of the SEP PCVs, their Ethiopia experiences eventually led to careers in the health field.

•

ACKNOWLEDGMENTS

The contributions of former Ethiopia PCVs Gene Bartley, Dave Bourne, Peter Carrasco, Scott Porterfield, Vince Radke, Jim Skelton, Robert Steinglass and Gary Urquhart to the completion of this chapter are gratefully acknowledged.

20

Can We Be Certain that Ethiopia and the Horn of Africa Are Really Smallpox-Free?

by Dr. D. A. Henderson, MD, MPH,
Director of WHO Global Smallpox Eradication Program, 1966-1977

We conclude our insiders' review of the history of the eradication of smallpox in Ethiopia with a report written by Dr. D.A. Henderson regarding his participation in the International Commission for the Certification of Smallpox Eradication in Ethiopia. This was one of four international commissions formed by the World Health Organization to confirm that smallpox had truly been eradicated from Ethiopia and three other countries in the Horn of Africa. Here Dr. Henderson describes the Commission's purpose and activities, as well as his role and thoughts as the group traveled to remote regions of Ethiopia and undertook their own surveillance work during a very unsettled period in the country.

This report chronicles the successful conclusion of the eradication effort in Ethiopia, more than two years after the discovery of the last smallpox case. We are very grateful to Dr. Henderson for the generous contribution of this valuable and insightful report, which provides a very fitting conclusion to this book. The full text of the report is set out below with only minimal editorial changes, such as standardizing spelling and the italicization of Amharic words.   — *The Editors*

•

NOTES ON A FIELD TRIP WITH THE INTERNATIONAL SMALLPOX COMMISSION, OCTOBER 1-17, 1979.

To confirm that a country was smallpox-free required at least two full years without cases during which there was an effective surveillance program. Surveillance programs varied from country to country but, basically, consisted of regular weekly reports about smallpox cases from health units and other government offices. Special search programs were conducted in high risk areas. In the concluding phases, a substantial reward was frequently offered to be given to anyone who reported a case. As a final step, an independent international group was selected by WHO to review the reports that had been prepared and to travel widely in the country over a two-to-three-week period to assure themselves of the certainty that smallpox had been eliminated.

The last of the International Smallpox Commission reviews were scheduled for October 1979. There would be four separate Commissions, one each for Ethiopia, Kenya, Djibouti and Somalia. It was more than two years since a case of smallpox had been detected in this entire region despite intensive surveillance. Elaborate search programs in each country had been completed and documented. If each of the Commissions agreed that the evidence was sufficient to be assured that the respective countries were smallpox-free, there would be a concluding joint meeting in Nairobi, Kenya on October 26 and the possibility of announcing that the last of the endemic countries was free of smallpox.

The major question mark was Ethiopia, where civil war compounded by the Ethiopian-Somali war had made surveillance activities difficult in many areas and impossible in some. Evidence that smallpox had been eradicated from Ethiopia was, of necessity, compounded by multiple pieces of epidemiological information and data. Could a Commission view this in its complexity and entirety and reach a reasonable conclusion?

The Ethiopian Commission was selected with care to assure adequate representation of individuals with experience in epidemiology in general and smallpox in particular. The chairman was Dr. Jan Kostrewski. He was Medical Secretary of the Polish Academy of Sciences, former Minister of Health of Poland, and Chairman of WHO's overall Global Commission on Smallpox Eradication. Dr. Keith Dumbell was Professor of Virology at St. Mary's Hospital, London, with a distinguished career of laboratory research, including smallpox virology and field epidemiology. Dr. David Robinson was formerly a WHO Smallpox Consultant in India and Nepal, formerly on the faculty of the Liverpool School of Tropical Medicine and now director of regional disease epidemiological and control units in the United Kingdom. Dr. Andre Stroganov, now on the faculty of the Central Institute for Advanced Medical Training in Moscow, served as a WHO smallpox consultant in Bangladesh. He was the personal choice of the Minister of Health of the Soviet Union. The final member, save myself, was Dr. Inusse Noor Muhammed, Deputy National Director of Preventive Medicine for Mozambique. He was a choice of the WHO Regional Director of Africa.

I departed Baltimore in less than an expectant or even cheerful frame of mind. To me, the joy in the program had been the struggle in achieving — the now more ritualistic recognition, the speeches to describe how the program came about and developed, the confirmation, the final pronouncements, although necessary, were often sad. Sad because I recognized that the exuberant, dedicated band — joined almost as brothers during innumerable field skirmishes in a seemingly impossible battle — were now reluctantly scattering to other challenges.

Addis Ababa, the capital of Ethiopia, had changed little during the three years since my last visit except for the addition of great red banners "Victory to the Proletariat" and such like. For the first time on my many visits, I was housed at the elegant Hilton, splendidly isolated from the city but near enough for international meetings to hold receptions. It might as well have been situated in Samoa or Timbuktu.

The Commission proceeded through a customary two-day review of the program, preceded by opening speeches by the Minister and other officials and the inevitable press conferences. Then, to the field. The Commission was divided into six groups to examine six different areas.

Assignments had to be made in advance since the Ministry of Internal Affairs insisted on special permits for all foreigners who leave the capital. My area was to be Bale and Arsi Regions—not a happy prospect. Arsi is small, prosperous and has been relatively untroubled by recent warfare. Bale is a different story. It is an enormous Region, perhaps 1,000 x 400-600 kilometers whose southernmost *awraja*, mostly consists of scrub desert. It is still beset by guerrilla warfare and a northern area riddled with areas which are "inaccessible" (translation—"security is a problem").

It was decided that I would endeavor to penetrate as far as possible into the less secure areas to determine how satisfactory surveillance might have been in such areas. For the first three days the helicopter C-GODY was at our disposal along with its Canadian pilot, Bill Waugh, an old friend from the first 1974 days of helicopter operations. The interim period had seen C-GODY portrayed on a now well-known Ethiopian smallpox poster; its partial destruction when it caught fire in the air (suspected bullet); and its return to Canada for reconstruction. Bill had continued to fly with equanimity, skill and cheerful good humor despite numerous risks and being captured by guerrillas and held for almost two weeks for ransom.

Accompanying me was *Ato* Ashagre Haile Mariam, a tall lanky sanitarian and an Oromo—the tribal group who inhabit the Bale-Arsi Region. *Ato* Ashagre was a sanitarian who had joined the program at its beginning and without a vehicle for nearly two years (the early lean years), had endeavored with success to search and control outbreaks through travel by bus, horseback and on foot. We had toured the Ogaden together during the concluding phases of the program and shortly before the Somalis invaded. A second companion was Dr. Alex Gromyko, a Russian now stationed at HQ in Geneva. He had done an excellent job as a WHO smallpox consultant in India.

It was a two-hour flight by helicopter to Goba, the capital of Bale — a small town similar to many in the highlands — cold and windy (11,000 foot altitude), comprised of small, single-story houses of simple wood frame with mud-daubed walls and corrugated iron roofs. Scattered about are the traditional round "*tukuls*" with peaked roofs of thatched grass. There is no electricity, no sewerage, casual drainage, rutted streets of rock and crushed gravel and the all-pervasive posters of heroic farmer-soldiers, banners proclaiming "Victory to the Proletariat." Goba represented the high-water mark of the Somali invasion.

After formalities with the military Regional Administrator, we decided that Alex and the Regional Surveillance Officer would stay that day in the highlands and survey by vehicle the resettlement villages — new villages of 300 to 4,000 which gather the typically widely scattered rural population of the Ethiopian highlands into compact villages for security and, eventually, to permit groupings large enough to supply electricity, water, education and health. *Ato* Ashagre and I would proceed by helicopter to Tedecha Alem, 150 km southeast of Goba, the southernmost "secure" village. Although we were advised to fly at high altitude, Bill was inclined to fly at a lower altitude where he feels that surprise and speed of transit provide better protection against possible use of SAM rocket missiles.

We soon passed from cold highland to hot scrub desert and landed between a small military encampment about 200 feet square, surrounded by shallow trenches and a village of some 250-300 persons, mostly assembled from the surrounding area for security. All were friendly and helpful. *Ato* Ashagre was clearly well-known and well-liked. Assembled under the shade of one of the area's few trees, they affirmed a knowledge of the smallpox program, the search for smallpox cases and the reward for reporting a case. None had seen cases, however, for at least five years and were sure that El Kere town (140 km south) to which they often traveled to get salt was likewise free. As we talked, there was an explosion in the distance and a puff of smoke. Conversation proceeded, however, and a survey for facial scars of smallpox revealed none among children. As we finished, the colonel suggested that in all probability the three-truck convoy en route to Tedecha Alem had experienced troubles. Could we take a look on our way back and report? Meanwhile, it would be best to fly at a high altitude. Some seven or eight kilometers from the camp, we saw the three-truck convoy, the first of the trucks with a wheel blown off and oil spread across the road.

We landed at a second camp some 20 km further north. The village was somewhat larger and more scattered; comparatively few Ethiopian

21

Experiences with Smallpox Eradication in Ethiopia

by Dr. Ciro de Quadros, MD, MPH,
WHO Epidemiologist in Charge of Field Operations in Ethiopia,
1970-1976

We are very grateful to Elsevier, the publishers of the Vaccine journal, *for granting us permission to reprint this article that appeared in Volume 29, Supplement 4 Vaccine D30-D35 (2011).*

•

I. INTRODUCTION

This article describes some of my experiences while I worked for the World Health Organization (WHO) in Ethiopia from November 1970 to February 1977, during the smallpox eradication pro-gramme in that country.

Ethiopia is the second largest country in Africa (about 1.2 million square kilometres). In 1970, Ethiopia had a population of about 25 million, most widely dispersed in rural areas. Infrastructure was rudimentary in all respects, including communications, schools and health facilities. At that time it had less than 5000 km of all-weather roads and access to rural areas was quite limited and difficult (Fig. 1A). The country has a very challenging topography with the central highlands, the Southwest forest

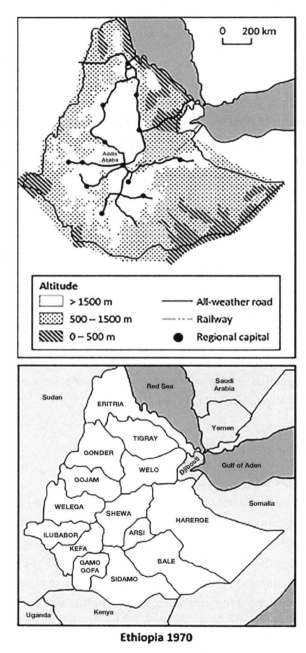

Fig. 1A. Topography and road system in Ethiopia, 1970.
Fig. 1B. Provinces

area, the Southeast Rift Valley and the Ogaden Desert. Addis Ababa, the capital of Ethiopia, is the third highest capital in the world. The country was divided into 14 provinces and the provinces were divided into *awrajas* (districts) and the *awrajas* into *woredas* (sub-districts).

In 1970, Ethiopia was a monarchy ruled by the Emperor Haile Selassie. Feudal landlords and the Ethiopian Coptic Church controlled most of the countryside. Travelling in the interior of the country felt as if you had stepped into the Middle Ages; people lived in small hamlets and, at night, shared their huts with their livestock.

At that time the country had only 84 hospitals, 64 health centres, fewer than 400 physicians and only about 2800 other health staff. Each province had a health department, called the Provincial Medical Department which was staffed by a medical officer, usually a European physician. In the South-western provinces, most of the physicians were Swedish. The other health departments were staffed with health officers who received training in a school of public health in the capital of Begemdir province in the north of the country. This school graduated what some call "Chinese barefoot doctor." These graduates were well prepared to deal with the major health problems in their area of responsibility, including performing minor surgeries, obstetrics, paediatrics and general medical care. Besides the health officer, the Provincial Medical Department had a sanitarian and some assistant nurses. This gives you an idea of the poor health infrastructure in the country at that time.

2. THE LAUNCHING OF THE PROGRAMME

In 1970, smallpox vaccination was essentially unknown. Variolation, the practice of inoculating material from a person with active smallpox into a healthy individual, was used in parts of the country.

Interestingly, the government had absolutely no interest in the eradication of smallpox, and like many other countries, argued that Ethiopia did not have a smallpox problem. Dr. Papaioannu, a Greek physician who directed the Anti-Epidemic Service in Addis Ababa, told the Emperor that Ethiopia did not have smallpox. As a result, when Dr. D.A. Henderson, from WHO, and his team came to Addis Ababa to plan the eradication programme they estimated that very few cases would be found. They went through all the records and concluded that smallpox was very rare in Ethiopia. This led them to believe that eradication could be achieved with fewer resources than were finally needed.

At that time, the Ministry of Health used most of its resources for malaria eradication. The malaria advisers were boycotting the smallpox eradication programme because they viewed smallpox as competing with their programme. Because of the boycott, when Dr. Henderson presented the smallpox initiative to ministry officials he was greeted very coldly. The situation changed when Dr. Henderson met Dr. Kurt Weithaler, an Austrian physician, who was the director of the Imperial Bodyguard Hospital that gave medical attention to the armed forces of the country. Dr. Weithaler was very well connected with the Emperor. This connection helped the Minister of Health to move forward with the programme, under the orders of the Emperor.

Nevertheless, because health officials were not very enthusiastic and because it was thought that smallpox was not a problem, they assigned a small number of personnel to the programme — about 25. Dr. Henderson succeeded in increasing the number of people working on the programme by reaching an agreement with the US Peace Corps. The Peace Corps added 17 volunteers to the programme for a period of two years. This arrangement lasted for about four years, with yearly replacement of the volunteers. Subsequently, the Japanese International Cooperation Agency (JICA) provided a few volunteers, some worked as surveillance officers and others helped manage the radio communication system and the car repair shop. The Austrian government also provided four volunteers who worked as surveillance officers.

After training the staff assigned to the programme on the techniques of surveillance and containment, the programme was launched at the beginning of 1971 in the provinces of Kaffa, Illubabor, Wollega and Gemu Goffa, with slightly better health infrastructure in the south and South-western parts of the country (Fig. 1B).

Ethiopia was the first country in the world to start its national smallpox eradication programme from day one with the strategy of "surveillance and containment," instead of mass vaccination. Mass vaccination was never used. The operational plan was searching for cases and outbreaks (surveillance), linked with vaccinating all contacts of smallpox cases discovered by surveillance (containment). At the start of operations in 1971, there were only six Land Rovers, one vehicle was deployed to each of the four provinces, and two surveillance officers (one Ethiopian sanitarian and one US Peace Corps volunteer).

Of course, the organization of a surveillance system in a country without an adequate health infrastructure was a challenge. We made personal contact with all the directors of the provincial medical departments, local governors and officials in all districts and sub-districts. We requested that all the available health facilities (hospitals, health centres and stations) report suspected smallpox cases. Surveillance officers searched for cases in schools and marketplaces. They showed a picture of a smallpox patient and asked, "Has anybody seen a case of smallpox similar to this one?" To our surprise almost everybody would answer, "Yes, I saw a case!" This strategy was very successful. In the first two to three years of operations transmission was interrupted in the initial four provinces.

3. THE EXPANSION OF THE PROGRAMME

By mid-1972 we received additional vehicles and camping equipment. We were then able to start organising the other provinces because until that time the two individuals had been working with the few resources they could find. If a car that would take them to investigate an outbreak was available they would go, if not, they could not go. Sometimes they would go on foot. In the first three to four years of the programme we walked like I had never walked in my life! Still today when I am invited to walk my answer is: "I have walked all the miles I had the right to in Ethiopia. I have no miles left!" Indeed, walking to hamlets was very challenging because it was usually in the mountains and the hamlets were far apart.

When Dr. Henderson asked the Malaria Director for logistical assistance, he was informed that the malaria programme had no cars. This was very interesting because we knew that the malaria eradication programme had received more than 40 vehicles before we arrived. Later on the WHO Malaria Advisor admitted that when they heard that the smallpox programme was going to start, they drove all the cars to Nazareth, a town near the Ogaden desert, to hide them and avoid lending the cars. It is unbelievable but it happened!

Furthermore, Dr. Papaioannu, the Greek director of the Anti- Epidemic Service opposed the programme, telling the Emperor and the Minister of Health that cases of smallpox were reported only after WHO started the programme. He argued that these were not smallpox cases and that the programme was not vaccinating enough people. He proposed that the programme be stopped.

At the end of the first year of the programme in 1971, we reported over 26,000 smallpox cases (variola minor only). Because this total was completely unexpected, even Dr. Henderson was suspicious. He wrote to us asking if we were "reporting rumours," However, we had an epidemiological record for every case reported. The surveillance system registered the patient, their entire family, and the number of contacts vaccinated in the outbreak. All this information was analysed and published in the Weekly Surveillance Bulletin. That article documented the accomplishments of the programme for those involved in the programme as well as to all health officials in Ethiopia.

The photograph (Fig. 2) was taken during my first trip to the southern province of Illubabor, on the border with Sudan. Shown in the picture are the district governor and the health officer in charge of the Health Centre in the area.

Fig. 2. Southern province of Illubabor, on the border with Sudan.

Accompanying me was a US Peace Corps volunteer, Mark Strassburg who often carried a violin which he played at the campsite at night. It was a quite an experience to hear this very nice violin in the middle of the jungle!

During one outbreak investigation we walked for 26 days going from village to village. We started the trip with the chief of the area and his three donkeys carrying our equipment. There were about five people in our group.

Because the river was dry, to get water we had to dig holes and wait for it to appear. To our dismay, the chief said "the first water to come out is for the donkeys because if not they will die." We asked, "Where is the next village?" and they replied: "Over that hill."

Fig. 3. Western Wollega province on border of Sudan near the Blue Nile River.

We started this long out-break investigation with about five people and ended it with more than 30. We were the first foreigners to visit that area. At each village we visited, people would join and go with us to the next village. (Fig. 3) During the investigation, we mapped this entire area and gave maps to the Ethiopian Map Institute. Before our maps, they did not have a clue of the layout of that area.

During the outbreak investigation trip, we unknowingly crossed the Sudanese border and were arrested and held for one day at the police station. We started a hunger strike which I think frightened them because soon after they released us. This release avoided a big fight. When we returned to Ethiopia, well-armed Ethiopians were on the way to rescue us.

Fig. 4. River crossing in Ethiopia.

The photo (Fig. 4) illustrates some of the bridges that we had to cross. In some rivers we had to pull the cars with winches so that the cars would essentially float during the crossing.

4. THE TRANSITION CHALLENGES

In 1974 we had a difficult transition when a military revolution overthrew Emperor Haile Selassie. It was of course a very difficult period in the

period, therefore had very few skin lesions and showed also a vaccination scar. This area was inhabited for only a few weeks in the year, as these pastoral, nomadic people roam the countryside, following the rain. They make fences out of thorn bushes to stop lions, hyenas and other wild animals from entering their houses (Fig. 10). All these desert areas were mapped by the surveillance teams, which could then trace the location of the nomads at any given time.

Fig. 10. Village of Dimo in the South-western part of the Ogaden.

The surveillance officer/vaccinator was dropped off by the helicopters in a given hamlet and two or three days later was picked up several kilometres away in another hamlet. He would walk for two or three days, following the pattern of the nomads and looking for cases and/or tracing the chains of smallpox transmission and vaccinating contacts of cases. This is how we came to meet the little girl by the name of Amina Salat. She had a mild case, because she had been vaccinated during the incubation period.

We were very excited because we thought that she was the last case of smallpox in the world. However, we strongly suspected transmission on the Somali side of the border. We insisted with Geneva that there were cases in Somalia, but Dr. Henderson and his team in Geneva kept telling us that there were no cases in Somalia, as reported by the WHO representative in Somalia and his team. Nevertheless, the people living in the Ogaden did not really know that a border existed. It was a virtual border, created somewhere in Europe after the Second World War, when somebody traced a line somewhere in the Horn of Africa, dividing the area inhabited by the same people into what is now known as Ethiopia and Somalia. Therefore, these nomadic people would travel on both sides of the border. They took their cattle and camels wherever they could find grass and water.

As the case in Dimo was thought to be the last case in the world, many people came to see the area and photograph the case. Dr. Henderson came, along with reporters from *National Geographic*, and we had a party at the end of the day. During the party we received a report of smallpox in a village north of the Ogaden, which brought a cloud over the celebration. The next morning we flew to the village where the report originated and found that the case was chickenpox.

The operations in the Ogaden were extremely difficult and dangerous. The gentleman who provided the fixed-wing aircrafts was Count Von Rosen, from Sweden, a famous humanitarian. He was eventually killed when guerrillas attacked the governor's compound in Gode, the capital of the province of Ogaden, less than a mile from the smallpox camp, which was not attacked! One helicopter pilot was also kidnapped and WHO received a note that the guerrillas [were] demanding 40,000 Ethiopian dollars (approximately $19,500 usd) for his release. Eventually the pilot was released without paying the ransom which was already on the way when the pilot was freed.

The programme in Ethiopia lasted six years with a lot of excitement. When you are working under such circumstances, with such a goal to be achieved, you do not even realise the real situation you are in. I only realised the extent of the situation when I left Ethiopia and read in the international press the daily dispatches about the war in the Horn of Africa. And apparently, in spite of these incidents, the general population appreciated the work that was being done and in general collaborated with the programme.

6. THE FUNDING OF THE PROGRAMME

The total funds received for this programme were about $14.3 million. WHO mobilised $13 million and most of that paid for the very expensive helicopter operations. We had five helicopters flying, each one flying seven to eight hours a day which greatly increased the cost of this operation. The government paid the salaries of the people they assigned to the programme and in many instances collaborated on logistical support in the different provinces.

7. CONCLUSION

Over the course of the seven-year campaign to eradicate smallpox in Ethiopia many challenges were overcome. Beginning with the overall lack of medical infrastructure and a variety of competing interests for the limited resources available to the Ministry of Health, smallpox was all but ignored for a long time. With the hard work of dedicated staff a successful surveillance and containment strategy made great strides toward the goal, but government instability, harsh working conditions and nomadic populations continued to present roadblocks. In the end the mission was accomplished through innovative interventions and continued persistence. Today, we see similarities with the problems the polio eradication initiative is having in the Ogaden desert to those we faced thirty years ago. It is my hope that this supplement will assist those working in the field today to reflect on the lessons learned from the smallpox eradication campaign.

•

Appendix

Biographies of the Contributors

Warren Barrash

Warren was always curious about different cultures and far-away places. Then he was taken by the idea of the Peace Corps when it was announced by President Kennedy. After graduating with
a BA in English from Dartmouth College in 1970, Warren worked in public health as a Peace Corps Volunteer in Malaysia (from 1970 to 1972) on Tuberculosis Control with Department of Aborigine Affairs, and then in Ethiopia (from 1973 to 1974) with Smallpox Eradication in the Amhara highlands. Along the way he realized that he was interested in geology.

Upon return to the U.S., Warren moved to Idaho for ready access to wild country, and to take a few classes in geology and wildlife before heading to South America to try freelance photojournalism. But instead, he got hooked on geology and Idaho, and went on to receive MS and PhD degrees in geology (focusing on hydrogeology) from the University of Idaho.

Warren has worked in government, consulting, and academia, and was a research professor at Boise State University from 1993 to 2014.

Since retiring in 2014, he has continued with some hydrogeology projects as an emeritus research professor at Boise State, as a visiting professor at Stanford (from 2012 to 2016), and as a part-time consulting hydrogeologist with Tetra Tech Inc. on a Superfund clean-up project (from 2014 to 2016).

Gene L. Bartley

Gene Bartley graduated from Westmar College, a small religious college in Iowa, in December 1968 with a major in biology and minors in psychology and teaching. After spending a year and a half as a substitute teacher in Denver, and as a full-time science teacher in a cow town on the eastern plains of Colorado, he decided to make a radical change in his life. After completing an application for the Peace Corps, he was offered a position as a teacher in a technical institution in India, which he declined, but he subsequently accepted an invitation to be a surveillance officer with the WHO-sponsored Smallpox Eradication Program in Ethiopia. Gene served as an SEP surveillance officer in Welega and Welo provinces during his first two years as a PCV.

Following his Peace Corps service, he stayed in Ethiopia for three more years as a high school teacher and then traveled back to the US to continue his education in public health. Gene received a MPH with specialization in public health education from the University of South Carolina in 1985, which set him on his path to work to improve the lives of children and mothers in developing countries. He continued his education online and received a PhD in health services in 2002 from Walden University while working.

As a result of his Peace Corps experience, and having Dr. Ciro de Quadros as his mentor, he worked for more than 25 years in Africa. In the next two decades he worked in Malawi with the International Eye Foundation, and 18 years as technical officer in the area of mother and child health for the WHO Africa Regional Office in Brazzaville, Congo.

Gene continued to work as a public health consultant for WHO/ Geneva, and as a director of operations for Africa 2010 Project in Washington, DC. In gratitude to Ciro, he recently completed work as a Senior Polio Consultant in Kenya and Uganda for the Gates Foundation to combat the re-infection of polio in East Africa. He also assisted in revitalizing the introduction of sustainable immunization financing with the

Sabin Vaccine Institute in Ethiopia, also as a result of a recommendation from Ciro.

David Bourne

During his senior year at the University of Utah, Dave completed an application to the Peace Corps. He had been generally interested in the Peace Corps, but doesn't recall having a burning interest in it at that time. Dave's preference was for a health-related job, and for country preferences he submitted Zaire, Thailand and Brazil. He was interested in medicine or a related field at the time, and his dad was a doctor and a District Health Officer in New Mexico. Dave basically forgot all about the application and was planning to apply to pharmacy school when, about a year after submitting the application, he was offered a position with the smallpox program in Ethiopia. He jumped at the chance. He was primarily driven by adventure, but wanted to help people as well.

During his time in the Peace Corps he encountered an epidemic intelligence officer from the CDC who told him about working for the CDC, and that everyone started out as a VD investigator. He applied to the CDC immediately upon returning home in early November, 1974 and started working for the CDC in Los Angeles in January 1975. He worked for the CDC in Los Angeles, Anchorage, and Gallup, New Mexico until 1982.

In 1982 Dave left the CDC, but remained in the federal government working for the U.S. General Accounting Office (GAO) as a congressional evaluator/investigator in the U.S. Department of Energy working as an environmental cleanup project manager, and finally at the U.S. National Nuclear Security Agency (NNSA). In his last position Dave worked as federal officer and Lead Internal Affairs Investigator for the NNSA. He retired in 2011 after 37 years of federal service.

Since 2005, when he was detailed to the Federal Emergency Management Agency to Hurricane Katrina, Dave has continued to serve as a volunteer disaster responder, responding to about 15 national disasters. He currently is the logistics lead for the New Mexico Chapter of the American Red Cross.

Peter Carrasco

Born in Ecuador in 1949 and schooled in Chicago, Peter left for Ethiopia in 1972, where he worked in the World Health Organization's (WHO) Smallpox Eradication Program (SEP) as a U.S. Peace Corps Volunteer until 1974. Peter subsequently served as a consultant to the WHO smallpox eradication efforts in Bangladesh and later in Somalia. In Somalia, he was one of the members of the team that controlled the last known outbreak of smallpox, including the last cases that occurred in Merka town in 1977.

In 1979 Peter completed his master's degree at Michigan State University and was offered a position in the WHO's Expanded Program on Immunization (EPI) in Washington, DC. He remained with the WHO's EPI until his retirement in 2010.

Some of the other notable accomplishments he recorded included being the team lead in working with the national team in Peru that eradicated the last cases of the indigenous circulation of the wild polio virus in the Americas. Peter was also responsible for overseeing the successful field operations that eliminated the circulation of the wild measles virus in the Americas in 2003.

In 2004 he left for WHO Geneva. During his tenure there, he successfully led the organization's effort to train all WHO regions in the use and deployment of the 2009 influenza pandemic vaccine.

From 2012 to 2016, Peter was the director for the Secretariat that established and organized the first International Association of Immunization Managers (IAIM), the membership of which included all health staff and other professionals working in or interested in the field of vaccine preventable disease. IAIM was housed in the Sabin Vaccine Institute in Washington.

Stuart Gold

Stuart Gold was born in 1949 in Los Angeles, California. He received his Bachelor of Science degree in physical anthropology from the University of California at Davis in 1972. In 1973, he joined the Peace Corps and served as a surveillance officer in the Smallpox Eradication Program in Ethiopia.

Upon returning to the U.S., he decided to pursue a career in art and reenrolled at UC Davis, where he studied with artists such as Wayne Thiebaud, Roland Peterson and Roy Deforest. In 1980, he received his Master's Degree in Fine Arts from San Francisco State University in printmaking.

After making a living for a number of years as a traditional painter/printmaker, he discovered an interest in computer generated imagery and animation, and in 1985 became one of the first generation of artists/non-technical programmers to be actively involved in the production of computer animation and graphics for the video industry. Hired by Pacific Bell Corporate Television in 1986 to create graphics and animations for in-house and satellite programming, he went on to  be one of two artists/animators creating work for Hewlett-Packard Media Services. In 1988, he became head of computer graphics and animation for Tandem Computers and Tandem Television Network.

In 1989, Stuart started Shadow and Light Productions, specializing in industrial and broadcast computer graphics, bio-medical animation, and the creation of forensic animation and multimedia. After 18 years in the computer graphics field, he came full circle, building himself a studio in the foothills south of Grass Valley, California, creating art once more and making stringed musical instruments. Sadly, Stuart passed away on June 3, 2018 after waging a fearless three-year battle with cancer. His work can be viewed at ShadowAndLight.com.

Russ Handzus

Russ Handzus grew up in Southern California, graduating from Loyola Marymount University in 1970 with a BS in biology. From an early age,

Russ loved reading "adventure in the jungle" type stories, and books about people who did good for others, such as Dr. Tom Dooley, an American doctor and humanitarian who helped people in Southeast Asia in the 1950s.

In his last year of college, Russ was casting about for what to do after graduation, and he started looking seriously into the Peace Corps. He thought "wouldn't it be great to live in the jungle and do some sort of humanitarian work." He felt he had hit the jackpot when he began working in the Smallpox Eradication Program in Ethiopia as a Peace Corps Volunteer from 1970 to 1972.

After the Peace Corps, Russ worked as a carpenter framing houses, as a high school math teacher and as a house painter. Then, from his 30s to his 60s he worked as an environmental health inspector for several county health departments in California. He retired in 2014.

Donald Ainslie Henderson, MD, MPH

By Leigh Henderson

Donald Ainslie (D.A.) Henderson, MD, MPH, was born on September 7, 1928, in Lakewood, Ohio. His parents were Canadian immigrants, and he retained hints of a Canadian accent all his life. He attended Oberlin College, where he honed his talents for circumventing bureaucracy. As editor of the yearbook, he wrangled a staff car when student cars were banned. Henderson clashed often with the managing editor Nana Bragg of Rochester, NY. They reconnected when he attended medical school at the University of Rochester, and they were wed in 1951.

Henderson interned at Bassett Hospital in Cooperstown, NY, where his daughter Leigh was born. Then, to fulfill his national service requirement, he joined the Public Health Service as preferable to examining Army recruits. He was assigned to the Communicable Disease Center (now the Centers for Disease Control and Prevention (CDC) in Atlanta (where his and Nana's son David was born) as deputy to Alex Langmuir, chief of the Epidemiology Branch. Langmuir was transforming the role of the branch from passive data collection to active surveillance and outbreak investigation.

Henderson became chief of the Epidemic Intelligence Service (EIS), and in 1956 saw his first case of smallpox during an EIS investigation in Argentina. In 1960, he earned an MPH at the Johns Hopkins School of Hygiene and Public Health (now the Johns Hopkins Bloomberg School of Public Health) in Baltimore, where son Douglas was born.

On returning to the CDC, Henderson became Langmuir's chief of surveillance. Langmuir believed that "surveillance" in public health meant the systematic reporting of infectious diseases, the analysis and epidemiological interpretation of data, and prompt and widespread dissemination of results. Henderson endorsed these principles and implemented them in the WHO's Smallpox Eradication Program (SEP).

In 1965, Henderson oversaw the approval by the National Institutes of Health (NIH) of an NIH-funded CDC/USAID measles control and

smallpox eradication program in West Africa. At the same time, he took the lead in drafting a global smallpox eradication plan for the WHO. On its approval in 1966, WHO requested that the U.S. Surgeon-General appoint Henderson as director of the SEP. The last case of smallpox in the world was discovered in Somalia in 1977.

In 1977, Henderson became dean of the Johns Hopkins School of Hygiene and Public Health, then in danger of being relegated to a division in the Medical School. Over the next 14 years, he used the precept "hire good people and get out of their way" to transform the School to a leader and innovator among schools of public health.

Henderson subsequently supported three presidents. From 1991-93, under George H. W. Bush, he served in the Executive Office of the President as the Associate Director for Life Sciences, Office of Science and Technology Policy. He was William Clinton's Deputy Assistant Secretary and Senior Science Advisor in the Department of Health and Human Services (DHHS) from 1993–95.

In 1998, following the revelations of Soviet defector and physician Ken Alibek about the Soviet bioweapons program in his book Biohazard, Henderson founded the Johns Hopkins Center for Civilian Biodefense Strategies (in 2005, the name and affiliation changed to University of Pittsburgh Center for Biosecurity, which in turn was renamed the Center for Health Security in 2013. As of January 17, 2017, the Center has rejoined the Johns Hopkins Bloomberg School of Public Health), the only such center in existence when the 2001 anthrax attacks occurred. Then, in November 2001, he was tapped by George W. Bush to create the DHHS Office of Public Health Emergency Preparedness (later merged with other agencies into the Department of Homeland Security), and served as DHHS Principal Science Advisor on this subject through 2007.

Over the following years, he saw the Center for Health Security expand its mandate to include new and emerging infections. He retired in 2016, but consulted on the ebola and zika epidemics, and continued to lecture to students of public health and medicine. At the time of his death on August 19, 2016, he was developing an online research archive of documents from the SEP (www.zero-pox.info) so that the lessons learned in the management of a large-scale international health program would not be lost.

Scott D. Holmberg

During Scott's senior year at Harvard majoring in English, he filled in a friend's extra Peace Corps application on a whim. When an invitation to serve in Ethiopia came through, he was actually negotiating to teach at a private prep school in Rhode Island.

The experience radically changed his life. Seeing so many diseases in addition to the smallpox outbreaks, he asked for his old biology books to be sent to him in Ethiopia and, reading at nights, discovered an interest that he never had when in school.

As if shot from a great bow, Scott came back to the States and worked through the necessary pre-medical courses, med school, and residency. In his last 30-plus years at CDC — through cholera, salmonella, HIV/AIDS, and now viral hepatitis — he has never regretted a life of chasing outbreaks.

John Scott Porterfield

Scott Porterfield was a PCV with the Smallpox Eradication Program in Ethiopia from 1971 to 1973 working in Kaffa province in the southwest, and Welo province in central Ethiopia.

Scott had volunteered for the military draft in the summer of 1971, but failed his physical. He then filled out an application for the Peace Corps. He was told by the agency that he could choose to serve in Ecuador or India. Scott chose Ecuador. When the contract arrived from the Peace Corps office, it stated that his country of service would be Ethiopia. Scott signed the contract and returned it to the Peace Corps. . . then he told his parents of his plans. He finished up his tour of duty in August 1973 and returned to college.

He graduated with a Bachelors in Public Administration and a Master's of Public Administration from Western Michigan University. His first position out of college was with the West Texas Council of Governments in El Paso, Texas.

In 1978, he relocated to Marietta, Ohio, with his wife and newborn daughter to take a position as a Certificate of Need reviewer for The Area Six Health Systems agency. Scott was appointed CEO of the agency in 1981.

In 1982, Scott and his four-year-old daughter relocated to Cleveland, Ohio, where he held the position of Administrator for the Rainbow Ambulatory Practice, an affiliate of University Hospitals of Cleveland. He was responsible for administering the practices of 140 pediatricians and 80 Pediatric residents. In 1985, Scott was promoted to Associate Director of Ambulatory Services for University Hospitals.

In 1988, Scott relocated to Sylvania, Ohio where he served as Vice

President of Physician Services for Promedica Flower Hospital.

In 1998, Scott joined Provider Solutions, a physician practice management company, which was owned by St. Luke's Hospital located in Maumee, Ohio. Scott purchased that company in 2002 and was the sole owner.

In 2010, Scott was hired to be the Administrator of The Toledo Clinic, a 170 plus multi-specialty group located in Toledo, Ohio.

Scott went into retirement in December 2015, which lasted about two weeks. He is now an independent health care consultant in the northwest Ohio area. Scott and his wife, Lindy, have four children.

Vince Radke

Vince Radke has worked in public health for 49 years.

Initially, he worked in the Smallpox Eradication Program, first as a Peace Corps Volunteer as a surveillance and assessment officer in Ethiopia from 1970 to 1974, and thereafter as a technical advisor with the World Health Organization in Bangladesh in 1976, and in Kenya from 1977 to 1979.

Vince received his BS from Michigan State University in 1970. He holds a Master's of Public Health degree from the University of Pittsburgh which was awarded in 1977.

Beginning in 1979, Vince spent 22 years dealing with environmental health in the states of Connecticut, West Virginia, Virginia and Minnesota. He was Director of Environmental Health for the City of Stamford, Connecticut (1979-83). In 2008, Vince became certified in public health (CPH). From 2001 to 2018, he worked at the Centers for Disease Control and Prevention (CDC).

He is a Registered Environmental Health Specialist and a Diplomate Laurate of the American Academy of Sanitarians (AAS). He was Chairman of the Board of the AAS from 2014 to 2015.

Vince received The Order of the Bifurcated Needle from the World Health Organization in 1980 for his work in the Smallpox Eradication

Program. He received the ADM Jerrold M. Michael Award from the National Capital Area Environmental Health Association in 1998 and 1999, the U.S. Department of Health and Human Services, Secretary's Award for Distinguished Service during Hurricanes Katrina, Rita and Wilma in 2005, and the Distinguished Service and Professional Achievement Award from the Environmental Section of the American Public Health Association in 2006. Vince was honored with the 2011 Environmental Protection Agency Bronze Medal Award, and received the Walter F. Snyder Award from NSF International and the National Environmental Health Association (NEHA). In 2013, he received the NEHA Past Presidents Award. Vince became the Second Vice-President of the NEHA Board of Directors in July, 2015, and served as President of the NEHA Board of Directors from 2018 to 2019.

Michael Santarelli

Right after graduating from San Francisco State College with a B.A. in Political Science and Anthropology in June 1970, Michael Santarelli joined the Peace Corps and was sent to Ethiopia where he served as a Volunteer until June 1973. For the first two years he served as an agricultural extension agent deep within Gurage country in a small village called Gofrer in Shoa Province where he conducted trial demonstrations of local grains, with and without manufactured fertilizers while  introducing vegetables into the Gurage's diet. In 1999, he returned to Gofrer to visit the people and upon return he wrote "Amongst the Gurage-27 Years Later" which is published online. Since that trip, he has continued to assist the villagers and a nearby health clinic.

During his service in Gofrer, Michael photographed the step by step construction of a Gurage tukul, known to be best in Ethiopia. After ten months it was completed and over 150 slide photos were taken documenting the hand crafting of a tukul 30 feet tall, 34 feet in diameter and 110 feet in circumference. During his 2nd trip to Gofrer in 2015 he saw

and has recently co-directed a graduate research seminar at the Folger Shakespeare Library in Washington, DC.

Jim has authored two books on Shakespeare, scholarly editions of individual plays by Shakespeare, Christopher Marlowe, and Thomas Preston, as well as numerous articles on early modern drama and culture. He edits the journal Shakespeare Studies and is furiously at work on a book about early modern English drama and social distinction

James W. Skelton, Jr.

Jim Skelton graduated from Arizona State University with a B.S. in Economics in 1968, and then served as a Peace Corps Volunteer in Group XIV in Ethiopia from 1970 to 1972. Although exempt from the draft

due to a back injury, he joined the Peace Corps because he wanted to do something that seemed meaningful and important.

His first Peace Corps assignment as the project accountant for the USAID's Food for Work Program in Mekele, Tigre did not work out, and he was very fortunate to be able to transfer to the Smallpox Eradication Program (SEP), where he worked as an operations officer in the SEP headquarters office in Addis Ababa.

After returning to the States from his Peace Corps/SEP Ethiopia adventure, Jim's next challenge was attending law school. He earned a Doctor of Jurisprudence degree from South Texas College of Law Houston in 1975, and then a Master of Laws degree in International Legal Studies from New York University School of Law in 1978. During his nearly 44 years of practicing law, he has primarily focused on international oil and gas transactions, which has taken him to 35 countries in the Former Soviet Union, the Middle East, Africa, Southeast Asia, Europe, and North and South America.

Jim began his legal career in private practice, then worked for Conoco/ConocoPhillips for nearly 28 years, retiring in 2008, and then returned to private practice. He taught the course in "Energy Law: Doing Business in Emerging Markets," as an Adjunct Professor of Law at the University of Houston Law Center from 2008 to 2016, and coauthored the second edition of the textbook Doing Business in Emerging Markets: A Transactional Course. In 2018, he was awarded the Lifetime Achievement Award by the Houston Journal of International Law for his nearly 40 years of service as a member and Chairman of its Board of Advisors.

He has published 24 articles in legal periodicals and books, and has made 18 presentations at international conferences in Houston, Dallas, London and Moscow. As part of his pro bono work, Jim has been an active member of the Council and Action Committees of the International Law Section of the State Bar of Texas since 2014, and served as the first Editor in Chief of the International Newsletter of the International Law Section from 2018 to 2019.

Nevertheless, Jim remained fascinated by his Peace Corps/SEP Ethiopia experience, which led him to write and publish, in 1991, a memoir entitled Volunteering in Ethiopia: A Peace Corps Odyssey. Years later, he spearheaded the 5-year effort to write and publish this book through his roles as the lead editor and a coauthor.

Robert Steinglass

Searching for a meaningful adventure outside his comfort zone, Robert Steinglass told the Peace Corps that he would only go to Ethiopia and only work in public health. He wanted to test himself in a remote country with a strong cultural heritage that owed little to the West.

After serving as a surveillance officer with the smallpox eradication program, and an administrator for the Relief and Rehabilitation Commission in Ethiopia, Robert studied public health at the Johns Hopkins School of Hygiene and Public Health.

He then worked for ten years as the resident technical officer for the World Health Organization (WHO), first proving the absence of smallpox in the Yemen Arab Republic ("North Yemen") and then starting the nationwide Expanded Programme on Immunization (EPI) programs in North Yemen, Sultanate of Oman and Kingdom of Nepal.

Based in Washington, DC starting in 1987 and for the next 30 years, Robert led immunization projects for John Snow, Inc. (JSI) on a succession of USAID-funded projects providing technical support to Ministries of Health in 50 resource-poor countries in Africa, Asia and the former Soviet Union to strengthen immunization programs and served on many global advisory committees at WHO, UNICEF, GAVI, and elsewhere.

At the time of his retirement in 2019, Robert was the founding Director of JSI's Immunization Center, which receives funding from the Bill and Melinda Gates Foundation, GAVI, WHO, UNICEF, International Organization for Migration, and others. He concurrently worked as Senior Immunization Advisor at the USAID-funded Maternal and Child Survival Program and served on several global advisory groups.

Robert has authored 30 peer-reviewed journal articles and several book chapters on immunization. He resides with his wife outside Asheville, North Carolina.

Marc Strassburg

After spending two years as a Peace Corps Volunteer working in the Smallpox Eradication Program (SEP) in Ethiopia, Marc returned to Los Angeles and earned his doctoral degree in epidemiology from UCLA. He was subsequently hired as an epidemiologist by the Los Angeles County Department of Public Health, where he held various positions, including: Chief Epidemiologist, Director of Immunization Program, and Head of the Web Informatics Division (Web). His interests in the Web included the development of policies governing the availability, use, and presentation of health data. After retirement in 2012, he continued to consult for the Los Angeles County on epidemiological and Web issues.

Outside of his Los Angeles County work, Marc worked as a consultant in the field of epidemiology and information systems. For the WHO, he consulted in over 20 countries. The objectives of these consultancies varied, but in general, focused on the control of vaccine preventable diseases. Two diseases, measles and polio, would receive much of his attention.

In 1986, he began consulting work for Ciro de Quadros, his former boss from the SEP in Ethiopia, who asked him to join the efforts to eradicate polio and control measles in the America's for the Pan American Health Organization (PAHO). Marc's principle role was to develop strategy guidelines and improve surveillance systems. He also served as support to the PAHO technical advisory committee. He has also worked with other state and county health departments in developing various health status indicators and in plans related to improving immunization levels and bioterrorism preparedness. After 2012, he consulted with the Gates Foundation on polio data systems; PAHO regarding future technologies for immunization programs; and SABIN on making Web resources available for members of the International Association of Immunization Managers.

Marc has taught at UCLA in the Epidemiology Department for over 30 years where he achieved the rank of professor (adjunct/part-time). He has also taught courses at the USC Keck School of Medicine and Claremont Graduate University. He has had a number of research interests including those related to vaccine preventable diseases and informatics, which resulted in over 50 publications.

In 2012, Marc was inducted into the UCLA School of Public Health's Hall of Fame.

.

Glossary of Amharic Words

Definitions of the Amharic words that are used in this book and written in italics with English phonetic spelling.

·

agilgel – leather–covered, circular reed basket with a carrying strap, used to carry food (a traditional version of a lunch box).

amora gadale – cliff where eagles live.

areki – alcoholic beverage distilled from *gesho* leaves and fermented barley.

asir–alika – military service rank equivalent to a corporal. (A similar rank was also used for the local militia. Most PCVs interacted with members of the local militia).

atbia danya – a local community leader and judge who had considerable knowledge of the regulations and laws of the land.

ato – mister

awraja – government administrative unit (one level below the provincial level).

ayib – local cheese, similar to cottage cheese.

balabat – landlord (often rich and powerful, respected and sometimes feared landowner in southwest provinces who had feudal powers over his tenant farmers).

balambaras – lower title of nobililty meaning commander of the fortress and bestowed by the emperor.

bekel – roasted kid goat.

berbere – very spicy red powder used in sauces (made from red pepper and other spices).

berele – round–based, narrow–necked glass flask used to drink *tej*.

bet – a house that is built with a more modern structure than the local thatched *tukul*.

birr – unit of Ethiopian currency (also referred to as Ethiopian "dollar").

bitweded – official title of a recognized important leader bestowed by H.I.M. (His Imperial Majesty) Haile Selassie, meaning "beloved."

buna – coffee.

buna bet – a restaurant and/or a bar that also serves coffee. (In some cases, a *buna bet* might also have prostitutes working there.)

chikashume – village official or chieftain.

dabo – locally baked bread.

dejazmatch – honorary senior title bestowed by H.I.M. Haile Selassie (a minister or provincial governor might be of this rank).

doro wot – highly spiced chicken stew made with a special combination of Ethiopian spices, including red pepper (*berbere*), eaten with *injera*.

dula – traditional cane/walking stick carried by men for protection, walking and carrying of goods.

enderassie – official Amharic title of a provincial governor.

ensera – a large, porous handmade clay pot used for keeping cool fermented liquid drinks and water.

ensete edulis – commonly known as the "false banana" plant, a principal source of nutrition for many peoples living in the lowlands in the southern part of Ethiopia.

Fasika – Ethiopian Orthodox Easter.

fentata – smallpox.

ferengi – foreigner, normally refers to a white–skinned person from outside Ethiopia.

fitawari – title of a local administrator.

gabi – a handwoven garment made locally of thickly spun cotton, which is wrapped around the shoulders and worn like a shawl to keep warm or to sleep in. (Worn by both men and women.)

gebs – barley.

gesho – similar to hops, used for fermenting local alcoholic beverages.

gile – large, curved knife customarily worn by an Afar male.

gorsha – traditional custom of hand feeding a guest or friend who was deemed to have not eaten enough.

grazmatch – honorary title bestowed by H.I.M. Haile Selassie (one rank below a *dejazmatch*).

Habisha – another name for Ethiopians.

habisha ketebat –local injection of traditional medicine given by a healer, including variolation for smallpox.

habisha medhanit – traditional medicine.

haji – title of local Moslem ruler; a title given to someone who has completed the pilgrimage to Mecca.

hakim – medical doctor.

hamsa–alika – military service rank equivalent to a sergeant. (A similar rank was also used for the local militia. Most PCVs interacted with members of the local militia.)

injera – circular sourdough flat bread usually made of *teff*, and cooked on a ceramic griddle.

jebena – handmade clay pot used to make coffee.

karare – a second brewing of *tella* (local beer) made of barley and hops, which is extremely sour tasting.

kerumpt – rainy season (big rains), from July to September, with duration and amount of rain varying by location in the country.

katikala – a strong traditional whiskey brewed locally.

kinay – traditional poem or prose with hidden or double meaning (also known as wax and gold).

kolo – roasted grains, usually barley or wheat, eaten as a snack, often with coffee or *tella*.

koshasha – dirty.

listro – shoe shine boy

madow – literally means "over the next hill," but the village, town or area to be visited could actually be over many hills and some distance from your location.

Merkato – large open-air market in Addis Ababa, Ethiopia.

medhanit – medicine.

mikitil woreda – a sub–sub district, an administrative unit located below the *woreda* level.

mohandies – engineer.

murfi –needle, used for medical injection.

netch libosh – a member of the local people's militia (who were usually clothed in white).

qoch'o – bread–like food baked primarily by the Guraghe people.

ras – senior official title given by the Emperor meaning leader like the Emperor.

sebseba – a meeting.

senyo gebaya – local weekly open market, held every Monday.

shankilla – an insulting term for a dark-skinned person of lower class. Also, in some contexts, had the connotation of a "slave."

shifta – armed highwayman, robber or thief.

siga – meat.

sini – traditional handmade small, ceramic cups without a handle for serving coffee.

souk – small local shop where one could purchase commonly used items.

tadius – has several meanings: can be used as a greeting, or, in some cases, as a "why not?" or "what did you expect?" response.

teff – an indigenous grass cultivated in Ethiopia as cereal grain for making *injera*.

tej – an alcoholic drink brewed by fermenting honey, similar to honey mead.

tella – local beer brewed with barley and hops.

tenayistilegne – hello (literally, May God grant you good health).

tibs – roasted meat.

tukul – circular hut/house made of mud and straw, with a dirt floor, and usually with a thatched roof.

wayna-dega – the geographic area/environment located between the highlands and semi-desert (not as cold as the highlands, not as hot as the desert lowlands).

werekut – paper.

woreda – name of administrative unit similar to a county in USA (one level below the *awraja* level).

wot – spicy stew containing vegetables and/or meat, eaten with *injera*.

zebanya – hired house guard or watchman.

•

About the SEP Ethiopia Painting

The photo of the SEP Ethiopia painting on the back cover of this book was also included on the inside cover pages of Dr. D.A. Henderson's book, *Smallpox: The Death of a Disease.*

This painting was created by Ethiopian artist *Ato* Tesfaye Tave in 1975. It is an oil-on-canvas work of art that was rendered in what is known as "the Queen of Sheba style." The painting portrays the activities and challenges of the health workers of the Smallpox Eradication Program (SEP) in Ethiopia, which included Ethiopian health personnel and Peace Corps Volunteers. The various scenes depict Ethiopian smallpox patients, vaccinations being given by bifurcated needles or jet injectors, and SEP health workers searching for possible cases and recording their findings.

The original painting is 54 x 29 inches (137 x 74 cm) and is included in the collection of the Institute of the History of Medicine, The Johns Hopkins University School of Medicine.

The following English language translations of the Amharic language captions provide a brief description of what is happening in each of the frames of the painting, viewing from left to right and top to bottom.

row 1

1 · Health workers telling community leaders that smallpox will be eradicated with the help of the helicopter.

2 · Health workers giving injections using the jet injector.

3 · A health worker taking smallpox scabs.

4 · The logos of the Ethiopia Smallpox Eradication Program and the World Health Organization.

row 1 (cont.)

5 · Smallpox affects children even more.

6 · Health workers teaching the community about the effects of smallpox using a poster.

7 · Health workers discussing where to go for suspected smallpox cases and how best to use the helicopter to eradicate the disease.

row 2

8 · Health workers encouraging men who refuse to be vaccinated.

9 · At health centers and clinics, health workers are examining people for symptoms of smallpox.

10 · To eradicate smallpox, health workers even travel by camel.

11 · Health workers traveling into the mountains to eradicate smallpox.

12 · Vaccinating the shankilla ethnic group against smallpox.

13 · Smallpox eradication workers rush to eradicate smallpox.

14 · Health workers traveling to eradicate smallpox by horse and mule.

15 · Smallpox causes blindness.

16 · Health workers giving smallpox vaccinations to the Guji ethnic group.

17 · Health workers explaining the effects of smallpox by loudspeaker with permission of the landlord.

18 · Health workers giving vaccinations to housewives by going house to house.

19 · The traditional Ethiopian vaccination is very dangerous.

row 4

20 · When health workers travel by vehicle, they occasionally face difficulties.

21 · Smallpox can result in suffering and death.

22 · A health worker explaining about smallpox to the community.

23 · Health workers giving vaccinations to ethnic groups in Hararghe and Dire Dawa.

24 · Smallpox eradication workers giving advice to mothers.

25 · When smallpox workers travel along the roads, they help car accident victims.

row 5

26 · Health workers giving smallpox vaccinations to the Oromo ethnic group.

27 · Health workers giving vaccinations to the population along the border regions.

28 · Health workers giving vaccinations to the Walamo ethnic group.

29 ·Health workers giving vaccinations to the Adal ethnic group.

30 ·Health workers giving vaccinations to children and adults everywhere.

31 ·Health workers giving vaccinations to the Arusi ethnic group.

Made in the USA
Monee, IL
16 May 2021